HMH

(into) Science™

Teacher Guide
Grade 5

All images ©Houghton Mifflin Harcourt, Inc., unless otherwise noted

Cover: ©Wachirawit Narkborvornwichit/Moment/Getty Images

Copyright © by Houghton Mifflin Harcourt Publishing Company

All rights reserved. No part of this work may be reproduced or transmitted in any form or by any means, electronic or mechanical, including photocopying or recording, or by any information storage or retrieval system, without the prior written permission of the copyright owner unless such copying is expressly permitted by federal copyright law. Requests for permission to make copies of any part of the work should be submitted through our Permissions website at https://customercare.hmhco.com/contactus/Permissions.html or mailed to Houghton Mifflin Harcourt Publishing Company, Attn: Compliance, Contracts, and Licensing, 9400 Southpark Center Loop, Orlando, Florida 32819-8647.

Next Generation Science Standards. Reprinted with permission by the National Academy of Sciences. Courtesy of the National Academies Press, Washington, D.C.

Printed in the U.S.A.

ISBN 978-0-358-39111-1

6 7 8 9 10 2331 29 28 27 26 25 24 23 22

4500844259

r2.21

D1211693

Program Authors

Michael A. DiSpezio

Global Educator
North Falmouth, Massachusetts

Michael DiSpezio has authored many HMH instructional programs for Science and Mathematics. He has also authored numerous trade books and multimedia programs on various topics and hosted dozens of studio and location broadcasts for various organizations in the U.S. and worldwide. Most recently, he has been working with educators to provide strategies for implementing the Next Generation Science Standards—particularly the Science and Engineering Practices and Crosscutting Concepts—and for using Evidence Notebooks. To all his projects, he brings his extensive background in science, his expertise in classroom teaching at the elementary, middle, and high school levels, and his deep experience in producing interactive and engaging instructional materials.

Marjorie Frank

***Science Writer and Content-
Area Reading Specialist***
Brooklyn, New York

An educator and linguist by training, a writer and poet by nature, Marjorie Frank has authored and designed a generation of instructional materials in all subject areas, including past HMH Science programs. Her other credits include authoring science issues of an award-winning children's magazine, writing game-based digital assessments, developing blended learning materials for young children, and serving as instructional designer and coauthor of pioneering school-to-work software. In addition, she has served on the adjunct faculty of Hunter, Manhattan, and Brooklyn Colleges, teaching courses in science methods, literacy, and writing. For *HMH Into Science,* she has guided the development of our K–2 strands and our approach to making connections between NGSS and Common Core ELA/literacy standards.

Michael R. Heithaus, PhD

***Dean, College of Arts,
Sciences & Education
Professor, Department of
Biological Sciences***
Florida International University
Miami, Florida

Mike Heithaus joined the FIU Biology Department in 2003 and has served as Director of the Marine Sciences Program and as Executive Director of the School of Environment, Arts, and Society, which brings together the natural and social sciences and humanities to develop solutions to today's environmental challenges. He now serves as Dean of the College of Arts, Sciences & Education. His research focuses on predator-prey interactions and the ecological importance of large marine species. He has helped guide the development of Life Science content in *HMH Into Science* with a focus on strategies for teaching challenging content as well as the science and engineering practices of analyzing data and using computational thinking.

Peter McLaren

***Executive Director of Next Gen
Education, LLC***
Providence, Rhode Island

Peter McLaren is Executive Director of Next Gen Education, LLC, consulting with schools implementing the Next Generation Science Standards. His previous roles in science education policy include: Director of State and District Support for Science at Achieve, Science and Technology Specialist at the Rhode Island Department of Education, and President of the Council of State Science Supervisors. He served on the writing committees for the Next Generation Science Standards, the National Academy of Engineering's *Guiding Implementation of K–12 Engineering Education*, and the National Academy of Science's *Developing Assessments for the Next Generation Science Standards*. McLaren helped guide the development of the three-dimensional formative assessments in *HMH Into Science.*

Bernadine Okoro

Social Emotional Learning Consultant
STEM Learning Advocate & Consultant
Washington, DC

Bernadine Okoro is a chemical engineer by training and a playwright, novelist, director, and actress by nature. Okoro went from working with patents and biotechnology to teaching in K–12 classrooms. A 12-year science educator and Albert Einstein Distinguished Fellow, Okoro was one of the original authors of the Next Generation Science Standards. As a member of the Diversity and Equity Team, her focus on alternative education and community schools and on integrating social emotional learning and brain-based learning into NGSS is the vehicle she uses as a pathway to support underserved groups from elementary school to adult education. An article and book reviewer for NSTA and other educational publishing companies, Okoro currently works as a STEM Learning Advocate & Consultant.

Cary I. Sneider, PhD

Associate Research Professor
Portland State University
Portland, Oregon

While studying astrophysics at Harvard, Cary Sneider volunteered to teach in an Upward Bound program and discovered his real calling as a science teacher. After teaching middle and high school science in Maine, California, Costa Rica, and Micronesia, he settled for nearly three decades at Lawrence Hall of Science in Berkeley, California, where he developed skills in curriculum development and teacher education. Over his career, Sneider directed more than 20 federal, state, and foundation grant projects and was a writing team leader for the Next Generation Science Standards. He has been instrumental in ensuring *HMH Into Science* meets the high expectations of the NGSS and provides an effective three-dimensional learning experience for all students.

Program Advisors

Paul D. Asimow, PhD
Eleanor and John R. McMillan Professor of Geology and Geochemistry
California Institute of Technology
Pasadena, California

Eileen Cashman, PhD
Professor of Environmental Resources Engineering
Humboldt State University
Arcata, California

Mark B. Moldwin, PhD
Professor of Climate and Space Sciences and Engineering
University of Michigan
Ann Arbor, Michigan

Kelly Y. Neiles, PhD
Associate Professor of Chemistry
St. Mary's College of Maryland
St. Mary's City, Maryland

Sten Odenwald, PhD
Astronomer
NASA Goddard Spaceflight Center
Greenbelt, Maryland

Bruce W. Schafer
Director of K–12 STEM Collaborations, retired
Oregon University System
Portland, Oregon

Barry A. Van Deman
President and CEO
Museum of Life and Science
Durham, North Carolina

Kim Withers, PhD
Assistant Professor
Texas A&M University-Corpus Christi
Corpus Christi, Texas

These are some smart people!

Educator Advisory Board Members

Julie Ahern
2nd Grade Teacher
Andrew Cooke Magnet School
Waukegan, Illinois

Kecia Allen-Rodgers
Science Lab Teacher
Idlewild Elementary School
Memphis, Tennessee

Amy Berke
Classroom Teacher
South Park Elementary School
Rapid City, South Dakota

Kelly Brotz
2nd Grade Teacher
Cooper Elementary School
Sheboygan, Wisconsin

Marsha Campbell
1st Grade Teacher
Murray Elementary School
Hobbs, New Mexico

Deborah Falaise
4th Grade Teacher
Benjamin Banneker Academy
East Orange, New Jersey

Noelle Foito
5th Grade Teacher
Madison School
Bridgeport, Connecticut

Theresa Gailliout
Classroom Teacher
James R. Ludlow Elementary
    School
Philadelphia, Pennsylvania

Robert Gray
Classroom Teacher
Essex Elementary School
Baltimore, Maryland

Bonnie Lock
Classroom Teacher
La Center Elementary School
La Center, Washington

Kara Miller
3rd Grade Teacher
Ridgeview Elementary School
Beckley, West Virginia

Dena Morosin
Classroom Teacher
Shasta Elementary School
Klamath Falls, Oregon

Joanna O'Brien
3rd Grade Teacher
Palmyra Elementary School
Palmyra, Missouri

Julie Padavic
Classroom Teacher
Lindsay Elementary School
Springfield, Illinois

Nora Rowe
Classroom Head Teacher
Peoria Traditional School
Peoria, Arizona

April Thompson
Classroom Teacher
Roll Hill School
Cincinnati, Ohio

Terri Trebilcock
Classroom Teacher
Fairmount Elementary School
Golden, Colorado

Classroom Reviewers

Julie Ahern
Andrew Cooke Magnet School
Waukegan, Illinois

Amy Berke
South Park Elementary School
Rapid City, South Dakota

Pamela Bluestein
Sycamore Canyon School
Newbury Park, California

Kelly Brotz
Cooper Elementary School
Sheboygan, Wisconsin

Andrea Brown
HLPUSD Science and STEAM
    TOSA, Retired
Hacienda Heights, California

Marsha Campbell
Murray Elementary School
Hobbs, New Mexico

Leslie C. Antosy-Flores
Star View Elementary School
Midway City, California

Theresa Gailliout
James R. Ludlow Elementary
    School
Philadelphia, Pennsylvania

Emily Giles
Assistant Principal
White's Tower Elementary
    School
Independence, Kentucky

Robert Gray
Essex Elementary School
Baltimore, Maryland

Stephanie Greene
Science Department Chair
Sun Valley Magnet School
Sun Valley, California

Roya Hosseini
Junction Avenue K–8 School
Livermore, California

Rana Mujtaba Khan
Will Rogers High School
Van Nuys, California

George Kwong
Schafer Park Elementary
    School
Hayward, California

Kristin Kyde
Templeton Middle School
Sussex, Wisconsin

Marie LaCross
Sulphur Springs United School
    District
Santa Clarita, California

Bonnie Lock
La Center Elementary School
La Center, Washington

Imelda Madrid
Assistant Principal
Montague Charter Academy
    for the Arts and Sciences
Pacoima, California

Susana Martinez O'Brien
Diocese of San Diego
San Diego, California

Kara Miller
Ridgeview Elementary School
Beckley, West Virginia

Mercy D. Momary
Local District Northwest
Los Angeles, California

Dena Morosin
Shasta Elementary School
Klamath Falls, Oregon

Craig Moss
Mt. Gleason Middle School
Sunland, California

Joanna O'Brien
Palmyra Elementary School
Palmyra, Missouri

Wendy Savaske
Education Consultant
Wisconsin Department of
    Public Instruction

Isabel Souto
Schafer Park Elementary
Hayward, California

Michelle Sullivan
Balboa Elementary School
San Diego, California

April Thompson
Roll Hill School
Cincinnati, Ohio

Tina Topoleski
District Science Supervisor
Jackson School District
Jackson, New Jersey

Terri Trebilcock
Fairmount Elementary School
Golden, Colorado

Emily R.C.G. Williams
South Pasadena Middle School
South Pasadena, California

Notes:

For the Teacher

Unit 1 Engineering and Technology 2

Look!

:Ed   GO ONLINE FOR

You Solve It: Cat Tree Simulation
Unit Project: Dropping Off, Picking Up
Unit Performance Task: Lunch Line Life Hack

Unit 2   Matter 28

GO ONLINE FOR

You Solve It: Maze Matters Simulation
Unit Project: Conservation of Matter
Unit Performance Task: Physical or Chemical?

Unit 3 Energy and Matter in Organisms

© Houghton Mifflin Harcourt Publishing Company • Image Credits: ©Ondrej Prosicky/Dreamstime

GO ONLINE FOR

You Solve It: What Do Plants Need? Simulation
Unit Project: The Best Light
Unit Performance Task: Business Has "Bean" Bad

Unit 4 Energy and Matter in Ecosystems

Ed GO ONLINE FOR

You Solve It: Build an Ecosystem Simulation
Unit Project: Self-Contained Ecosystem
Unit Performance Task: Design an Ecosystem

Unit 5 Earth Interactions and Resources

GO ONLINE FOR

You Solve It: Earth's Systems Simulation
Unit Project: My Environmental Impact
Unit Performance Task: Protecting a Sphere

Unit 6 Patterns in the Sky 262

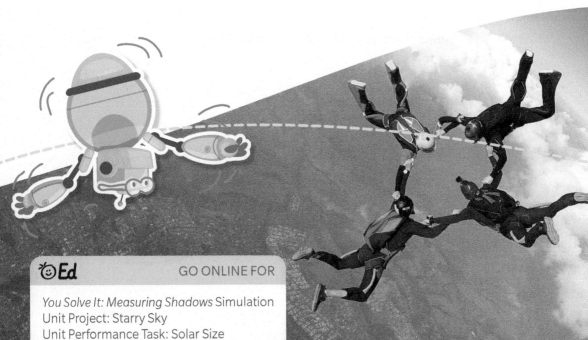

⊙Ed GO ONLINE FOR

You Solve It: Measuring Shadows Simulation
Unit Project: Starry Sky
Unit Performance Task: Solar Size

 Ed *your friend in learning*

GO ONLINE FOR

Professional Development

Calendar Pacing Guide

Reading in the Science Content Area

English Language Arts Correlations

Math Correlations

Instructional Model

PRINT

Student Activity Guide

- Introduces the Anchoring Phenomenon
- Includes Hands-On Investigations for exploring investigative phenomena

FUNomenal Readers

- Leveled by reading levels
- Model investigative sensemaking

Teacher Guide

- Provides strategies for
    - Introducing phenomena
    - Guiding Student Explorations
    - Supporting student sensemaking through 3D learning
    - Assessing students

- Provides point-of-use strategies for
    - Incorporating readers into an ELA lesson
    - Incorporating Social Emotional Learning (SEL) strategies
    - Leveling strategies

ONLINE

Go online to access components that include

Student Ebook: Provides additional in-depth materials and explorations for early finishers/motivated students

Teacher Ebook: Provides additional teaching information and strategies that help focus on 3D learning

ASSESSMENT

- Scaffolds toward higher-level thinking
- Provides formative and summative options to help you identify how your students are progressing toward mastering Performance Expectations
- Helps determine if students are making sense of phenomena
- Provides modified options for students that struggle with reading

Student Sensemaking Journey

The student journey is a five-step process centered around a phenomenon.

1
Students experience a phenomenon requiring explanation. (a sense of wonder)

5
Students revisit phenomenon to revise or augment their explanations supported by their previous understandings and by the new evidence they have gathered.

2
Students wonder, talk, share and try to explain using what they already know.

ANCHORING PHENOMENON

4
Students conduct activities, read, talk to experts, gather information from the Internet, and analyze all that they discover.

3
Students ask questions about the phenomenon and their explanations.

Your Teacher Journey—What Happens in a Lesson

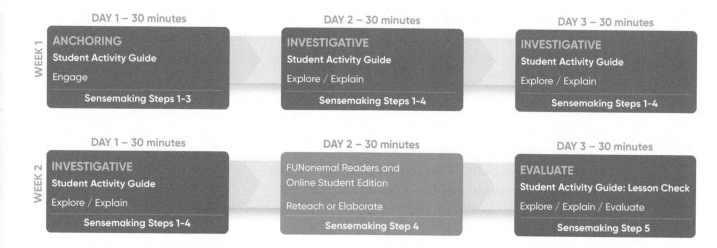

WEEK 1

DAY 1 – 30 minutes

ANCHORING
Student Activity Guide

Engage

Sensemaking Steps 1–3

DAY 2 – 30 minutes

INVESTIGATIVE
Student Activity Guide

Explore / Explain

Sensemaking Steps 1–4

DAY 3 – 30 minutes

INVESTIGATIVE
Student Activity Guide

Explore / Explain

Sensemaking Steps 1–4

WEEK 2

DAY 1 – 30 minutes

INVESTIGATIVE
Student Activity Guide

Explore / Explain

Sensemaking Steps 1–4

DAY 2 – 30 minutes

FUNonemal Readers and
Online Student Edition

Reteach or Elaborate

Sensemaking Step 4

DAY 3 – 30 minutes

EVALUATE
Student Activity Guide: Lesson Check

Explore / Explain / Evaluate

Sensemaking Step 5

Your Teaching Journey and the Student Sensemaking Journey are tightly interlinked.

Week 1/Day 1: Introduce Anchoring Phenomenon (*Reinforces Steps 1–3 of Student Sensemaking Journey*).
- Students discuss and begin exploration.
- Students offer initial explanations.
- Students begin to ask questions that should be recorded.

Week 1/Day 2–3, Week 2: Students explore the Anchoring Phenomenon through Investigative Phenomena (*Step 4 of Student Sensemaking Journey*).
- Students conduct the investigations in the Student Activity Guide.
- They relate their discoveries back to the Anchoring Phenomenon to show how what they have discovered relates to part of the explanation of the Anchoring Phenomenon.

Week 2 /Day 2: Use the FUNomenal Readers and the Online Student Edition to continue Exploration and do the Elaborate part of the lesson cycle (*Step 4 of Student Sensemaking Journey*).
- FUNomenal Readers allow students to explore the same Performance Expectations using the same or alternative phenomenon.

Week 2/Day 3: Formative Assessment (*Step 5 of Student Sensemaking Journey*) is administered using the Can You Explain It? in Lesson Check.
- Formative Assessment continues the explore/explain and allows you to enter the evaluate phase.
- Students return to the Anchoring Phenomenon with what they have learned as they have explored.
- Student explanations should be richer, more elaborate, and more connected to a claims, evidence, reasoning model of understanding and argument.
- If student sensemaking is still in need of formation, reteach using the Online Student Edition or by revisiting the FUNomenal Reader.

Claims, Evidence, Reasoning (CER) for Sensemaking

Making sense of phenomena requires a bookended approach of initial explanation followed by a revised understanding after a series of explorations. CER is part of both.

A student makes a **claim**, which can be an explanation or a prediction based on evidence. Ideally, the claim is something that should be subject to a fair test.

The evidence can include
- prior knowledge
- data gathered in hands-on explorations
- observations both within and outside explorations
- information gathered from research and reading
- discussion with other students and other people who could be sources of information

In reasoning,
- students evaluate the quality of the evidence
- students relate the evidence to the explanation by explaining how that piece of evidence supports the explanation

But it doesn't stop here: students continue to discuss and critique explanations offered using the same claim-evidence-reasoning chain until they come to a conclusion that provides a "best-fit" explanation for the phenomenon that incorporates all of the available, valid evidence.

Your role in this? Be ready with questions such as, "What is your evidence for that conclusion?" "How does the evidence support your claim?" "What evidence do you have?" You guide the sensemaking by constantly returning students to the central ideas of CER.

Download *Think Like a Scientist* posters for your classroom.

Getting students comfortable thinking like scientists is no small feat, but it's the best way to teach science.

Search (HMH Think Like a Scientist)

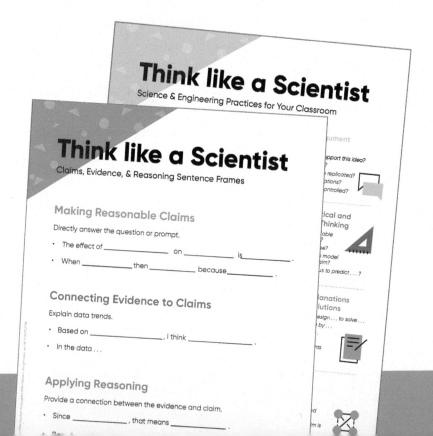

Think like a Scientist
Science & Engineering Practices for Your Classroom

Think like a Scientist
Claims, Evidence, & Reasoning Sentence Frames

Making Reasonable Claims
Directly answer the question or prompt.
- The effect of _____ on _____ is_____ .
- When _____ then _____ because_____ .

Connecting Evidence to Claims
Explain data trends.
- Based on _____ , I think _____ .
- In the data . . .

Applying Reasoning
Provide a connection between the evidence and claim.
- Since _____ , that means _____ .

Social Emotional Learning at HMH

We believe that learning is an intellectual, social, and emotional process for the whole child. Learning has highs and lows, victories and setbacks—each of which causes emotions that drive and affect how students learn and view themselves. Learning goes beyond acquiring facts and expanding knowledge and becomes a personal story of curiosity, perseverance, and growth.

We believe that schools—and those who collaborate with them—have a responsibility to empower learners and educators by providing opportunities in safe environments that allow every child to be engaged and supported in the interwoven cognitive, behavioral, social, and emotional facets of learning.

We commit to empowering ALL students to author their own learning story.

Research suggests integrating Social Emotional Learning (SEL) directly into the core curriculum every day is the most effective practice. Our activities provide daily opportunities to practice SEL skills within real-world contexts in an encouraging and safe environment. We offer teacher support in the form of teacher blogs, courses focused on SEL competencies, and supplemental supports aligned with practical ways to integrate SEL skills into your curriculum.

Benefits:

- Improved quality of instruction and teacher-student interactions
- Improved student performance
- Ease of social adjustments for students

HMH SEL activities foster mastery of competencies and transfer of skills because students are consistently practicing over time. We invite you to find relevancy in your classroom communities through HMH learning products, and we are here to support your SEL endeavors.

HMH Into Science™ Pacing Guide

Common Pacing Guide Model—Applicable to All Units

HMH Into Science is designed with the time constraints of the K–5 science classroom in mind. The chart below identifies recommended choices for learning experiences within units and lessons. You can also customize your own pacing to meet your classroom needs.

- **Core Path** The Core path is recommended as it covers all of the Next Generation Science Standards. At Grade 5, this will require about 120 days of 30-minute instructional segments.

- **Extended Path** If you have additional time, the Extended path provides additional opportunities to explore and reinforce the science content.

- **Short on Time Path** If you have less time than the Core path assumes, the Short on Time path highlights key pieces to focus on. However, this may not cover all of the standards thoroughly.

- **Blended Path** If you are short on time, we recommend using the Blended path. In the Blended path, you use available science instruction time plus 30 minutes of English Language Arts instruction time to explore the FUNomenal Reader in order to more thoroughly cover all of the standards.

Section	Short on Time	Core	Extended	Blended
Lessons 1–4				
Engage: Can You Explain It?	✓	✓	✓	✓
Explorations 1–2: Hands-On Activity	✓	✓	✓	✓
Explorations 3–5		✓	✓	
Elaborate: FUNomenal Reader			✓	📕 ELA
Elaborate: Take It Further (digital-only)			✓	
Evaluate: Can You Explain It?	✓	✓	✓	✓
Evaluate: Checkpoints			✓	
Unit				
You Solve It (digital-only)			✓	
Unit Project (digital-only)			✓	
Unit Performance Task (digital-only)			✓	
Unit Review		✓	✓	
Unit Test (Assessment Guide)	✓	✓	✓	✓

Specific pacing information for learning experiences is found at point-of-use throughout your Teacher Guide. Those point-of-use timings are summarized in the chart below.

1 Instructional Day = 30 min

Section	Short on Time	Core	Extended	Blended
Unit 1 Engineering and Technology	**5 days**	**10 days**	**19.5 days**	**6 days**
Lesson 1 Engineering and Society	4 days	8 days	10.5 days	5 days
Unit 1 Resources	1 day	2 days	9 days	1 day
Unit 2 Matter	**15 days**	**22 days**	**37 days**	**18 days**
Lesson 1 Matter Has Mass and Volume	4.5 days	6 days	8.5 days	5.5 days
Lesson 2 Matter Has Many Properties	4.5 days	7 days	9.5 days	6 days
Lesson 3 Matter Can Change	4.5 days	7 days	10 days	5.5 days
Unit 2 Resources	1.5 days	2 days	9 days	1 day
Unit 3 Energy and Matter in Organisms	**14.5 days**	**20 days**	**34.5 days**	**17.5 days**
Lesson 1 Plants Transform and Use Energy and Matter	4.5 days	5.5 days	8.5 days	5.5 days
Lesson 2 Organisms Use Matter and Energy	4.5 days	5.5 days	9.5 days	5.5 days
Lesson 3 Energy and Matter Move Between Organisms	4.5 days	7 days	10 days	5.5 days
Unit 3 Resources	1 day	2 days	6.5 days	1 day
Unit 4 Energy and Matter in Ecosystems	**10.5 days**	**16 days**	**28.5 days**	**12.5 days**
Lesson 1 Organisms Interact in Ecosystems	5 days	8 days	10.5 days	6 days
Lesson 2 Organisms Change Their Ecosystems	4.5 days	6 days	9 days	5.5 days
Unit 4 Resources	1 day	2 days	9 days	1 day
Unit 5 Earth Interactions and Resources	**21 days**	**30 days**	**48.5 days**	**25 days**
Lesson 1 Earth's Systems Interact	4 days	6 days	9 days	5 days
Lesson 2 Water in Earth's Systems	5.5 days	7.5 days	10 days	6.5 days
Lesson 3 Resource Use Affects the Environment	5.5 days	7.5 days	10 days	6.5 days
Lesson 4 People Can Protect the Environment	5 days	7 days	10 days	5 days
Unit 5 Resources	1 day	2 days	9.5 days	2 days
Unit 6 Patterns in the Sky	**15 days**	**22 days**	**37.5 days**	**18 days**
Lesson 1 Gravity Affects Matter on Earth	4.5 days	6 days	8.5 days	5.5 days
Lesson 2 Sky Patterns over Time	4.5 days	7 days	10 days	5.5 days
Lesson 3 The Sun	5 days	7 days	10 days	6 days
Unit 6 Resources	1 day	2 days	9 days	1 day

Grade 5 Unit Correlations and K–8 Program Storyline

This chart shows the Unit-level Grade 5 correlations and how the Next Generation Science Standards and the three dimensions of learning build across the grades. Detailed correlations are also available at the Lesson level. This chart also shows the completely coherent program storyline that grows in sophistication across K–8.

Grades K–2 Storyline	Grades 3–5 Storyline
	Gr 5 Unit 1 Engineering and Technology
K-2-ETS1-1 Ask questions, make observations, and gather information about a situation people want to change to define a simple problem that can be solved through the development of a new or improved object or tool.	**Gr 5** **3-5-ETS1-1** Define a simple design problem reflecting a need or a want that includes specified criteria for success and constraints on materials, time, or cost.
K-2-ETS1-2 Develop a simple sketch, drawing, or physical model to illustrate how the shape of an object helps it function as needed to solve a given problem.	**Gr 5** **3-5-ETS1-2** Generate and compare multiple possible solutions to a problem based on how well each is likely to meet the criteria and constraints of the problem.
K-2-ETS1-3 Analyze data from tests of two objects designed to solve the same problem to compare the strengths and weaknesses of how each performs.	**Gr 5** **3-5-ETS1-3** Plan and carry out fair tests in which variables are controlled and failure points are considered to identify aspects of a model or prototype that can be improved.
	Gr 5 Unit 2 Matter
2-PS1-1 Plan and conduct an investigation to describe and classify different kinds of materials by their observable properties. **2-PS1-3** Make observations to construct an evidence-based account of how an object made of a small set of pieces can be disassembled and made into a new object.	**Gr 5** **5-PS1-1** Develop a model to describe that matter is made of particles too small to be seen.
2-PS1-4 Construct an argument with evidence that some changes caused by heating or cooling can be reversed and some cannot.	**Gr 5** **5-PS1-2** Measure and graph quantities to provide evidence that regardless of the type of change that occurs when heating, cooling, or mixing substances, the total weight of matter is conserved.
2-PS1-1 Plan and conduct an investigation to describe and classify different kinds of materials by their observable properties.	**Gr 5** **5-PS1-3** Make observations and measurements to identify materials based on their properties.
2-PS1-3 Make observations to construct an evidence-based account of how an object made of a small set of pieces can be disassembled and made into a new object.	**Gr 5** **5-PS1-4** Conduct an investigation to determine whether the mixing of two or more substances results in new substances.
K-2-ETS-1 Ask questions, make observations, and gather information about a situation people want to change to define a simple problem that can be solved through the development of a new or improved object or tool.	**Gr 5** **3-5-ETS1-1** Define a simple design problem reflecting a need or a want that includes specified criteria for success and constraints on materials, time, or cost.

Performance Expectations

Grades 6–8 Storyline

MS-ETS1-1 Define the criteria and constraints of a design problem with sufficient precision to ensure a successful solution, taking into account relevant scientific principles and potential impacts on people and the natural environment that may limit possible solutions.

MS-ETS1-2 Evaluate competing design solutions using a systematic process to determine how well they meet the criteria and constraints of the problem.

MS-ETS1-3 Analyze data from tests to determine similarities and differences among several design solutions to identify the best characteristics of each that can be combined into a new solution to better meet the criteria for success.

MS-ETS1-4 Develop a model to generate data for iterative testing and modification of a proposed object, tool, or process such that an optimal design can be achieved.

MS-PS1-1 Develop models to describe the atomic composition of simple molecules and extended structures.

MS-PS1-2 Analyze and interpret data on the properties of substances before and after the substances interact to determine if a chemical reaction has occurred.

MS-PS1-5 Develop and use a model to describe how the total number of atoms does not change in a chemical reaction and thus mass is conserved.

MS-PS1-3 Gather and make sense of information to describe that synthetic materials come from natural resources and impact society.

MS-PS1-4 Develop a model that predicts and describes changes in particle motion, temperature, and state of a pure substance when thermal energy is added or removed.

MS-ETS1-1 Define the criteria and constraints of a design problem with sufficient precision to ensure a successful solution, taking into account relevant scientific principles and potential impacts on people and the natural environment that may limit possible solutions.

Notes:

Performance Expectations

Grade 5 Unit Correlations and K–8 Program Storyline

Grades K–2 Storyline	Grades 3–5 Storyline

Gr 5 Unit 2 Matter *cont.*

K-2-ETS1-2 Develop a simple sketch, drawing, or physical model to illustrate how the shape of an object helps it function as needed to solve a given problem.

Gr 5 3-5-ETS1-2 Generate and compare multiple possible solutions to a problem based on how well each is likely to meet the criteria and constraints of the problem.

K-2-ETS1-3 Analyze data from tests of two objects designed to solve the same problem to compare the strengths and weaknesses of how each performs.

Gr 5 3-5-ETS1-3 Plan and carry out fair tests in which variables are controlled and failure points are considered to identify aspects of a model or prototype that can be improved.

Gr 5 Unit 3 Energy and Matter in Organisms

K-LS1-1 Use observations to describe patterns of what plants and animals (including humans) need to survive.

1-LS1-1 Use materials to design a solution to a human problem by mimicking how plants and/or animals use their external parts to help them survive, grow, and meet their needs.

Gr 4 4-LS1-1 Construct an argument that plants and animals have internal and external structures that function to support survival, growth, behavior, and reproduction.

Gr 5 5-LS1-1 Support an argument that plants get the materials they need for growth chiefly from air and water.

K-ESS3-1 Use a model to represent the relationship between the needs of different plants or animals (including humans) and the places they live.

2-LS2-1 Plan and conduct an investigation to determine if plants need sunlight and water to grow.

Gr 5 5-LS2-1 Develop a model to describe the movement of matter among plants, animals, decomposers, and the environment.

Gr 5 5-PS3-1 Use models to describe that energy in animals' food (used for body repair, growth, motion, and to maintain body warmth) was once energy from the sun.

Gr 5 Unit 4 Energy and Matter in Ecosystems

K-ESS3-1 Use a model to represent the relationship between the needs of different plants or animals (including humans) and the places they live.

2-LS2-1 Plan and conduct an investigation to determine if plants need sunlight and water to grow.

Gr 5 5-LS2-1 Develop a model to describe the movement of matter among plants, animals, decomposers, and the environment.

Gr 5 Unit 5 Earth Interactions and Resources

K-ESS2-1 Use and share observations of local weather conditions to describe patterns over time.

2-ESS2-1 Compare multiple solutions designed to slow or prevent wind or water from changing the shape of the land.

Gr 3 3-ESS2-1 Represent data in tables and graphical displays to describe typical weather conditions expected during a particular season.

Gr 4 4-ESS1-1 Identify evidence from patterns in rock formations and fossils in rock layers to support an explanation for changes in a landscape over time.

Gr 4 4-ESS2-1 Make observations and/or measurements to provide evidence of the effects of weathering or the rate of erosion by water, ice, wind, or vegetation.

Gr 5 5-ESS2-1 Develop a model using an example to describe ways the geosphere, biosphere, hydrosphere, and/or atmosphere interact.

Performance Expectations

MS-ETS1-2 Evaluate competing design solutions using a systematic process to determine how well they meet the criteria and constraints of the problem.

MS-ETS1-3 Analyze data from tests to determine similarities and differences among several design solutions to identify the best characteristics of each that can be combined into a new solution to better meet the criteria for success.

MS-LS1-6 Construct a scientific explanation based on evidence for the role of photosynthesis in the cycling of matter and flow of energy into and out of organisms.

MS-LS2-1 Analyze and interpret data to provide evidence for the effects of resource availability on organisms and populations of organisms in an ecosystem.

MS-LS2-2 Construct an explanation that predicts patterns of interactions among organisms across multiple ecosystems.

MS-ESS3-3 Apply scientific principles to design a method for monitoring and minimizing a human impact on the environment.

MS-ESS3-1 Construct a scientific explanation based on evidence for how the uneven distributions of Earth's mineral, energy, and groundwater resources are the result of past and current geoscience processes.

MS-LS2-1 Analyze and interpret data to provide evidence for the effects of resource availability on organisms and populations of organisms in an ecosystem.

MS-LS2-2 Construct an explanation that predicts patterns of interactions among organisms across multiple ecosystems.

MS-ESS2-1 Develop a model to describe the cycling of Earth's materials and the flow of energy that drives this process.

Notes:

Performance Expectations

Grade 5 Unit Correlations and K–8 Program Storyline

Grades K–2 Storyline	Grades 3–5 Storyline

Grades K–2 Storyline

2-ESS2-2 Develop a model to represent the shapes and kinds of land and bodies of water in an area.

2-ESS2-3 Obtain information to identify where water is found on Earth and that it can be solid or liquid.

K-ESS3-1 Use a model to represent the relationship between the needs of different plants or animals (including humans) and the places they live.

K-PS2-1 Plan and conduct an investigation to compare the effects of different strengths or different directions of pushes and pulls on the motion of an object.

1-ESS1-1 Use observations of the sun, moon, and stars to describe patterns that can be predicted.

1-ESS1-2 Make observations at different times of year to relate the amount of daylight to the time of year.

1-ESS1-1 Use observations of the sun, moon, and stars to describe patterns that can be predicted.

2-ESS1-1 Use information from several sources to provide evidence that Earth events can occur quickly or slowly.

Grades 3–5 Storyline

Gr 5 Unit 5 Earth Interactions and Resources *cont.*

Gr 4 **4-ESS2-2** Analyze and interpret data from maps to describe patterns of Earth's features.

Gr 5 **5-ESS2-2** Describe and graph the amounts and percentages of water and fresh water in various reservoirs to provide evidence about the distribution of water on Earth.

Gr 3 **3-ESS3-1** Make a claim about the merit of a design solution that reduces the impacts of a weather-related hazard.

Gr 4 **4-ESS3-1** Obtain and combine information to describe that energy and fuels are derived from natural resources and their uses affect the environment.

Gr 4 **4-ESS3-2** Generate and compare multiple solutions to reduce the impacts of natural Earth processes on humans.

Gr 5 **5-ESS3-1** Obtain and combine information about ways individual communities use science ideas to protect the Earth's resources and environment.

Gr 5 Unit 6 Patterns in the Sky

Gr 3 **3-PS2-1** Plan and conduct an investigation to provide evidence of the effects of balanced and unbalanced forces on the motion of an object.

Gr 5 **5-PS2-1** Support an argument that the gravitational force exerted by Earth on objects is directed down.

Gr 5 **5-ESS1-1** Support an argument that differences in the apparent brightness of the sun compared to other stars is due to their relative distances from Earth.

Gr 5 **5-ESS1-2** Represent data in graphical displays to reveal patterns of daily changes in length and direction of shadows, day and night, and the seasonal appearance of some stars in the night sky.

Performance Expectations

MS-ESS2-4 Develop a model to describe the cycling of water through Earth's systems driven by energy from the sun and the force of gravity.

MS-ESS2-2 Construct an explanation based on evidence for how geoscience processes have changed Earth's surface at varying time and spatial scales.

MS-ESS3-3 Apply scientific principles to design a method for monitoring and minimizing a human impact on the environment.

MS-ESS3-1 Construct a scientific explanation based on evidence for how the uneven distributions of Earth's mineral, energy, and groundwater resources are the result of past and current geoscience processes.

MS-PS2-1 Apply Newton's Third Law to design a solution to a problem involving the motion of two colliding objects.

MS-PS2-4 Construct and present arguments using evidence to support the claim that gravitational interactions are attractive and depend on the masses of interacting objects.

MS-ESS1-3 Analyze and interpret data to determine scale properties of objects in the solar system.

MS-ESS1-1 Develop and use a model of the Earth-sun-moon system to describe the cyclic patterns of lunar phases, eclipses of the sun and moon, and seasons.

Notes:

Performance Expectations

Grade 5 Unit Correlations and K–8 Program Storyline

Grades K–2 Storyline	Grades 3–5 Storyline
	Gr 5 Unit 1 Engineering and Technology
Asking Questions and Defining Problems (define a problem that can be solved with a tool or object)	**Asking Questions and Defining Problems** (define a problem that includes criteria and constraints)
Planning and Carrying Out Investigations (plan and conduct an investigation with peers; plan and conduct an investigation collaboratively to produce data; make observations or measurements to collect data for comparisons)	**Planning and Carrying Out Investigations** (plan and conduct an investigation collaboratively to produce data)
Constructing Explanations and Designing Solutions (generate or compare multiple solutions to a problem)	**Constructing Explanations and Designing Solutions** (generate or compare multiple solutions to a problem based on criteria and constraints)
	Gr 5 Unit 2 Matter
Planning and Carrying Out Investigations (plan and conduct an investigation with peers; plan and conduct an investigation collaboratively to produce data; make observations or measurements to collect data for comparisons)	**Planning and Carrying Out Investigations** (make observations or measurements to produce data to explain a phenomenon; plan and conduct an investigation collaboratively to produce data)
Developing and Using Models (develop a simple model based on evidence; develop a model to represent amounts, relationships, scales, or patterns)	**Developing and Using Models** (develop models to describe or predict phenomena)
	Using Mathematics and Computational Thinking (describe, measure, estimate, or graph quantities such as area, volume, weight, time)
	Engaging in Argument from Evidence (evaluate claims about cause and effect)
	Gr 5 Unit 3 Energy and Matter in Organisms
Developing and Using Models (develop a simple model based on evidence; develop a model to represent amounts, relationships, scales, or patterns)	**Developing and Using Models** (develop models to describe or predict phenomena)
Engaging in Argument from Evidence (support a claim with evidence)	**Engaging in Argument from Evidence** (support an argument with evidence, data, model)
Obtaining, Evaluating, and Communicating Information (read texts and use media to obtain information; obtain information from text and media to answer a question or support a claim; communicate information or design ideas/solutions orally or in writing)	**Obtaining, Evaluating, and Communicating Information** (obtain and combine information from books and media to explain phenomena or solutions)
	Using Mathematics and Computational Thinking (describe, measure, estimate, or graph quantities such as area, volume, weight, time)

Science and Engineering Practices

Asking Questions and Defining Problems (define a problem that includes criteria and constraints, including scientific knowledge)

Planning and Carrying Out Investigations (collect data about the performance of an object, tool, process, system; conduct an investigation or revise the experimental design; plan an investigation individually and collaboratively; identify independent and dependent variables)

Constructing Explanations and Designing Solutions (design, construct, and test the design of an object, tool, process, or system; construct or implement a solution that meets specific criteria and constraints)

Planning and Carrying Out Investigations (collect data to answer questions or design solutions; conduct an investigation or revise the experimental design; plan an investigation individually and collaboratively; identify independent and dependent variables)

Developing and Using Models (develop models to describe or predict phenomena)

Using Mathematics and Computational Thinking (use mathematical representations to describe/support conclusions and solutions)

Developing and Using Models (develop models to describe or predict phenomena)

Engaging in Argument from Evidence (support an oral or written argument with empirical evidence and scientific reasoning)

Obtaining, Evaluating, and Communicating Information (integrate text, media, and visual displays to clarify claims and findings; gather, read, and synthesize information from multiple appropriate sources and assess credibility, accuracy, bias)

Notes:

Science and Engineering Practices

Grade 5 Unit Correlations and K–8 Program Storyline

Grades K–2 Storyline	Grades 3–5 Storyline
	Gr 5 Unit 3 Energy and Matter in Organisms *cont.*
Science Models, Laws, Mechanisms, and Theories Explain Natural Phenomena (scientists search for cause and effect relationships)	**Science Models, Laws, Mechanisms, and Theories** (science explanations describe the mechanisms for natural events)
	Gr 5 Unit 4 Energy and Matter in Ecosystems
Developing and Using Models (develop a simple model based on evidence; develop a model to represent amounts, relationships, scales, or patterns)	**Developing and Using Models** (develop models to describe or predict phenomena)
Science Models, Laws, Mechanisms, and Theories Explain Natural Phenomena (scientists search for cause and effect relationships)	**Science Models, Laws, Mechanisms, and Theories** (science explanations describe the mechanisms for natural events)
	Gr 5 Unit 5 Earth Interactions and Resources
Developing and Using Models (develop a simple model based on evidence; develop a model to represent amounts, relationships, scales, or patterns)	**Developing and Using Models** (develop a model using an analogy, example, or abstract representation)
	Using Mathematics and Computational Thinking (describe, measure, estimate, or graph quantities such as area, volume, weight, time)
Obtaining, Evaluating, and Communicating Information (read texts and use media to obtain information; obtain information from text and media to answer a question or support a claim; communicate information or design ideas/solutions orally or in writing)	**Obtaining, Evaluating, and Communicating Information** (obtain and combine information from books and media to explain phenomena or solutions)
Engaging in Argument from Evidence (support a claim with evidence)	**Engaging in Argument from Evidence** (support an argument with evidence, data, model)
	Gr 5 Unit 6 Patterns in the Sky
Engaging in Argument from Evidence (support a claim with evidence)	**Engaging in Argument from Evidence** (support an argument with evidence, data, model)
Analyzing and Interpreting Data (use observations to describe patterns and relationships)	**Analyzing and Interpreting Data** (represent data in various graphical displays to reveal relationships)

Science and Engineering Practices

Science Models, Laws, Mechanisms, and Theories Explain Natural Phenomena (laws are regularities or mathematical descriptions of natural phenomena)

Developing and Using Models (develop models to describe or predict phenomena)

Science Models, Laws, Mechanisms, and Theories Explain Natural Phenomena (laws are regularities or mathematical descriptions of natural phenomena)

Developing and Using Models (develop a model of unobservable mechanisms)

Using Mathematics and Computational Thinking (use mathematical representations to describe/support conclusions and solutions)

Obtaining, Evaluating, and Communicating Information (integrate text, media, and visual displays to clarify claims and findings; gather, read, and synthesize information from multiple appropriate sources and assess credibility, accuracy, bias)

Engaging in Argument from Evidence (support an oral or written argument with empirical evidence and scientific reasoning)

Engaging in Argument from Evidence (support an oral or written argument with empirical evidence and scientific reasoning)

Analyzing and Interpreting Data (analyze and interpret data to determine similarities and differences; construct, analyze, and interpret data or data sets to identify relationships)

Notes:

Science and Engineering Practices

Grade 5 Unit Correlations and K–8 Program Storyline

Grades K–2 Storyline	Grades 3–5 Storyline
	Gr 5 Unit 1 Engineering and Technology
DCI.K-2-ETS1.A: Defining and Delimiting Engineering Problems (asking questions, making observations, and gathering information help in thinking about problems to be solved)	**DCI.3-5-ETS1.A: Defining and Delimiting Engineering Problems** (solutions can be compared by how well they meet criteria and take constraints into account)
DCI.K-2-ETS1.B: Developing Possible Solutions (designs can be conveyed through sketches, drawings, and physical models)	**DCI.3-5-ETS1.B: Developing Possible Solutions** (carry out research before designing a solution; communicate with others about your solution; test the solution)
DCI.K-2-ETS1.C: Optimizing the Design Solution (there is always more than one possible solution; compare and test designs)	**DCI.3-5-ETS1.C: Optimizing the Design Solution** (test different solutions to determine which best solves the problem)
DCI.2-PS1.A: Structure and Properties of Matter (matter exists in different forms, has properties, and can be combined to make objects) **DCI.2-PS1.B: Chemical Reactions** (heating or cooling a substance can cause changes)	**DCI.5-PS1.A: Structure and Properties of Matter** (matter is made up of particles too small to be seen and has properties useful for identification; when matter changes form, the same amount is present)
	Gr 5 Unit 2 Matter
DCI.2-PS1.A: Structure and Properties of Matter (matter exists in different forms, has properties, and can be combined to make objects)	**DCI.5-PS1.A: Structure and Properties of Matter** (matter is made up of particles too small to be seen and has properties useful for identification; when matter changes form, the same amount is present)
DCI.2-PS1.B: Chemical Reactions (heating or cooling a substance can cause changes)	**DCI.5-PS1.B: Chemical Reactions** (when two or more different substances are mixed, a new substance may be formed that has the same weight as the original substances)
DCI.K-2-ETS1.A: Defining and Delimiting Engineering Problems (asking questions, making observations, and gathering information help in thinking about problems to be solved)	**DCI.3-5-ETS1.A: Defining and Delimiting Engineering Problems** (solutions can be compared by how well they meet criteria and take constraints into account)
DCI.K-2-ETS1.B: Developing Possible Solutions (designs can be conveyed through sketches, drawings, and physical models)	**DCI.3-5-ETS1.B: Developing Possible Solutions** (carry out research before designing a solution; communicate with others about your solution; test the solution)
DCI.K-2-ETS1.C: Optimizing the Design Solution (there is always more than one possible solution; compare and test designs)	**DCI.3-5-ETS1.C: Optimizing the Design Solution** (test different solutions to determine which best solves the problem)

Disciplinary Core Ideas

DCI.MS-ETS1.A: Defining and Delimiting Engineering Problems (the more precisely a design task's criteria and constraints are defined, the more likely it is that the solution will be successful)

DCI.MS-ETS1.B: Developing Possible Solutions (evaluate solutions with respect to criteria and constraints; use models to test solutions and then modify a solution based on test results)

DCI.MS-ETS1.C: Optimizing the Design Solution (iterative process of testing and modifying based on test results leads to an optimal solution)

DCI.MS-PS1.A: Structure and Properties of Matter (substances consist of different combinations of atoms and occur in different states; they have different physical and chemical properties)

DCI.MS-PS1.B: Chemical Reactions (substances react in ways that preserve the original number and type of atoms; reactions store or release energy)

DCI.MS-ESS2.A: Earth's Materials and Systems (Earth processes are the result of energy flowing and matter cycling through the planet's systems)

DCI.MS-PS1.A: Structure and Properties of Matter (substances consist of different combinations of atoms and occur in different states; they have different physical and chemical properties)

DCI.MS-ESS2.A: Earth's Materials and Systems (Earth processes are the result of energy flowing and matter cycling through the planet's systems)

DCI.MS-PS1.B: Chemical Reactions (substances react in ways that preserve the original number and type of atoms; reactions store or release energy)

DCI.MS-ETS1.A: Defining and Delimiting Engineering Problems (the more precisely a design task's criteria and constraints are defined, the more likely it is that the solution will be successful)

DCI.MS-ETS1.B: Developing Possible Solutions (evaluate solutions with respect to criteria and constraints; use models to test solutions and then modify a solution based on test results)

DCI.MS-ETS1.C: Optimizing the Design Solution (iterative process of testing and modifying based on test results leads to an optimal solution)

Notes:

Disciplinary Core Ideas

Grade 5 Unit Correlations and K–8 Program Storyline

Gr 5 Unit 3 Energy and Matter in Organisms

DCI.K-LS1.C: Organization for Matter and Energy Flow in Organisms (animals need food in order to live and grow; plants need water and light)

DCI.K-ESS3.A: Natural Resources (living things need water, air, and resources)

DCI.2-LS2.A: Interdependent Relationships in Ecosystems (plants depend on water and light to grow and animals to help in reproduction)

Gr 4 **DCI.4-PS3.D: Energy in Chemical Processes and Everyday Life** (stored energy can be converted into a form for practical use)

Gr 4 **DCI.4-LS1.A: Structure and Function** (plants and animals have structures that help them survive and reproduce)

Gr 5 **DCI.5-LS1.C: Organization for Matter and Energy Flow in Organisms** (plants acquire material for growth chiefly from air and water; animals get these materials from food)

DCI.K-PS3.B: Conservation of Energy and Energy Transfer (sunlight warms Earth's surface)

DCI.2-LS2.A: Interdependent Relationships in Ecosystems (plants depend on water and light to grow and animals to help in reproduction)

Gr 4 **DCI.4-PS3.A: Definitions of Energy** (energy can be moved from place to place; faster objects have greater energy)

Gr 4 **DCI.4-PS3.B: Conservation of Energy and Energy Transfer** (energy is present whenever there are moving objects, sound, light, or heat and can be transferred from one object or place to another)

Gr 5 **DCI.5-PS3.D: Energy in Chemical Processes and Everyday Life** (energy released from food was once energy from the sun)

DCI.K-LS1.C: Organization for Matter and Energy Flow in Organisms (animals need food in order to live and grow; plants need water and light)

DCI.K-ESS3.A: Natural Resources (living things need water, air, and resources)

Gr 3 **DCI.3-LS2.C: Ecosystem Dynamics, Functioning, and Resilience** (when the environment changes in an area, the organisms adjust, move away, or die off)

Gr 4 **DCI.4-ESS2.E: Biogeology** (living things affect the physical characteristics of their regions)

Gr 5 **DCI.5-LS2.A: Interdependent Relationships in Ecosystems** (the relationships of organisms in an ecosystem can be shown by food webs)

DCI.K-LS1.C: Organization for Matter and Energy Flow in Organisms (animals need food in order to live and grow; plants need water and light)

DCI.2-PS1.A: Structure and Properties of Matter (matter exists in different forms, has properties, and can be combined to make objects)

DCI.2-LS2.A: Interdependent Relationships in Ecosystems (plants depend on water and light to grow and animals to help in reproduction)

DCI.2-LS4.D: Biodiversity and Humans (different kinds of living things in an area live in different places on land and in water)

Gr 4 **DCI.4-ESS2.E: Biogeology** (living things affect the physical characteristics of their regions)

Gr 5 **DCI.5-LS2.B: Cycles of Matter and Energy Transfer in Ecosystems** (matter cycles among the living and nonliving parts of an ecosystem)

Disciplinary Core Ideas

DCI.MS-LS1.C: Organization for Matter and Energy Flow in Organisms (some organisms make food through photosynthesis; food is broken down to release energy and support growth)

DCI.MS-LS2.A: Interdependent Relationships in Ecosystems (in any ecosystem, organisms with similar requirements compete with each other for limited resources, which can limit growth and population size)

DCI.MS-LS2.B: Cycle of Matter and Energy Transfer in Ecosystems (food webs are models of how energy transfer occurs in ecosystems)

DCI.MS-PS3.D: Energy in Chemical Processes and Everyday Life (sunlight provides energy for photosynthesis; cellular respiration provides energy to organisms)

DCI.MS-LS2.A: Interdependent Relationships in Ecosystems (in any ecosystem, organisms with similar requirements compete with each other for limited resources, which can limit growth and population size)

DCI.MS-LS2.B: Cycle of Matter and Energy Transfer in Ecosystems (food webs are models of how energy transfer occurs in ecosystems)

DCI.MS-LS2.C: Ecosystem Dynamics, Functioning, and Resilience (ecosystem characteristics, including biodiversity, change over time)

Notes:

Disciplinary Core Ideas

Grade 5 Unit Correlations and K–8 Program Storyline

Grades K–2 Storyline	Grades 3–5 Storyline

DCI.K-LS1.C: Organization for Matter and Energy Flow in Organisms (animals need food in order to live and grow; plants need water and light)

DCI.K-ESS3.A: Natural Resources (living things need water, air, and resources)

Gr 3 **DCI.3-LS2.C: Ecosystem Dynamics, Functioning, and Resilience** (when the environment changes in an area, the organisms adjust, move away, or die off)

Gr 4 **DCI.4-ESS2.E: Biogeology** (living things affect the physical characteristics of their regions)

Gr 5 **DCI.5-LS2.A: Interdependent Relationships in Ecosystems** (the relationships of organisms in an ecosystem can be shown by food webs)

DCI.K-LS1.C: Organization for Matter and Energy Flow in Organisms (animals need food in order to live and grow; plants need water and light)

DCI.2-PS1.A: Structure and Properties of Matter (matter exists in different forms, has properties, and can be combined to make objects)

DCI.2-LS2.A: Interdependent Relationships in Ecosystems (plants depend on water and light to grow and animals to help in reproduction)

DCI.2-LS4.D: Biodiversity and Humans (different kinds of living things in an area live in different places in water and on land)

Gr 4 **DCI.4-ESS2.E: Biogeology** (living things affect the physical characteristics of their regions)

Gr 5 **DCI.5-LS2.B: Cycles of Matter and Energy Transfer in Ecosystems** (matter cycles among the living and nonliving parts of an ecosystem)

DCI.K-ESS2.D: Weather and Climate (weather is a combination of atmospheric conditions in a certain region at a certain time)

DCI.K-ESS3.A: Natural Resources (living things need water, air, and resources)

DCI.2-ESS2.A: Earth Materials and Systems (wind and water can change the shape of the land)

Gr 3 **DCI.3-ESS2.D: Weather and Climate** (scientists use patterns to make weather predictions and describe climate)

Gr 4 **DCI.4-ESS2.A: Earth Materials and Systems** (Earth's rocks and landforms can be changed by water, ice, wind, living things, and gravity)

Gr 4 **DCI.4-ESS2.B: Plate Tectonics and Large-Scale System Interactions** (locations of major Earth features such as mountain ranges, etc., occur in patterns)

Gr 5 **DCI.5-ESS2.A: Earth Materials and Systems** (Earth's major systems are the geosphere, hydrosphere, atmosphere, and biosphere)

DCI.K-2-ETS1.B: Developing Possible Solutions (designs can be conveyed through sketches, drawings, and physical models)

Gr 5 **DCI.3-5-ETS1.B: Developing Possible Solutions** (carry out research before designing a solution; communicate with others about your solution; test the solution)

Disciplinary Core Ideas

DCI.MS-LS2.A: Interdependent Relationships in Ecosystems (in any ecosystem, organisms with similar requirements compete with each other for limited resources, which can limit growth and population size)

DCI.MS-LS2.B: Cycle of Matter and Energy Transfer in Ecosystems (food webs are models of how energy transfer occurs in ecosystems)

DCI.MS-PS3.D: Energy in Chemical Processes and Everyday Life (sunlight provides energy for photosynthesis; cellular respiration provides energy to organisms)

DCI.MS-LS1.C: Organization for Matter and Energy Flow in Organisms (some organisms make food through photosynthesis; food is broken down to release energy and support growth)

DCI.MS-LS2.B: Cycle of Matter and Energy Transfer in Ecosystems (food webs are models of how energy transfer occurs in ecosystems)

DCI.MS-LS2.C: Ecosystem Dynamics, Functioning, and Resilience (ecosystem characteristics, including biodiversity, change over time)

DCI.MS-PS3.D: Energy in Chemical Processes and Everyday Life (sunlight provides energy for photosynthesis; cellular respiration provides energy to organisms)

DCI.MS-ESS1.C: The History of Planet Earth (the geologic time scale provides a way to organize Earth's history)

DCI.MS-ESS2.A: Earth's Materials and Systems (Earth processes are the result of energy flowing and matter cycling through the planet's systems)

DCI.MS-ESS2.C: The Roles of Water in Earth's Surface Processes (movement of Earth's water causes changes in all Earth systems, determining weather, shaping landforms, and causing ocean currents)

DCI.MS-ESS2.D: Weather and Climate (weather and climate are influenced by interactions of the atmosphere with sunlight and the ocean)

DCI.MS-ETS1.B: Developing Possible Solutions (evaluate solutions with respect to criteria and constraints; use models to test solutions and then modify a solution based on test results)

Notes:

Disciplinary Core Ideas

Grade 5 Unit Correlations and K–8 Program Storyline

Grades K–2 Storyline	Grades 3–5 Storyline

DCI.K-ESS2.D: Weather and Climate (weather is a combination of atmospheric conditions in a certain region at a certain time)

DCI.K-ESS3.A: Natural Resources (living things need water, air, and resources)

DCI.2-ESS2.A: Earth Materials and Systems (wind and water can change the shape of the land)

Gr 3 **DCI.3-ESS2.D: Weather and Climate** (scientists use patterns to make weather predictions and describe climate)

Gr 4 **DCI.4-ESS2.A: Earth Materials and Systems** (Earth's rocks and landforms can be changed by water, ice, wind, living things, and gravity)

Gr 4 **DCI.4-ESS2.B: Plate Tectonics and Large-Scale System Interactions** (locations of major Earth features such as mountain ranges, etc. occur in patterns)

Gr 5 **DCI.5-ESS2.A: Earth Materials and Systems** (Earth's major systems are the geosphere, hydrosphere, atmosphere, and biosphere)

DCI.2-ESS2.C: The Roles of Water in Earth's Surface Processes (water is found in many forms in oceans, on land, and in the air)

Gr 5 **DCI.5-ESS2.C: The Roles of Water in Earth's Surface Processes** (nearly all of Earth's water is in the ocean)

DCI.K-ESS2.E: Biogeology (plants and animals can change their environment)

DCI.K-ESS3.A: Natural Resources (living things need water, air, and resources)

DCI.K-ESS3.C: Human Impacts on Earth Systems (things people do can affect the world around them)

Gr 4 **DCI.4-ESS2.E: Biogeology** (living things affect the physical characteristics of their regions)

Gr 4 **DCI.4-ESS3.A: Natural Resources** (energy and fuels are derived from natural sources)

Gr 5 **DCI.5-ESS3.C: Human Impacts on Earth Systems** (human activities have had major effects on Earth and even in outer space)

DCI.K-2-ETS1.B: Developing Possible Solutions (designs can be conveyed through sketches, drawings, and physical models)

Gr 5 **DCI.3-5-ETS1.B: Developing Possible Solutions** (carry out research before designing a solution; communicate with others about your solution; test the solution)

DCI.K-2-ETS1.C: Optimizing the Design Solution (there is always more than one possible solution; compare and test designs)

Gr 5 **DCI.3-5-ETS1.C: Optimizing the Design Solution** (test different solutions to determine which best solves the problem)

DCI.K-PS2.B: Types of Interactions (when objects touch or collide, they push on one another and can change motion)

Gr 3 **DCI.3-PS2.B: Types of Interactions** (objects in contact exert forces on each other; electromagnetic forces do not require contact)

Gr 5 **DCI.5-PS2.B: Types of Interactions** (the gravitational force of Earth pulls objects toward the planet's center)

Disciplinary Core Ideas

DCI.MS-ESS1.C: The History of Planet Earth (the geologic time scale provides a way to organize Earth's history)

DCI.MS-ESS2.A: Earth's Materials and Systems (Earth processes are the result of energy flowing and matter cycling through the planet's systems)

DCI.MS-ESS2.D: Weather and Climate (weather and climate are influenced by interactions of the atmosphere with sunlight and the ocean)

DCI.MS-ESS2.C: The Roles of Water in Earth's Surface Processes (movement of Earth's water causes changes in all Earth systems, determining weather, shaping landforms, and causing ocean currents)

DCI.MS-ESS3.A: Natural Resources (humans depend on Earth's land, ocean, atmosphere, and biosphere for resources)

DCI.MS-ESS3.C: Human Impacts on Earth Systems (as resource consumption increases, so do negative impacts on Earth)

DCI.MS-ESS3.D: Global Climate Change (human activities are a major factor in the current rise in Earth's mean surface temperature)

DCI.MS-ETS1.B: Developing Possible Solutions (evaluate solutions with respect to criteria and constraints; use models to test solutions and then modify a solution based on test results)

DCI.MS-ETS1.C: Optimizing the Design Solution (iterative process of testing and modifying based on test results leads to an optimal solution)

DCI.MS-ESS1.B: Earth and the Solar System (the solar system formed from a disk of dust and gas and consists of many objects held in orbit by the sun's pull on them; motions of these objects can explain eclipses and seasonal variations)

DCI.MS-PS2.B: Types of Interactions (non-contact forces can be explained by fields that extend through space)

Notes:

Disciplinary Core Ideas

Grade 5 Unit Correlations and K–8 Program Storyline

Grades K–2 Storyline	Grades 3–5 Storyline
	Gr 5 Unit 6 Patterns in the Sky *cont.*

DCI.1-ESS1.A: The Universe and Its Stars
(patterns of motion of objects in the sky can be described)

DCI.1-ESS1.B: Earth and the Solar System
(seasonal patterns of sunrise and sunset can be predicted)

Gr 3 **DCI.3-PS2.A: Forces and Motion** (every force has a strength and direction; patterns of motion can be used to predict future motion)

Gr 5 **DCI.5-ESS1.B: Earth and the Solar System** (motion of Earth and the moon cause observable patterns)

DCI.1-ESS1.A: The Universe and Its Stars
(patterns of motion of objects in the sky can be described)

Gr 5 **DCI.5-ESS1.A: The Universe and its Stars** (the sun is the closest, and therefore the brightest star seen from Earth)

Disciplinary Core Ideas

DCI.MS-ESS1.B: Earth and the Solar System (the solar system formed from a disk of dust and gas and consists of many objects held in orbit by the sun's pull on them; motions of these objects can explain eclipses and seasonal variations)

DCI.MS-ESS1.A: The Universe and Its Stars (patterns of apparent motion of objects in the sky can be described and explained with models; the solar system is one part of the Milky Way galaxy)

Notes:

Disciplinary Core Ideas

Grade 5 Unit Correlations and K–8 Program Storyline

Grades K–2 Storyline	Grades 3–5 Storyline
	Gr 5 Unit 1 Engineering and Technology
Influence of Engineering, Technology, and Science on Society and the Natural World (human life would be very different without technology; products are designed using knowledge of natural world and natural materials)	**Influence of Engineering, Technology, and Science on Society and the Natural World** (engineers improve technologies or develop new ones; people's needs, wants, and demands change over time)
	Gr 5 Unit 2 Matter
Cause and Effect (events have causes that generate patterns; simple tests can provide evidence to support or refute ideas)	**Cause and Effect** (cause and effect relationships are identified, tested, and used to explain change)
	Scale, Proportion and Quantity (objects and phenomena exist in various scales and for various times; standard units measure and describe physical quantities)
	Science Is a Human Endeavor (science affects everyday life; creativity and imagination are important to science)
Scientific Knowledge Assumes an Order and Consistency in Natural Systems (natural events happen today as in the past; many events are repeated)	**Scientific Knowledge Assumes an Order and Consistency in Natural Systems** (science assumes consistent patterns)
Systems and System Models (systems have parts that work together)	**Systems and System Models** (system can be described by its components and their interactions)
	Gr 5 Unit 3 Energy and Matter in Organisms
	Energy and Matter (energy can be transferred in various ways and between objects; total weight of substances does not change in a process; matter moves in and out of systems)
Systems and System Models (systems have parts that work together)	**Systems and System Models** (system can be described by its components and their interactions)
	Gr 5 Unit 4 Energy and Matter in Ecosystems
Systems and System Models (systems have parts that work together)	**Systems and System Models** (system can be described by its components and their interactions)
	Gr 5 Unit 5 Earth Interactions and Resources
Systems and System Models (systems have parts that work together)	**Systems and System Models** (system can be described by its components and their interactions)

Crosscutting Concepts

Influence of Engineering, Technology, and Science on Society and the Natural World (technology use is driven by needs, desires, values, research, and other factors; technologies enhance scientific investigations)

Cause and Effect (correlation does not necessarily imply causation; cause and effect relationships can predict phenomena)

Scale, Proportion, and Quantity (models can be used to study phenomena at various scales; proportional relationships provide information about magnitude; phenomena may not be observable at all scales)

Science is a Human Endeavor (science and technology influence each other; scientists and engineers are guided by habits of mind)

Scientific Knowledge Assumes an Order and Consistency in Natural Systems (natural systems and consistent patterns are understandable through measurement and observation)

Systems and System Models (systems interact; may have subsystems and be part of complex systems)

Energy and Matter (transfer of energy drives motion and cycling of matter in a system; energy may take different forms; transfer of energy can be tracked as energy flows through a system)

Systems and System Models (systems interact; may have subsystems and be part of complex systems)

Systems and System Models (systems interact; may have subsystems and be part of complex systems)

Systems and System Models (systems interact; may have subsystems and be part of complex systems)

Notes:

Crosscutting Concepts

Grade 5 Unit Correlations and K–8 Program Storyline

Grades K–2 Storyline	Grades 3–5 Storyline
	Gr 5 Unit 5 Earth Interactions and Resources *cont.*
	Scale, Proportion, and Quantity (objects and phenomena exist in various scales and for various times)
Science Addresses Questions About the Natural and Material World (scientists study natural and material world)	**Science Addresses Questions About the Natural and Material World** (science findings are limited to empirical evidence)
	Gr 5 Unit 6 Patterns in the Sky
Cause and Effect (events have causes that generate patterns; simple tests can provide evidence to support or refute ideas)	**Cause and Effect** (cause and effect relationships are identified, tested, and used to explain change)
Patterns (patterns can describe phenomena and be used as evidence)	**Patterns** (patterns can be used to sort, classify, communicate, and analyze rates of change)
	Scale, Proportion and Quantity (objects and phenomena exist in various scales and for various times)

Crosscutting Concepts

Scale, Proportion, and Quantity (models can be used to study phenomena at various scales; phenomena may not be observable at all scales)

Science Addresses Questions About the Natural and Material World. (science can describe consequences of actions but is not responsible for society's decisions)

Cause and Effect (correlation does not necessarily imply causation; cause and effect relationships can predict phenomena)

Patterns (macroscopic patterns are related to microscopic and atomic-level structure)

Scale, Proportion, and Quantity (models can be used to study phenomena at various scales; phenomena may not be observable at all scales)

Notes:

Crosscutting Concepts

HMH Into Science™ and the EQuIP Rubric

The **EQuIP Rubric** is an instrument for evaluating a curriculum's conformance with the contours of an authentic NGSS program. As such, one needs to bear in mind the known limitations and proper usages of the rubric:

- The rubric is intended to be applied to lessons or units, not to entire curricula.
- The rubric itself indicates that it is unlikely that a single lesson will lead to mastery of a Performance Expectation. High-Quality Units may do so.
- The evaluation process is intended to be done in a group, not by an individual.

- The rubric requires familiarity with the Performance Expectation and its supporting Dimensions of Learning. The **HMH Into Science Trace Tool to the NGSS** can help provide this orientation.

Throughout the **HMH Into Science Teacher Guide**, you will find features to help you orient toward the critical dimensions of the EQuIP Rubric. Using the book, you are well beyond the evaluation phase of considering a program, but these features will demonstrate the best practices of NGSS summarized by the evaluation instrument. Highlights of critical EQuIP Rubric evaluation points are summarized in the reduced pages you see here.

UNIT OPENER PAGES

I.F ELA and Math connections

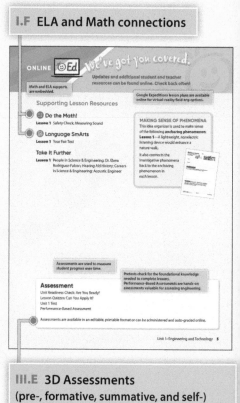

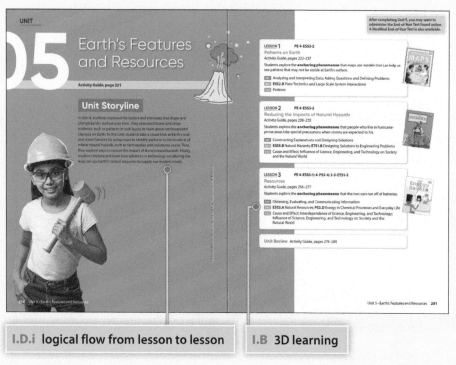

I.D.i logical flow from lesson to lesson

I.B 3D learning

III.E 3D Assessments
(pre-, formative, summative, and self-)

LESSON OPENER PAGES

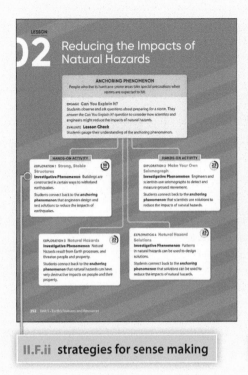

II.F.ii strategies for sense making

II.A.i authentic and meaningful scenarios

FUNonemal READER

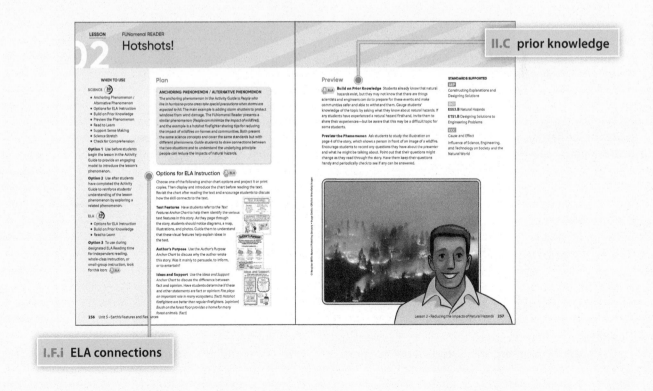

II.C prior knowledge

I.F.i ELA connections

ONLINE RESOURCES

III.F multiple opportunities to learn

I.C interdisciplinary connections

II.B collaborative opportunities to express ideas and respond

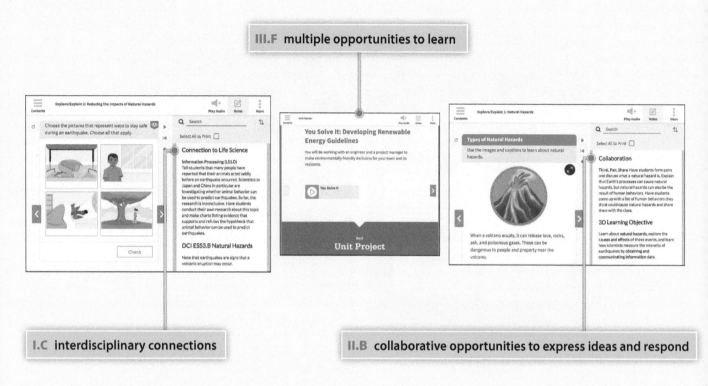

LESSON PAGES

III.B formative assessments embedded throughout instruction

II.E differentiating instruction

II.F.ii strategies for sense making

III.C rubrics for interpreting student performance

II.D scientifically accurate and grade-appropriate content

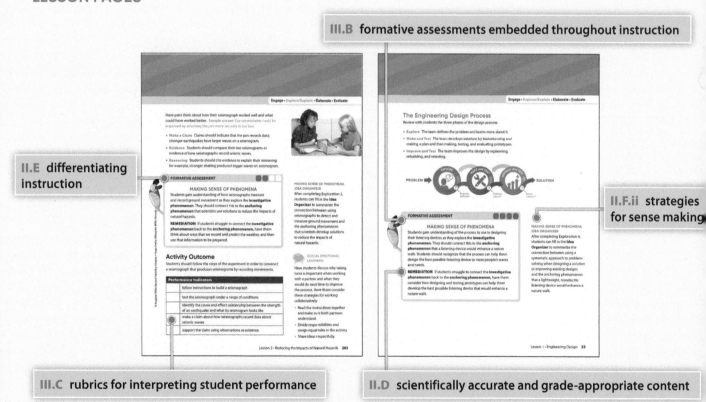

LESSON CLOSER PAGES

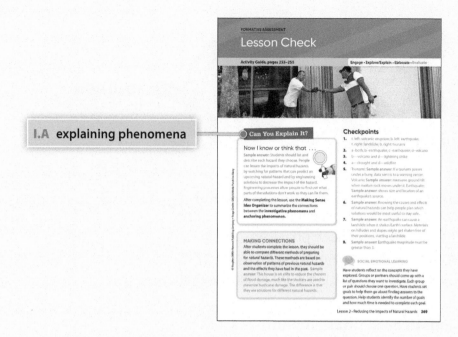

I.A explaining phenomena

UNIT CLOSER PAGES

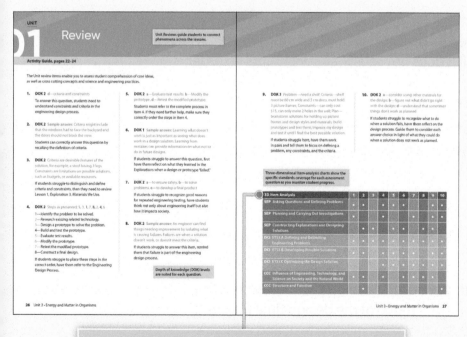

III.A eliciting direct observable evidence of 3D learning

Engineering

Have students examine the diagram by looking at the icons and tracing the arrows. The arrows within each phase show how you may repeat steps within a phase multiple times. The questions for each phase are checks to help identify what result you should have before moving on to the next phase. The return arrows show how you may return to a previous phase at any time.

Ask: What do you think the icons in each phase mean? Students may notice that in the first phase a person is asking questions. In the second phase, there is a pencil representing the idea of using a pencil to plan, but also to record data from tests. The wrench indicates making changes to a possible solution. The icon in the third phase shows repeated improvements by the arrows increasing to a plus sign.

EXPLORE

Discuss with students how to gather information about a problem to understand it and identify what features an acceptable solution would have. A solution is unacceptable if it does not satisfy all constraints. In order to define a problem, one must state the problem clearly and identify the criteria and constraints for an acceptable solution.

Ask: Look at the diagram. What should you do when you answer 'yes' to the question "Problem defined"? Students should identify that if the problem is defined, they go on to the Make and Test phase. If not, they should repeat the steps in the Explore phase to gather the necessary information.

MAKE and TEST

Discuss with students how to brainstorm and develop potential solutions in the Make and Test phase. Explain that much of the design time may be spent in the Make and Test phase. Students can modify, test, and evaluate one or more prototypes to find an acceptable solution. Point out that a solution can be a tool or process that solves a problem.

Discuss with students how testing is needed to gather the data needed to make decisions. New information might arise during this phase that makes it necessary to return to the Explore phase. During testing, students may realize that even though a solution seems to satisfy the criteria, it doesn't really solve their problem. This may mean that they need to adjust their problem definition.

Ask: How are criteria and constraints used during the MAKE and TEST phase? Criteria and constraints are used to evaluate a solution. If a solution satisfies the criteria and constraints it should solve the problem.

Remind students that multiple solutions may solve the problem. One solution may work better than another, and features of different solutions may be combined to make a better solution.

IMPROVE and TEST

Discuss with students why you should repeat the steps of changing, testing, and evaluating a prototype to improve it. Each change should improve how well the solution satisfies the criteria to get the best possible solution. If new information makes it necessary, you may return to the Explore or Make and Test phase.

Discuss with students that engineers often work in groups and design solutions for other people. They need to communicate during all phases of the process to gather and share information. This includes presenting a solution so that other people can use it.

Ask: How might you communicate a solution to other people? Students may say that a model can be used to explain how a solution works or what it looks like so that other people can use it.

Hana wants to attract pretty birds to her backyard. Talk with a partner about how Hana might use an engineering design process to solve this problem. Sample answer: Students should consider all the parts of the engineering design process presented here and discuss how Hana might use this process to solve the problem of attracting birds to her backyard.

Claims, Evidence, and Reasoning

Use the following discussion points to introduce the Claims, Evidence, and Reasoning strategy that will be used throughout the program.

Materials

Prepare the following materials before starting:

- clear container, 50 mL vinegar
- clear container, 100 mL vinegar
- clear container, 200 mL vinegar
- tablespoon
- baking soda, 3 tablespoons
- safety goggles

Procedure

Ask for three volunteers. Before you begin the activity, have students write a claim about which amount of vinegar will react the most.

1. Have one volunteer put one tablespoon of baking soda in the 50 mL of vinegar. Pause to observe.

2. Have the next volunteer put one tablespoon of baking soda in the 100 mL of vinegar. Pause to observe.

3. Have the last volunteer put one tablespoon of baking soda in 200 mL of vinegar. Pause to observe.

4. Have students share their observations.

Discuss with students that a claim can be made about an observation either before or after you do a scientific investigation or solve an engineering problem.

Have students work independently to formulate questions and identify one to investigate. Students should use this investigation to practice making a claim, supporting it with evidence, and using reasoning to connect and explain the evidence. They can use sentence frames such as, The evidence supports my claim because _____.

Ask: In a scientific investigation, what can you use as evidence to support a claim? Sample answer: Data collected from the investigation, observations, research or things you read about

 Find more support in the **Claims, Evidence, and Reasoning** section of the online Science and Engineering Practices Handbook.

Safety in Science

Safety in the Lab

Use the following discussion points to emphasize key safety rules for indoor science activities.

Ask: Why is it important to understand safety reminders before you begin an activity? You may get hurt if you don't follow the reminders during the activity.

Ask: Why do you need to keep long sleeves and hair out of the way during science activities? Hair and clothes can snag equipment and get stained. They can also catch fire.

Ask: Tell me what you would do if you spilled some water. Students should mention informing the teacher and helping clean up.

Ask: What could happen if the spill wasn't cleaned up? Students should realize that water makes the floor slippery and increases the risk of falls.

Ask: First, put on a pair of safety goggles. What are the differences between safety goggles and ordinary glasses? Students should recognize the sturdy material and protection all around the sides of the lenses.

Ask: Why are these differences important during science activities? The lenses are less likely to break. The protection on the sides keeps liquid and objects from getting into your eyes.

Ask for a student volunteer. Tell them to walk up to and point at a piece of safety equipment in the classroom, then tell the class when and how you would use it.

Safety in the Field

Use the following discussion points to emphasize key safety rules for outdoor science activities.

Ask: How does your clothing affect your safety outdoors? Covering up your arms and legs protects you from scratches and from the sun.

Ask: Why do you think open-toed or dressy shoes are poor choices for exploring outdoors? Sturdy shoes can protect your feet from sharp objects, plants, and biting insects.

Ask: Why is it unsafe to taste anything outdoors? Many plants and animals are poisonous. Even adults can be fooled.

Ask: Why is it important to stay with your group and stay on marked trails? With a group, someone will be there to help if you get hurt or have a problem. Marked trails are safer; walking through wild areas may damage habitats.

Ask: Why are running and horseplay riskier outdoors? You don't know the area. The ground level may change quickly. If you're moving fast, it's easier to fall and get hurt before you can stop.

Ask: Why is it especially important to wash your hands when you come back indoors? It helps keep you from getting sick and from rubbing grit into your eyes by accident.

Safety Symbols

Safety symbols will appear in the instructions for each Hands-On Activity to emphasize important notes of caution. Make sure students learn what they represent and understand the appropriate precautions to take.

Use the following discussion points to emphasize key safety rules for each Hands-On Activity.

Ask: How are safety goggles different from regular eyeglasses? Safety goggles are made of sturdy material and have protection around the sides of the lenses.

Ask: Why should you tie back long hair? Loose, long hair could obstruct the materials in the activity or become contaminated.

Ask: If chemicals get on your skin, clothing, or in your eyes, why is it important to rinse it immediately? Chemicals can burn or stain skin or clothing. Rinsing immediately helps to reduce the impact of the chemicals.

Ask: Why should you wash your hands thoroughly after each activity? Hands can get contaminated from the materials in the activity. Washing hands helps to ensure that materials from the activity are not ingested when eating. Washing hands also keeps you from rubbing things into your eyes.

Dress Code	
Glassware and Sharp Object Safety	
Electrical Safety	
Chemical Safety	
Heating and Fire Safety	
Plant and Animal Safety	
Cleanup	

Safety Quiz

Use this quiz to check student understanding of lab safety practices and procedures.

It is important that students take responsibility for their safety and the safety of others. Be sure to discuss with students each question and answer to help them understand the importance of safe conduct during an activity.

1. At the end of any activity you should
    a—wash your hands thoroughly before leaving the lab.
2. If you get hurt or injured in any way, you should
    a—tell your teacher immediately.
3. Before starting an activity, you should
    c—read all directions and make sure you understand them
4. When working with materials that might fly into the air and hurt someone's eye, you should wear
    a—goggles.
5. If you get something in your eye you should
    d—tell your teacher right away.

Find more support in the online **Lab Safety Handbook**.

Notes:

Notes:

Engineering and Technology

Activity Guide, page 1

Unit Storyline

In this unit, students will explore how people study, interact with, and manage technology. They will revisit and practice the engineering design process to define problems and build, test, evaluate, and optimize solutions to those problems. This will help students in their explorations in Units 2 through 6.

Before starting Unit 1, you may want to
administer the Beginning-of-Year Readiness
Check found online.

LESSON 1   PE 3-5-ETS1-1, 3-5-ETS1-2, 3-5-ETS1-3
Engineering and Society
Activity Guide, pages 2–25

Students explore the **anchoring phenomenon** that a car from 60 years ago looks
different from cars today but has the same basic function.

SEP Asking Questions and Defining Problems; Constructing Explanations and
Designing Solutions; Planning and Carrying Out Investigations

DCI **ETS1.A** Defining and Delimiting Engineering Problems; **ETS1.B** Developing
Possible Solutions; **ETS1.C** Optimizing the Design Solution;
PS1.A Structure and Properties of Matter*

CCC Influence of Science, Engineering, and Technology on Society and the
Natural World

*Engineering and science are interconnected, and engineering does not occur in
isolation from science. To help students make this connection, the physical science
concepts in this DCI are introduced briefly in this lesson. However, this lesson does
not prepare students for mastery of the physical science content. Full coverage of DCI
PS1.A occurs in Unit 2.

Unit Review   Activity Guide, pp. 26–28

Engineering is embedded throughout each
grade level and covered in depth in the first
unit to provide a solid foundation for students.

Engineering Design Process

PROBLEM ➡️ EXPLORE   MAKE and TEST   IMPROVE and TEST ➡️ SOLUTION

Problem
defined?

Problem
solved?

Better
solution?

Online-Only Resources

01

Online, the NGSS Trace Tool unpacks the standards and displays the connectedness and spiraling within and across grade levels.

Supporting Unit Resources

You Solve It SUPPORTS LESSON 1

Cat Tree is a virtual lab that offers practice in support of **Performance Expectations 3-5-ETS1-1** and **ETS1-3.** Students will design a scratching post for cats and optimize their solutions to better meet criteria and constraints.

- **SEP** Asking Questions and Defining Problems
- **DCI** **ETS1.C** Optimizing the Design Solution
- **CCC** Influence of Science, Engineering, and Technology on Society and the Natural World

You Solve It activities are engaging open-ended computer simulations that offer alternative, easy lab options.

Unit Project SUPPORTS LESSON 1

90 min

Dropping Off, Picking Up provides students an opportunity to practice aspects of **Performance Expectations 3-5-ETS1-1, ETS1-2,** and **ETS1-3.** Students will ask questions and define problems in order to redesign a school entranceway.

- **SEP** Asking Questions and Defining Problems; Constructing Explanations and Designing Solutions
- **DCI** **ETS1.A** Defining and Delimiting Engineering Problems; **ETS1.B** Developing Possible Solutions; **ETS1.C** Optimizing the Design Solution
- **CCC** Influence of Science, Engineering, and Technology on Society and the Natural World

Optional Unit Projects can be used to tie together bigger concepts across the unit.

Unit Performance Task SUPPORTS LESSON 1

90 min

Lunch Line Life Hack provides an opportunity for students to practice or be assessed on aspects of **Performance Expectations 3-5-ETS1-1** and **ETS1-2.** Students design a lunch line that moves faster.

- **SEP** Asking Questions and Defining Problems; Constructing Explanations and Designing Solutions; Planning and Carrying Out Investigations
- **DCI** **ETS1.A** Defining and Delimiting Engineering Problems; **ETS1.B** Developing Possible Solutions
- **CCC** Influence of Science, Engineering, and Technolog on Society and the Natural World; Systems and System Models

Hands-On Unit Performance Tasks provide tactile assessment options.

Language Development

This worksheet is used as students progress through the unit. As they come to a highlighted vocabulary term, they should fill in this chart with words or phrases.

Embedded ELA best practices and strategies allow teachers to cover both science and ELA in the same lesson.

We've got you covered.

Updates and additional student and teacher resources can be found online. Check back often!

Math and ELA supports are embedded.

Google Expeditions lesson plans are available online for virtual-reality field-trip options.

Supporting Lesson Resources

 Do the Math!

Lesson 1 Fuel Efficiency

 Language SmArts

Lesson 1 Tech Knowledge, Background Research, Connecting, Posing Questions

Take It Further

Lesson 1 Careers in Science & Engineering: Safety Engineer; Go Further: Self-Driving Cars; Safety Survey

MAKING SENSE OF PHENOMENA

This idea organizer is used to make sense of the following **anchoring phenomenon**: **Lesson 1**—A car from 60 years ago looks different from cars today but has the same basic function.

It also connects the investigative phenomena back to the anchoring phenomenon in the lesson.

Assessments are used to measure student progress over time.

Pretests check for the foundational knowledge needed to complete lessons.
Performance-Based Assessments are hands-on assessments valuable for assessing engineering.

Assessment

Unit Readiness Check: Are You Ready?

Lesson Quiz: Can You Apply It?

Unit 1 Test

Performance-Based Assessment

Assessments are available in an editable, printable format or can be administered and auto-graded online.

01

Engineering and Society

ANCHORING PHENOMENON

A car from 60 years ago looks different from cars today but has the same basic function.

ENGAGE Can You Explain It?

Students observe and ask questions about cars from different eras. They answer the Can You Explain It? question to identify what they will gather evidence about in the lesson.

EVALUATE Lesson Check

Students gauge their understanding of the anchoring phenomenon.

Lessons begin with phenomena- and problem-driven three-dimensional learning.

Every lesson clearly shows how the phenomena relate to a coherent storyline.

HANDS-ON ACTIVITY

EXPLORATION 1
What Makes a Good Toy Car? (50 min)
Investigative Phenomenon
Before designing a car, engineers seek to understand what matters in a good car.

Students connect back to the **anchoring phenomenon** that both cars meet the need for transportation, but they meet wants to different degrees.

HANDS-ON ACTIVITY

EXPLORATION 2
Improving Toy Cars (60 min)
Investigative Phenomenon
Engineers improve existing car solutions according to clear priorities.

Students connect back to the **anchoring phenomenon** that the most desirable car technology depends on what users consider valuable and important, which can change.

EXPLORATION 3
Technology, Engineering, and Science (15 min)
Investigative Phenomenon
Engineers apply science knowledge to make technology that solves problems.

Students connect back to the **anchoring phenomenon** that engineers applied science to develop technology to solve the problem of getting around quickly and safely.

EXPLORATION 4 How Do Engineers Solve Problems? (60 min)
Investigative Phenomenon Engineers use a systematic approach to problem solving when designing cars or improving existing car technology.

Students connect back to the **anchoring phenomenon** that the engineering design process was used to improve transportation technology to make the cars in use today.

EXPLORATION 5 Improving Over Time (15 min)
Investigative Phenomenon Technology, including cars, changes over time as user priorities change and engineers make tradeoffs.

Students connect back to the **anchoring phenomenon** that engineers improved car technology to better meet government rules and the needs and wants of car buyers.

Making 3D Connections

Focal points of the three dimensions of learning for each lesson are defined.

The **anchoring phenomenon** in this lesson supports students' understanding of and application of these Next Generation Science Standards.

Building to the Performance Expectations

3-5-ETS1-1 Define a simple design problem reflecting a need or a want that includes specified criteria for success and constraints on materials, time, or cost.

3-5-ETS1-2 Generate and compare multiple possible solutions to a problem based on how well each is likely to meet the criteria and constraints of the problem.

3-5-ETS1-3 Plan and carry out fair tests in which variables are controlled and failure points are considered to identify aspects of a model or prototype that can be improved.

SEP

Asking Questions and Defining Problems Define a simple design problem that includes several criteria and constraints. *(Explorations 1, 4, 5)*

Constructing Explanations and Designing Solutions Generate and compare multiple solutions to a problem based on the criteria and constraints. *(Explorations 1, 2)*

Planning and Carrying Out Investigations Plan and conduct an investigation to produce data to serve as the basis for evidence, using fair tests. *(Explorations 1, 2, 4)*

Language development support options are embedded for students, and strategies are called out for teachers.

DCI

ETS1.A Defining and Delimiting Engineering Problems Different proposals for solutions can be compared. *(Explorations 1, 2, 4, 5)*

ETS1.B Developing Possible Solutions Research on a problem should be carried out. Testing a solution involves investigating how it performs. *(Explorations 1, 2, 3, 4)*

Communicating with peers is an important part of the design process. *(Explorations 2, 5)*

Tests are often designed to identify failure points or difficulties. *(Exploration 2)*

ETS1.C Optimizing the Design Solution Different solutions need to be tested. *(Explorations 2, 4, 5)*

DCI

PS1.A Structure and Properties of Matter Matter of any type can be subdivided into particles that are too small to see. **(Exploration 2)*

*This lesson briefly introduces the science concepts in this DCI. Full coverage of DCI PS1.A occurs in Unit 2.

CCC

Influence of Science, Engineering, and Technology on Society and the Natural World People's needs and wants change over time. *(Exploration 5)*

Engineers improve existing technologies or develop new ones. *(Explorations 1, 2, 3, 5)*

Vocabulary

| Word Wall | A word wall, anchor chart, or Language Development chart can be used to support vocabulary.

criteria the desirable features of a solution

constraint an absolute limit on possible solutions

prototype a model for testing

tradeoff a decision to give up a quality or feature of a solution to gain a different quality or feature

You may want to include additional academic terms such as *factor* and *limitation* and any other terms students might struggle with.

Language Development Prompt students to complete the chart when they come to these highlighted terms within the lesson.

Anchor Chart As you progress through the unit, you may want to make a vocabulary-based Anchor Chart using the Language Development chart as a guide that can be displayed and filled out as a whole group during each lesson.

01 Engineering and Society

Activity Guide, pages 2–3

Online, students can view videos, play animations, and interact with instructional images and text.

Students can engage in the Can You Explain It? content by observing the photograph or by exploring the corresponding video online.

ONLINE View a video related to older and newer cars.

ANCHORING PHENOMENON

A car from 60 years ago looks different from cars today but has the same basic function.

PHENOMENON EXPLAINED

Cars have changed over time based on changes in user needs and wants, government laws, and scientific advances.

Explanations of lesson phenomena provide useful instructional background information.

Lessons supported by the 5E instructional model are flexible so you can adjust them to your classroom needs.

Engage • Explore/Explain • Elaborate • Evaluate

Lesson Objective

Students can use evidence to support a claim that engineers use a systematic approach to design and improve technology to meet people's wants and needs, which change over time.

Support Discovery

The following prompts can be used to guide student-led discovery.

> Discussion prompts allow teachers to easily facilitate classroom explorations.

I notice . . .

After observing the photograph or watching the video, students should record what they noticed about the cars. If students struggle to record observations, ask them to focus on the similarities and differences between the cars.

Sample answer: I notice that both cars have windows and doors and tires.

I wonder . . .

After observing the photograph or watching the video, students should record what they want to find out more about cars from different time periods. If students struggle to record what they wonder about the cars, have them work with a partner to brainstorm a list of questions.

Sample answer: I wonder why the newer car is more rounded than the older car and if they both work with the same kind of fuel.

> Alternative phenomena provide additional instructional flexibility or can be used as an assessment to measure students' ability to apply learning to a new situation.

Can You Explain It?

In the Can You Explain It?, students make an initial claim that explains the **Anchoring Phenomenon.**
Sample answer: Students may draw a model of a process to change car technology or write a sentence about how engineers design improvements to technology.

In the lesson, students gather evidence about the engineering design process and changes in automobile design. This will enable them to give a more complete explanation of the **Anchoring Phenomenon** at the end of the lesson.

→ Alternative Phenomenon

If students are unfamiliar with the changes in automobiles over time, guide them to think of other examples of design changes over time, such as athletic shoes or mobile phones.

SOCIAL EMOTIONAL LEARNING

Have each student set a personal goal for this lesson and make a plan for how to achieve the goal. Throughout the lesson, take daily breaks for students to track their progress in meeting their goals. As students move from lesson to lesson, they can continue to work toward their initial goals or set new ones. If students struggle setting goals for this lesson, share with them some of the following ideas: identifying how engineers solve problems, determining how wants and needs influence technology, participating during activity/group work, or persevering when an activity or topic is difficult.

> Friendly robots guide students throughout the lessons and across elementary grade levels.

Lesson 1 • Engineering and Society **9**

01

A Pressure Problem

The FUNomenal Leveled Readers model how students should use scientific processes to resolve phenomena.

WHEN TO USE

SCIENCE **30 min**

- Anchoring Phenomenon / Alternative Phenomenon
- Options for ELA Instruction
- Build on Prior Knowledge
- Preview the Phenomenon
- Read to Learn
- Support Sense Making
- Science Stretch
- Check for Comprehension

Option 1 Use before students begin the lesson in the Activity Guide to provide an engaging model to introduce the lesson's phenomenon.

Option 2 Use after students have completed the Activity Guide to reinforce students' understanding of the lesson phenomenon by exploring a related phenomenon.

ELA **20 min**

- Options for ELA Instruction
- Build on Prior Knowledge
- Read to Learn

Option 3 To use during designated ELA Reading time for independent reading, whole-class instruction, or small-group instruction, look for this icon: **ELA**

Options on when to use your FUNomenal Readers can be found here.

Plan

ANCHORING PHENOMENON / ALTERNATIVE PHENOMENON

The anchoring phenomenon in the Activity Guide is *A car from 60 years ago looks different from cars today but has the same basic function.* The main example is a comparison of a modern car with an older-model car. The FUNomenal Reader presents a similar phenomenon (*The properties of matter can be used to design a solution for properly inflating a soccer ball*), and the example is a soccer ball that has gone flat. Both present the same science concepts and cover the same standards but with different phenomena. Guide students to draw connections between the two situations and to understand the underlying principle: the engineering design process can be used to solve problems.

Follow the ELA icon to use readers during your reading time.

Options for ELA Instruction   ELA

Choose one of the following anchor chart options and project it or print copies. Then display and introduce the chart before reading the text. Revisit the chart after reading the text and encourage students to discuss how the skill connects to the text.

Ask and Answer Questions Use the *Ask and Answer Questions Anchor Chart* when introducing, developing, or reviewing those skills. Have students consider how questioning helps the characters in the story define and delimit the problem they want to solve.

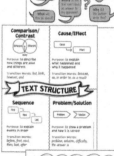

Text Structure Refer to the *Text Structure Anchor Chart* when discussing text structure in the context of this story. Guide students to an understanding of the problem-solution structure of the story. Have them identify the problem and the solution.

Make Connections Use the *Make Connections Anchor Chart* to help students relate what they read to their own experiences, to other stories they have read, and to the larger world. Give them these sentence starters: *This reminds me of when I . . ., This is like another story I read . . ., This is like something that happened in my community . . .*

Preview

ELA **Build on Prior Knowledge** Students should already know that the engineering design process involves defining a problem, designing a solution, considering the positive and negative impacts, and testing and improving those designs. Review the properties of matter by identifying an object in the classroom (such as a chair or a piece of paper) and having students describe these properties: color, shape, texture, hardness, flexibility, and absorbency. Tell students that knowing about the properties of matter can help them design solutions to many problems.

Preview the Phenomenon Have students study the illustration on p. 7 of the story, which shows three kids, two balls, and an air pump. Encourage students to record any questions they have, reminding them that this story is part of a lesson on engineering design. Is there anything in the illustration that represents a problem to solve? Point out that their questions might change as they read through the story. Have them keep their questions handy and periodically check to see if they can answer any.

STANDARDS SUPPORTED

SEP
Asking Questions and Defining Problems

Constructing Explanations and Designing Solutions

DCI
ETS1.A Defining and Delimiting Engineering Problems

ETS1.B Developing Possible Solutions

ETS1.C Optimizing the Design Solution

PS1.A Structure and Properties of Matter

CCC
Influence of Science, Engineering, and Technology on Society and the Natural World

A Pressure Problem (continued)

Discover

Read to Learn

The **Read to Learn** suggestions inside the book's front cover encourage students to interact with the book multiple times for different purposes.

> **Preview** Students look for unfamiliar words and share them with a partner. New terms may include *pressure* and *engineering design process*. Have students look up words they aren't sure about and notice how they are used in the context of the story.

> **Skim** Students skim the illustrations in the story. Have them turn to a partner and share their predictions of what the story will be about.

> **Read** As students read the story, ask them to look for connections to one of the following anchor chart skills.
> **Ask and Answer Questions, Text Structure, Make Connections**

Support Sense Making

Choose one or more of the following:

- ▶ Be sure students can identify the phenomenon presented on the opening pages of the story: Ana, Toshiro, and Leo need to inflate a soccer ball, but they don't know how to get the correct pressure. The story follows their efforts to explore the problem, make a plan, and test and improve several solutions.

- ▶ Discuss the criteria and constraints the characters identify. Project the Engineering Design Process graphic from the Teacher Guide introduction to this unit, and have students list the steps in the engineering design process that the characters follow under the three heads: Explore, Make and Test, Improve and Test.

- ▶ Encourage a student-led discussion of the tests the characters use to determine the correct pressure for a soccer ball. Can students think of other tests they might try, especially if there is no second ball for comparison purposes? Interested students can do research to find out how an everyday item was developed and tested.

- ▶ Remind students that engineers learn from their failures. In the engineering design process, there are no "right answers." Instead, getting things wrong is an important part of problem solving. Invite volunteers to describe failures they have experienced that led to new understandings or other breakthroughs.

Extend

Science Stretch

The **Science Stretch** suggestions inside the book's back cover help students think about what they read. Students can complete one or more as time allows.

> List the factors the characters used to evaluate their solution. Support a claim about how well their solution met the desired features. Students can work in pairs to come up with a claim that is supported by evidence and reasoning.

> Make a poster showing how you could use an engineering design process to solve a problem. Remind students that the steps in the engineering design process can be repeated and done in any order.

> Research how soccer balls have changed over time. Provide books, magazines, and approved online links for students to use in their research.

SOCIAL EMOTIONAL LEARNING

How did working together help the characters solve their problem?
Sample answer: They listened to each other's ideas and tried them all.

Check for Comprehension Have students write a paragraph in response to this question: *Why is it important that multiple solutions be developed and tested?* Be sure students understand that an engineering design solution might not actually work when tested. It is important to try several alternatives to improve the chances of success.

Engineer It • What Makes a Good Toy Car?

Activity Guide, pages 4–7

Engineer It explorations allow students to apply the engineering design process.

TIME ESTIMATE

50 min

POSSIBLE MATERIALS

- ☐ balloons
- ☐ bendable straws, 3
- ☐ cardboard, rectangle
- ☐ paper cups, 4, 12 oz
- ☐ ruler
- ☐ scissors
- ☐ stir straws, 2
- ☐ tape
- ☐ additional varieties of the above, and alternatives such as CDs, toothpicks, wooden craft sticks, index cards, poly beads, and plastic bottle caps with pre-drilled holes

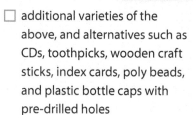

Hands-on materials kits are available and easy to use.

PREPARATION

The quantities for the paper cups and straws are required to build the toy car in Step 1. The cardboard must be at least 4 cm narrower than the length of the stir straws. The cardboard depicted is 9 cm x 15 cm. Provide additional materials for improving the toy cars. Students won't use the extra materials until the next activity, but access now will inform their design process. Also prepare a place to store students' toy cars, as the cars will be used in the next activity.

INVESTIGATIVE PHENOMENON
Before designing a car, engineers seek to understand what matters in making a good car.

Phenomenon Explained Students explore the **investigative phenomenon** by exploring and preparing to improve a toy car. Students gather evidence through their process to support their solution.

Identify a Problem After reading the introductory paragraph, students should identify the problem they are trying to solve. If students struggle to identify the problem, ask them to consider what the text in the introductory paragraph asks them to do. Sample answer: I need to improve the toy car from the version built from the kit.

STEP 1   Students build the balloon-powered car using the directions provided. Students then investigate how it works, and they propose how it might be improved. Students record their testing actions and observations in the table. For safety and sanitation, remind groups to have the same student blow up the balloon for each test.

- **Make a Claim** Students should make a claim about how the car could be better.
- **Evidence** Students should support their claim with evidence from their investigation.
- **Reasoning** Students should explain why the change would improve the car.

Having students make claims aids in gathering student background knowledge.

STEP 2 Students define the problem by listing desired features and limitations for a good solution. Desired features: easy to build, works reliably, rolls in straight line; Limitations: available materials

STEPS 3 and 4 Students brainstorm to come up with at least three possible improvements to the toy car solution and then evaluate them against the desired features and limitations. Possible improvements could include adding tape to keep the axle housings from wiggling, adjusting the wheel width, moving the wheels closer to the car body, moving the balloon forward or backward, or strengthening the connection between the wheel and the axle.

STEP 5 Students sketch and label a model of their possible solution. Have students label ways they plan to change the base toy car solution.

FORMATIVE ASSESSMENT ▢▢▢▢▢

MAKING SENSE OF PHENOMENA

Students gain understanding that engineers seek to understand the problem in the process of designing a car as they explore the **investigative phenomenon.** They should connect this to the **anchoring phenomenon** that cars are designed to meet wants and needs. Students should understand that both the older car and the modern car meet the need for transportation, but they meet different wants to different degrees.

REMEDIATION If students struggle to connect the **investigative phenomenon** back to the **anchoring phenomenon,** have them consider the needs or wants the older and modern cars meet and why engineers would explore problems before making solutions.

MAKING SENSE OF PHENOMENA IDEA ORGANIZER

After completing Exploration 1, students can fill in the **Idea Organizer** to summarize the connection between engineers understanding what matters before designing solutions and the anchoring phenomenon that what matters, the needs and wants, were different for the older car and the modern car, which engineers needed to understand to design the cars.

> Formative assessment and remediation options are provided at point of use.

Activity Outcome

Students should model an improved toy car and recognize that exploring and defining the problem is also important in improving real cars.

> Activity rubrics aid in grading.

Performance Indicators	
	explore the base car solution through testing
	make a claim about how to improve the solution
	support the claim using reasoning and evidence

Engineer It • Improving Toy Cars

Activity Guide, pages 8–11

TIME ESTIMATE

60 min

POSSIBLE MATERIALS

☐ basic toy car from previous Hands-On Activity

☐ additional materials provided to students in the previous Hands-On Activity

PREPARATION

In advance, gather the basic toy cars students built and tested in the previous Hands-On Activity, as well as any additional materials you previously provided to students.

> Preparation notes and easy-to-source materials typify each hands-on activity.

INVESTIGATIVE PHENOMENON
Engineers improve existing car solutions according to clear priorities.

Phenomenon Explained Students explore the **investigative phenomenon** by building, testing, and improving their toy car solution. Students gather evidence to support their explanation for the importance of clear priorities.

Form a Question Clarify that in their modified solution, students will be improving their toy car solution, just as automotive engineers who work on real cars make improvements on their cars. Then have students read the paragraph about school leaders' concerns and form a question to summarize those concerns. If students struggle to form a question, ask them to think about what the school leaders want to know. Sample answer: Does the modified solution work as well as or better than the original solution? How do we know?

STEP 1 Students modify the basic toy car according to the improved solution model they made in the previous activity.

STEPS 2 and 3 Students plan a test of their solution. Clarify with students that their test plan should involve several trials, each changing only one factor. Students carry out their tests and record their data.

STEP 4 Students use their test results to evaluate their possible solution against the desired features and limitations. Then, students sketch a model of their plan to improve their solution.

STEP 5 Students test their improved solutions and evaluate the results. Remind students to use test data to support their evaluations.

STEP 6 Students share their solutions with other groups and compare different groups' solutions, recording their observations.

- **Make a Claim** Students make a claim in the response to the teacher's concerns in the introductory paragraph, describing how much better their solution works than the original toy car.

- **Evidence** Students should cite as evidence data from their testing and information about their testing process.

- **Reasoning** Students should reason that a well-planned test with multiple trials and only one factor changed each time gives confidence that their solution has the desired features within the limitations.

Each activity guides students through using evidence to either support or refute a claim.

FORMATIVE ASSESSMENT

MAKING SENSE OF PHENOMENA

Students gain understanding that engineers make and improve solutions to meet priorities as they explore the **investigative phenomenon.** They should connect this to the **anchoring phenomenon** that the most desirable car depends on what users consider important, which explains the differences between the older and more modern car. Students should recognize that engineers changed car technology because user priorities changed.

REMEDIATION If students struggle to connect the **investigative phenomenon** back to the **anchoring phenomenon,** have them first imagine changes to their toy cars if the desired features and limitations changed, and then consider related real car technology.

Activity Outcome

Students should build, test, and improve the toy car solution making decisions based on the problem definition.

Performance Indicators	
	iteratively improve the toy car solution
	make a claim about the effectiveness of the improved toy car
	support the claim with evidence from their testing

MAKING SENSE OF PHENOMENA IDEA ORGANIZER

After completing Exploration 2, students can fill in the **Idea Organizer** to summarize the connection between improving the toy car solution to meet clear desired features and limitations, and the anchoring phenomenon that engineers used similar processes in changing real car technology over time from the older car to the more modern car.

 SOCIAL EMOTIONAL LEARNING

Discuss with students the value of working on a team. Point out that working with a team means there are more ideas to pool and discuss. Stress the importance making sure everyone's input is encouraged and recognized as valuable. Team members contribute in a variety of ways, including sharing ideas, making models, carrying out investigations, recording observations, and reflecting on the process.

Technology, Engineering, and Science

Activity Guide, pages 12–14

TIME ESTIMATE

15 min

INVESTIGATIVE PHENOMENON
Engineers apply science knowledge to make technology that solves problems.

Phenomenon Explained Students explore the **investigative phenomenon** by learning about the different things engineers do in order to explain how engineering and science are related.

What Is Technology, and What Is Not?

Everyday Phenomenon **Everyday items that are designed by humans are examples of technology, whether simple or complex.**

Discuss patterns in what is and is not technology based on the matching activity. Have small groups of students collect two items of technology from around the classroom and, if possible, identify one item that is not technology. Compare the collected items and facilitate a class discussion to determine that anything designed and made by humans is technology, and anything found in nature is not technology.

Embedded Social Emotional Learning activities and strategies build student confidence and healthy learning environments.

Classroom Technology

Students can match the items to the descriptions either working independently or in pairs. Consider providing printed materials or devices with internet access to allow students to research the various engineering specialties mentioned in the descriptions.

Looking at What They Do

Students should understand that engineers are often working to solve a specific problem or improve a specific technology—building a better mousetrap, for example. Scientists conduct research to add to the knowledge of a subject—to learn more about mice and their behavior, for example. Have students do the classifying activity individually and discuss their responses in small groups.

 SOCIAL EMOTIONAL LEARNING

Before students hold their partner conversations, have them consider how to communicate effectively with another person. Model and then have students participate in reflective listening, in which one pair member conveys his or her thoughts and the other sums them up before conveying his or her own. Stress the importance of listening respectfully and not interrupting until one's partner is finished.

FORMATIVE ASSESSMENT

MAKING SENSE OF PHENOMENA

Students gain understanding of the connection as well as the distinction between science and engineering as they explore the **investigative phenomenon.** They should connect this to the **anchoring phenomenon** that engineers apply science knowledge to make car technology that solves human problems, including both the car from 60 years ago and the modern car that solve the problem of transportation.

REMEDIATION If students struggle to connect the **investigative phenomenon** back to the **anchoring phenomenon,** have them share ideas about what scientific understanding engineers would need to have to design cars and to improve them over time.

MAKING SENSE OF PHENOMENA IDEA ORGANIZER

After completing Exploration 3, students can fill in the **Idea Organizer** to summarize the connection between engineers using science to make technology and the anchoring phenomenon that car technology is one area that engineers applied science knowledge to make and improve solutions to problems over time.

How Do Engineers Solve Problems?

Activity Guide, pages 15–20

TIME ESTIMATE

60 min

INVESTIGATIVE PHENOMENON
Engineers use a systematic approach to problem solving when designing cars or improving existing car technology.

Phenomenon Explained Students explore the **investigative phenomenon** by applying aspects of the engineering design process in the context of various problems to explain how the systematic process can be used to develop good solutions.

Explore and In the Background

Remind students that a STEM night is devoted to science, technology, engineering, and mathematics. Have students discuss the criteria and constraints for a game for that event. Point out that in the Hands-On Activities, criteria were referred to as *desired features* and constraints were referred to as *limitations*. As students consider the reasons for research, remind them that research can include many activities such as talking to people, reading materials, and conducting investigations.

Make and Test

Point out that brainstorming yields a wide range of responses. Then have students work in small groups to brainstorm ideas for the STEM night game.

Make a Decision

Review the decision matrix for Shania's bicycle purchase. Help students understand how the written information about Shania's needs translates into the criteria in the left column of the decision matrix and how the details about the possible bicycles translate into the numerical values.

What Is Fair?

Be sure students understand the terms *prototype, variable,* and *trial.* Clarify that a test consists of several trials, and only one variable can be modified in each test.

Improve and Test

Facilitate a discussion about the arrow target images to understand how each trial that did not hit the center of the target provided information that the archer could use to modify the next trial and get closer to the center. These trials were not failures—they were learning opportunities

It's a Process

Review the diagram, which shows the phases in the process that engineers follow to develop solutions. When students work on the sorting task, point out that some activities happen in more than one phase; for example, "Analyze test results," "Modify the prototype," and "Test the prototype" all happen in both the second and third phases.

SOCIAL EMOTIONAL LEARNING

As partners share recollections of projects that did not go right the first time, encourage them to think about how they can re-frame these failures as learning opportunities. In engineering problem solving as in other areas of life, learning from unsuccessful attempts can make the next attempt better.

MAKING SENSE OF PHENOMENA IDEA ORGANIZER

After completing Exploration 4, students can fill in the **Idea Organizer** to summarize the connection between the systematic process engineers go through to solve problems and the anchoring phenomenon that engineers have improved car technology over the last 60 years.

FORMATIVE ASSESSMENT ■■■■

MAKING SENSE OF PHENOMENA

Students gain understanding that engineers go through a process to solve problems as they explore the **investigative phenomenon.** They should connect this to the **anchoring phenomenon** that engineers used a systematic design process to make improvements to transportation technology, which resulted in the modern car looking different from the car from 60 years ago.

REMEDIATION If students struggle to connect the **investigative phenomenon** back to the **anchoring phenomenon,** ask them to consider how steps in the process, such as designing and testing prototypes, played a role in the improvement of cars over 60 years.

Improving Over Time

Activity Guide, pages 21–22

TIME ESTIMATE

15 min

INVESTIGATIVE PHENOMENON
Technology, including cars, changes over time as user priorities change and engineers make tradeoffs.

Phenomenon Explained Students explore the **investigative phenomenon** by reading about how engineers improve designs over time and discussing how they would make tradeoffs when faced with conflicting priorities.

So Many Changes!

Direct students' attention to the photos of the seat belts on page 21. Explain that seat belts were not a feature of the earliest cars but began to be used in the 1950s. Ten years later, seat belts were a required design feature. Point out that other everyday features, such as tires and doors, have always been parts of cars but have had changes in design. Have students discuss improvements engineers might have tried to make to tires over the years.

FORMATIVE ASSESSMENT

MAKING SENSE OF PHENOMENA

Students gain understanding that engineers make changes to technology over time as user priorities change, as they explore the **investigative phenomenon.** They should connect this to the **anchoring phenomenon** that engineers changed and improved car technology over the past 60 years to meet changing needs and wants of car buyers and to meet new government regulations.

REMEDIATION If students struggle to connect the **investigative phenomenon** back to the **anchoring phenomenon,** ask them to compare the photos of the two cars on page 2 and consider what wants and needs might have changed to explain the differences between the cars.

MAKING SENSE OF PHENOMENA IDEA ORGANIZER

After completing Exploration 5, students can fill in the **Idea Organizer** to summarize the connection between technology changing in response to changing priorities and the anchoring phenomenon that engineers made changes and tradeoffs over the last 60 years of developments in car technology to meet wants and needs of car buyers and to comply with government regulations.

You Can't Have Everything

Have students discuss the tradeoffs involved in Shania's bike choices, making sure they understand that a tradeoff is when one particular quality or feature is given up in order to have another. Then, have students mark their preferences for car technology tradeoffs and discuss their different views on which qualities or features matter most to them.

← **better power** — **better mileage** →

← **better appearance** — **lower cost** →

Take It Further

The Take it Further section of each lesson showcases diverse People and Careers in Science & Engineering. These features show students the real-world applications of what they're learning.

Engage • Explore/Explain • **Elaborate** • Evaluate

TIME ESTIMATE

45 min

These Take It Further paths may be completed to enrich and extend students' comprehension of content covered within this lesson.

Online, students have different pathways from which to choose, increasing differentiation options.

ONLINE

Careers in Science & Engineering: Safety Engineer

Students learn about the roles of safety engineers in keeping technologies safe.

Go Further: Self-Driving Cars

Students research self-driving cars and come up with a list of pros and cons about them.

Safety Survey

Students work with partners or in small teams of mixed ability to develop a list of safety criteria for cars. They then research online the types of safety checks that automobile manufacturers perform on their cars. See whether students found a lot of the same answers.

Lesson Check

Activity Guide, pages 23–25

Engage • Explore/Explain • Elaborate • **Evaluate**

Online, self-checks are autograded, so students get immediate feedback.

Can You Explain It?

Now I know or think that. . .

Sample answer: Engineers used the systematic approach of the engineering design process and their knowledge of science to improve car technology, which is why cars look different today than they did 60 years ago. As priorities, needs, wants, and societal expectations changed over time, engineers changed car technology to meet those factors.

After completing the lesson, use the **Making Sense Idea Organizer** to summarize the connections between the **investigative phenomena** and **anchoring phenomenon.**

MAKING CONNECTIONS

After students complete the lesson, they should be able to answer a question about an alternative phenomenon to explain how developments in vision technology are similar to those in car technology. **Sample answer:** As with car technology, engineers made changes in vision technology to meet changing user needs and priorities.

Making Connections helps students apply what they have learned to a new real-world phenomenon.

Checkpoints

1. b; c; e

2. **Sample answer:** He could come up with a list of criteria and constraints that would describe a good solution and then use a decision matrix to evaluate possible solutions.

3. c; d

4. a; c

5. **Sample answers:** Will measurements be made in the same way for all trials? Will all factors but one be the same for all trials? Will anything in the environment change the test results?

6. a; b; d

7. problem; background research; criteria/constraints; constraints/criteria

8. **Sample answer:** Cellphone technology has been changing to larger screens because people want to play games and watch videos on their devices, not just use them to make phone calls.

🗨 SOCIAL EMOTIONAL LEARNING

Have students reflect on the goals they set at the beginning of the lesson. Ask them to think about whether the goals were accomplished or if there were challenges. Have students share the factors that contributed to their success. If the goals were not achieved, talk about what students can do to help them achieve the goals.

UNIT

01

Review

Unit Reviews guide students to connect phenomena across the lessons.

Activity Guide, pages 26–28

The Unit review items enable you to assess student comprehension of core ideas, as well as cross cutting concepts and science and engineering practices.

1. **DOK 2** **Sample answer:** The chain on the bicycle is broken. Because the chain component of the bicycle is broken, the bicycle system cannot perform its function.

   If students are unfamiliar with bicycles, explain that the chain is meant to connect the gears turned by the pedals to the gears around the hub of the rear wheel. You may choose to find a close-up video of a bicycle for students to watch.

2. **DOK 3** **Sample answer:** I would need to research materials that can repair a chain to know whether it is fixable or needs to be replaced. I would need to research how the chain functions on the bicycle to know what I should observe when the problem is solved.

   If students are very familiar with bicycles and have trouble thinking of new information they would need, have them list what they think they know about bicycle chains that would help solve the problem. Remind them that research provides evidence to confirm assumptions.

3. **DOK 1** **b.** use scientific discoveries to develop technology; **c.** discover things about the world and universe.

   If students struggle to answer the question, have them review the activities in Exploration 3.

4. **DOK 2** **a.** new legal requirements, **b.** new scientific knowledge. **c.** new understanding of risks, **d.** new needs and wants

   If students struggle to answer the question, have them consider whether each answer option would change the problem definition, criteria and constraints, or list of possible solutions.

5. **DOK 1** criterion; constraint; constraint

   If students struggle with the distinction between a criterion and a constraint, have them review the stem night game problem in Exploration 4.

6. **DOK 2** Students may or may not use the language of independent and controlled variables but should clearly identify that a fair test requires that only one factor changes between trials and all other factors stay the same. With a fair test, the test results from multiple trials can be compared because the conditions for the trials were the same except for the one factor that changed.

   If students struggle to describe a fair test, review the discussion of testing game night ideas in Exploration 4.

7. **DOK 2** 3, 5, 1, 2, 4

   If students do not order the steps in this sequence, have them write the steps on index cards. They can physically arrange the cards, taking two at a time and considering which step would need to happen first until they have all five in order.

8. **DOK 1** **b.** investigate how a computer battery might fail, **c.** model how long a pen will work if used daily

   If students choose *a* or *d*, remind them that engineers deal with solving problems and developing technology, whereas scientists conduct investigations of natural phenomena.

   Depth of knowledge (DOK) levels are noted for each question.

9. **DOK 3** **Sample answer:** Testing is necessary because testing shows how well a system solves the problem. Our first toy car system did not work the way we had thought, and we found that out through testing. We also found ways to improve the solution.

If students struggle to answer the question, encourage them to reflect on how they used testing and test results while developing their toy car solution in the two Hands-On Activities.

10. **DOK 3** **Sample answer:** Car users want fuel efficiency, which the rounded structure of the car improves. Car users need the vehicle to be safe, which seat belts and airbags in the car provide.

If students struggle to answer the question, ask them to think about what car users want and need, and identify specific components of a car, such as wheels, that contribute to meeting those wants and needs.

Three-dimensional item-analysis charts show the specific standards coverage for each assessment question as you monitor student progress.

3D Item Analysis	1	2	3	4	5	6	7	8	9	10
SEP Asking Questions and Defining Problems	•	•		•	•		•			•
SEP Constructing Explanations and Designing Solutions					•		•			•
SEP Planning and Carrying Out Investigations						•	•	•	•	
DCI Defining and Delimiting Engineering Problems	•	•		•	•		•			
DCI Developing Possible Solutions		•	•	•	•	•	•	•	•	•
DCI Optimizing the Design Solution								•	•	
CCC Influence of Science, Engineering, and Technology on Society and the Natural World			•	•				•		•

02

Matter

Activity Guide, page 29

Unit Storyline

In Unit 1, students explored the design and engineering process and how it relates to technology and problem solving. In Unit 2, they will explore matter, its properties, and its different forms. This will lay the foundation for Units 3 through 6.

LESSON 1   PE 5-PS1-1
Matter Has Mass and Volume
Activity Guide, pp. 30–45

Students explore the **anchoring phenomenon** that people use properties of plastic, water, and air to make the rocket fly.

SEP Planning and Carrying Out Investigations; Developing and Using Models

DCI **PS1.A** Structure and Properties of Matter

CCC Scale, Proportion, and Quantity

LESSON 2   PE 5-PS1-3, 3–5 ETS1-1, 3–5 ETS1-2, 3–5 ETS1-3
Matter Has Many Properties
Activity Guide, pp. 46–61

Students explore the **anchoring phenomenon** that sitting in a beanbag chair feels different from sitting in a typical classroom chair.

SEP Using Mathematics and Computational Thinking; Engaging in Argument from Evidence

DCI **PS1.A** Structure and Properties of Matter; **ETS1.A** Defining and Delimiting Engineering Problems; **ETS1.B** Developing Possible Solutions; **ETS1.C** Optimizing the Design Solution

CCC Scale, Proportion, and Quantity; Science Is a Human Endeavor

LESSON 3   PE 5-PS1-2, 5-PS1-4
Matter Can Change
Activity Guide, pp. 62–77

Students explore the **anchoring phenomenon** that this metal sculpture has dark and shiny areas.

SEP Planning and Carrying Out Investigations; Using Mathematics and Computational Thinking

DCI **PS1.A** Structure and Properties of Matter; **PS1.B** Chemical Reactions

CCC Cause and Effect; Systems and System Models ; Scientific Knowledge Assumes an Order and Consistency in Natural Systems

Unit Review   Activity Guide, pp. 78–80

Supporting Unit Resources

You Solve It SUPPORTS LESSONS 1, 2, AND 3

Maze Matters is a virtual lab that offers practice in support of **Performance Expectation 5-PS1-2** and **5-PS1-3.** Students will apply understanding of the properties of matter to solve problems and identify substances.

> **SEP** Planning and Carrying Out Investigations
> **DCI** **PS1.A** Structure and Properties of Matter; **PS1.B** Chemical Reactions
> **CCC** Patterns

Unit Project SUPPORTS LESSONS 2 AND 3 (90 min)

Conservation of Matter provides students an opportunity to practice aspects of **Performance Expectation 5-PS1-1, 5-PS1-2, 5-PS1-3,** and **5-ETS1-3.** Groups will design an experiment to prove that matter is conserved during physical or chemical changes.

> **SEP** Asking Questions and Defining Problems; Using Mathematics and Computational Thinking; Developing and Using Models; Planning and Carrying Out Investigations
> **DCI** **PS1.A** Structure and Properties of Matter; **PS1.B** Chemical Reactions; **ETS1.B** Developing Possible Solutions
> **CCC** Scale, Proportion, and Quantity

Unit Performance Task SUPPORTS LESSONS 1, 2, AND 3 (90 min)

Physical or Chemical? provides an opportunity for students to practice or be assessed on aspects of **Performance Expectation 5-PS1-4.** Students plan and carry out investigations to exhibit cause and effect of certain types of matter.

> **SEP** Developing and Using Models; Planning and Carrying Out Investigations
> **DCI** **PS1.B** Chemical Reactions
> **CCC** Cause and Effect

Language Development

This worksheet is used as students progress through the unit's lessons. As they come to a highlighted vocabulary term, they should come back to this chart and fill in the blanks with words or phrases.

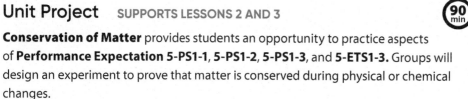

ONLINE  We've got you covered.

Updates and additional student and teacher resources can be found online. Check back often!

Supporting Lesson Resources

Do the Math!

Lesson 1 Matter Math
Lesson 2 Interpret a Graph
Lesson 3 Explaining Patterns in Melting

Language SmArts

Lesson 1 Implicit and Explicit Language; Understanding Vocabulary
Lesson 2 Researching Insulators and Conductors; Providing Evidence
Lesson 3 Recall and Summarize Experiences; Visual Summary

Take It Further

Lesson 1 Careers in Science and Engineering: Materials Scientists and Engineers; Organizing Particles; More States of Matter
Lesson 2 People in Science and Engineering: Shirley Ann Jackson and Anthony Atala; Healthy Mixtures; People in Science and Engineering: Dr. Jani Ingram and Ciarra Greene
Lesson 3 People in Science and Engineering: Antoine Lavoisier; Slow Down the Spoil; Acids and Bases; Careers in Science and Engineering: Flavor Chemist

MAKING SENSE OF PHENOMENA

This idea organizer is used to make sense of the following **anchoring phenomena**:
Lesson 1—People use properties of air, plastic, and water to make the rocket fly.
Lesson 2—Sitting in a beanbag chair feels different from sitting in a typical classroom chair.
Lesson 3—This metal sculpture has dark and shiny areas.

It also connects the investigative phenomena back to the anchoring phenomenon in each lesson.

Assessment

Unit Readiness Check: Are You Ready?
Lesson Quizzes: Can You Apply It?
Unit 2 Test
Performance-Based Assessment

Assessments are available in an editable, printable format or can be administered and auto-graded online.

01 Matter Has Mass and Volume

ANCHORING PHENOMENON

People use properties of water, plastic, and air to make the rocket fly.

ENGAGE Can You Explain It?

Students observe and ask questions about a homemade rocket. They answer the Can You Explain It? question to identify what they will gather evidence about in the lesson.

EVALUATE Lesson Check

Students gauge their understanding of the anchoring phenomenon.

HANDS-ON ACTIVITY

EXPLORATION 1 Measuring Mass and Volume

Investigative Phenomenon Matter takes up space and has mass.

Students connect back to the **anchoring phenomenon** that matter of all types and at all scales has mass and volume and two forms of matter cannot occupy the same space.

HANDS-ON ACTIVITY

EXPLORATION 2 Evidence of Matter

Investigative Phenomenon Gases are made of matter, can be compressed, and affect objects in ways we can observe.

Students connect back to the **anchoring phenomenon** that air has mass and volume and its effects on other objects can be observed.

EXPLORATION 3 A Matter of Particles

Investigative Phenomenon The properties of solids, liquids, and gases can be used to explain how these forms of matter interact in a system.

Students connect back to the **anchoring phenomenon** that the rocket system is made up of matter in all three states interacting in ways, based on their properties, that cause the rocket to fly.

Making 3D Connections

The **anchoring phenomenon** in this lesson supports students' understanding of and application of these Next Generation Science Standards.

Building to the Performance Expectations

5-PS1-1 Develop a model to describe that matter is made of particles too small to be seen.

SEP	DCI	CCC

Planning and Carrying Out Investigations Make observations and measurements to produce data to serve as the basis for evidence for an explanation of a phenomenon. *(Exploration 1)*

Developing and Using Models Use models to describe phenomena. *(Explorations 2, 3)*

PS1.A Structure and Properties of Matter Matter of any type can be subdivided into particles that are too small to see, but even then the matter still exists and can be detected by other means. A model showing that gases are made from matter particles that are too small to see and are moving freely around in space can explain many observations, including the inflation and shape of a balloon and the effects of air on larger particles or objects. *(Explorations 1, 2, 3)*

Scale, Proportion, and Quantity Natural objects exist from the very small to the immensely large. *(Explorations 1, 2, 3)*

Vocabulary

Word Wall A word wall, anchor chart, or Language Development chart can be used to support vocabulary.

matter anything that takes up space and can be measured

gas state of matter with neither definite shape nor definite volume

solid state of matter that has definite shape and volume

liquid state of matter without definite shape but with definite volume

You may want to include additional academic terms such as *state* and *arrangement* and any other terms students might struggle with.

Language Development Prompt students to complete the chart when they come to these highlighted terms within the lesson and to add their own terms as they come across unknown science terms.

Anchor Chart As you progress through the unit, you may want to use the Language Development chart as a guide to make a vocabulary-based anchor chart that can be displayed and filled out as a whole group during each lesson.

Activity Guide, pages 30–31

Students can engage in the Can You Explain It? content by observing the photograph or by exploring the corresponding video online.

ONLINE  View a video related to homemade water rockets.

ANCHORING PHENOMENON
People use properties of plastic, water, and air to make the rocket fly.

PHENOMENON EXPLAINED
The rocket system includes a solid body and a gas and liquid propellant system. The particles in each state of matter are arranged in different ways. Because the particles in a gas can be compressed, compressed air is used to rapidly push incompressible water out of the plastic bottle to make the rocket fly.

Lesson Objective

Students can use models and conduct investigations to identify properties of matter and to demonstrate that matter is made of particles too small to be seen, from the very small to the immensely large, but whose effects can be observed.

Support Discovery

The following prompts can be used to guide student-led discovery.

I notice . . .

After observing the photograph or watching the video, students should record what they noticed about the rocket. If students struggle to record observations, ask them to focus on the substances that appear to spray out of, and propel, the rocket into the air.

Sample answers: It's clear; it's spraying water; it has fins.

I wonder . . .

After observing the photograph or watching the video, students should record what more they want to find out about the rocket.

Sample answer: I wonder what part of the system makes the rocket move.

Alternative Phenomenon

If students are unfamiliar with the water rocket, guide them to think of other examples of devices, models, or experiments that involve a device that can move due to expelling matter, such as a balloon-driven boat or a firehose. You can show one or more of these alternative phenomena to help students infer what might be happening in a homemade model rocket.

Can You Explain It?

In Can You Explain It?, students make an initial claim that explains the **Anchoring Phenomenon.** Sample sketches might show some kind of reaction in the rocket causing a rapid expansion of air and water out of the opening. Students will expand on their explanations as they progress through the lesson.

Students will gather evidence about matter and how it can change states and become new forms of matter. This will enable them to give a more complete explanation of the **Anchoring Phenomenon** at the end of the lesson.

SOCIAL EMOTIONAL LEARNING

Guide students to reflect on their goals from previous lessons and on any feedback they received from their teachers or peers. Then have each student set a personal goal for this lesson and make a plan for how to achieve the goal. Throughout the lesson, take daily breaks for students to track their progress in meeting their goals. As students move from lesson to lesson, they can continue to work toward their initial goals or set new ones. If students struggle to set goals for this lesson, share with them some of the following ideas: modeling matter, planning an investigation, participating more during activity/group work or ensuring everyone in the group has a chance to share an idea, or persevering when an activity or topic is difficult.

01

Everyone Loves a Parade

WHEN TO USE

SCIENCE 30 min

- Anchoring Phenomenon / Alternative Phenomenon
- Options for ELA Instruction
- Build on Prior Knowledge
- Preview the Phenomenon
- Read to Learn
- Support Sense Making
- Science Stretch
- Check for Comprehension

Option 1 Use before students begin the lesson in the Activity Guide to provide an engaging model to introduce the lesson's phenomenon.

Option 2 Use after students have completed the Activity Guide to reinforce students' understanding of the lesson phenomenon by exploring a related phenomenon.

ELA 20 min

- Options for ELA Instruction
- Build on Prior Knowledge
- Read to Learn

Option 3 To use during designated ELA Reading time for independent reading, whole-class instruction, or small-group instruction, look for this icon: ELA

Plan

ANCHORING PHENOMENON / ALTERNATIVE PHENOMENON

The anchoring phenomenon in the Activity Guide is *People use properties of water, plastic, and air to make the rocket fly*, and the main example is a model rocket made from a plastic bottle. The FUNomenal Reader presents a similar phenomenon *(People use properties of matter to make parades)*, and the example is students who want to make a parade float that represents the states of matter. Both present the same science concepts and cover the same standards but with different phenomena. Guide students to draw connections between the two situations and to understand the underlying principle: the most common states of matter on Earth are solids, liquids, and gases.

Options for ELA Instruction ELA

Choose one of the following anchor chart options and project it or print copies. Then display and introduce the chart before reading the text. Revisit the chart after reading the text and encourage students to discuss how the skill connects to the text.

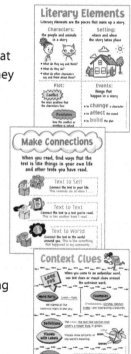

Literary Elements Refer to the *Literary Elements Anchor Chart* and guide students to identify the characters, setting, plot, and events in the story. What problem do the main characters face and how do they resolve it?

Make Connections Display the *Make Connections Anchor Chart* to help students relate what they read to their own experiences, to other stories they have read, and to the larger world. Give them these sentence starters: *This reminds me of when I . . ., This is like another story I read . . ., This is like something that happened in my community . . .*

Context Clues Use the *Context Clues Anchor Chart* if students struggle to understand the meaning of some words in the story. For example, the word *particles* on page 6 has a clue to its meaning when Elena says, "That's because they are too small to be seen."

Preview

ELA **Build on Prior Knowledge** Discuss the word *matter* as used in science and in everyday conversation. Students may know it to mean that something is wrong or that something is important. In science, the word *matter* refers to any physical substance or material that takes up space. Have volunteers use the common and scientific meanings appropriately in sentences. Challenge students to name things that are not matter and explain why. Examples might include light, heat, and sound.

Preview the Phenomenon Ask students to study the illustration on page 4 of the story, which shows kids looking at posters on the wall. Encourage students to record the first questions that come into their minds about what the posters might represent. Point out that their questions might change as they read through the selection. Have them keep their questions on hand and periodically check to see if any can be answered.

STANDARDS SUPPORTED

SEP
Planning and Carrying Out Investigations

Developing and Using Models

DCI
PS1.A Structure and Properties of Matter

CCC
Scale, Proportion, and Quantity

Everyone Loves a Parade (continued)

Discover

Read to Learn

The **Read to Learn** suggestions inside the book's front cover encourage students to interact with the book multiple times for different purposes.

> **Preview** Students look for unfamiliar words and share them with a partner. New terms may include *states of matter, particles,* and *volume.* Have students look up words they aren't sure about and notice how they are used in the context of the story.

> **Skim** Students skim the illustrations. Have them turn to a partner and share their predictions of what the story will be about.

> **Read** As students read the story, ask them to look for connections to one of the following anchor chart skills. **Literary Elements, Make Connections, Context Clues**

Support Sense Making

Choose one or more of the following:

▶ Be sure students can identify the phenomenon presented on the opening pages of the reader: Mrs. Rivera's students want to build a parade float that represents the three states of matter. The remaining pages describe their efforts to carry out this task while learning about the properties of matter and about scale models.

▶ Discuss the steps the characters in the story take to make their float. Write the steps on the board as students name them. The steps include doing research, brainstorming ideas, drawing plans, gathering materials, testing their ideas, and making changes as needed. Would students follow these same steps? Why or why not?

▶ Students may find it difficult to think of gases as matter because most aren't visible. Have volunteers read aloud and act out the story scene in which Elena, Mason, and Taylor discuss gas particles and use a balloon to represent Saturn on their float. Demonstrate that gases are matter by inflating a balloon. The air you blow into the balloon pushes out its sides because air takes up space.

▶ Have interested students do research about maquettes, preliminary models used by sculptors, and report their findings to the class. Discuss why a sculptor would make a small-scale model before creating a full-size statue out of a valuable material such as marble.

Extend

Science Stretch

The **Science Stretch** suggestions inside the book's back cover help students think about what they read. Students can complete one or more as time allows.

> Describe an object using volume, weight, and other properties of matter. You may want to review the properties of matter with students before they begin.

> Look around the room. Find one solid, one liquid, and one gas. **Sample answer:** Solid—desk; liquid—water in watering can; gas—fire extinguisher.

> Compare a pile of salt with salt seen through a microscope. **Sample answer:** I see tiny white crystals when I look at salt. Through a microscope, I see that the crystals are cube-shaped and clear.

 SOCIAL EMOTIONAL LEARNING

Why is communication important when working on a team project? **Sample answer:** Communicating helps keep everyone working toward the same goal and helps prevent misunderstandings.

Check for Comprehension Ask: *How did understanding the properties of their materials help Elena, Mason, and Taylor solve problems as they designed and built their float?* Have students share their responses with a partner.

Measuring Mass and Volume

Activity Guide, pages 32–34

TIME ESTIMATE

(50 min)

....

SHORT ON TIME?

Conduct the test as a class or divide students into larger groups to reduce the number of activities happening at one time.

POSSIBLE MATERIALS

- ☐ objects to measure
- ☐ balance
- ☐ beaker
- ☐ graduated cylinder
- ☐ metric ruler or tape
- ☐ unit cubes
- ☐ other objects as needed

PREPARATION

Collect materials in advance. Provide a variety of measuring tools and give students a chance to explore each one.

INVESTIGATIVE PHENOMENON
Matter takes up space and has mass.

Phenomenon Explained Students explore the **investigative phenomenon** by planning and conducting an investigation to answer questions they develop about measuring matter.

Form a Question After observing the photograph and reading the text, students should form a question about how or why we measure matter. If students struggle to form a question, have them describe what is happening in the photo and why. Sample answer: How can matter be measured?

STEP 1 Call on several students to share their question, and write questions down on the board to discuss as a group. You can have students vote for their favorite question and take the top three choices, or steer them toward a few questions that are feasible for investigation.

STEP 2 Explain that students will investigate properties of different objects. Show them the materials they can use for the investigation. The materials listed here are a starting point; include objects for students to measure, such as rocks, pennies, tissue boxes, or classroom objects. Ask students what tools they think will work best for measuring each of the following: mass (the balance); volume of rectangular objects (metric ruler, unit cubes); volume of a rock (beaker or graduated cylinder, water).

Help students formulate their plans and allow time to review them yourself before investigations begin. Remind students that different objects contain different amounts of matter and are measured in different ways.

STEP 3 Circulate and make sure students are measuring and recording their results appropriately, as outlined in their plan. Remind them that scientists use the metric system as a common system of measurement. As time allows, have students share their findings. Encourage students to think about why they used different tools to measure different objects.

- **Make a Claim** Claims will vary based on students' investigations but should communicate that matter can be measured.

- **Evidence** Students should cite as evidence their recorded data.

- **Reasoning** Students should explain their reasoning by using the data to answer their research questions and to support their claim.

FORMATIVE ASSESSMENT

MAKING SENSE OF PHENOMENA

As they explore the **investigative phenomenon**, students gain understanding that measuring mass and volume are ways to show that matter takes up space and has mass. They should connect this to the **anchoring phenomenon** that all matter has mass and volume and therefore takes up space. As demonstrated by the rocket, two forms of matter cannot occupy the same space.

REMEDIATION If students struggle to connect the **investigative phenomenon** back to the **anchoring phenomenon,** have them consider whether two types of matter can occupy the same space, and why not.

Activity Outcome

Students should follow the steps to design an investigation to measure mass and volume.

Performance Indicators
develop a thorough investigation and record measurements accurately
make a claim about measuring matter
support the claim using recorded observations as evidence

MAKING SENSE OF PHENOMENA
IDEA ORGANIZER
After completing Exploration 1, students can fill in the **Idea Organizer** to summarize the connection between their observations while measuring mass and volume and the anchoring phenomenon that the rocket moves because two forms of matter cannot take up the same space.

Materials Alert All materials should be able to be reused or shared among groups.

Evidence of Matter

TIME ESTIMATE

45 min

SHORT ON TIME?

Have groups perform their investigations at the same time. If needed, omit the third activity.

POSSIBLE MATERIALS

- ☐ dosing tube
- ☐ clear plastic cups of water
- ☐ paper towel
- ☐ bowl of water
- ☐ sugar cube
- ☐ spoon or stir stick

PREPARATION

Preassemble the materials for each group. Divide the class into three groups, with each group performing a different activity. Distribute materials accordingly.

Materials Alert Caution students not to drink any of the water in these activities and to dispose of it properly.

INVESTIGATIVE PHENOMENON

Gases are made up of tiny particles of matter, can be compressed, and affect objects in observable ways.

Phenomenon Explained Students explore the **investigative phenomenon** by observing that particles of air are present even if they are invisible to an unaided eye, and that air can be compressed.

Form a Question After observing the photograph and reading the text, students should form a question about particles of matter. If students struggle to form a question, remind them that air is a form of matter with mass and volume. **Sample answer:** How does air fit in a bicycle tire?

STEPS A: 1–4 Make sure students use the dosing tube correctly. Remind them that air is a type of matter called a gas. The tube provides a shape and space for the air. The plunger can't go all the way down because the air inside has been compressed as much as possible by squeezing.

STEPS A: 5–6 Students repeat the activity with water. They should observe that the plunger can't compress the water. This is because liquid water particles are already close together.

STEPS B: 1–4 Help students in Group B insert their cups into the bowl of water so that the paper towel stays dry. Particles of air already fill the cup, so there's no room for water.

STEPS C: 1–2 Discuss with students what is happening to the sugar as they stir, and ask if it is still present in the water (it is). They should understand that it has dissolved. Stirring helped break the sugar into tiny particles and mix them evenly and completely with the water.

Have representatives from each group share their observations and thinking with the class.

- **Make a Claim** Claims will vary based on students' investigations but should relate to the behavior of different states of matter.
- **Evidence** Students should cite as evidence their observations and models, for example, something kept water away from the towel.
- **Reasoning** Students should explain their reasoning that matter takes up space and air (gases) can be compressed.

FORMATIVE ASSESSMENT

MAKING SENSE OF PHENOMENA

As they explore the investigative phenomenon, students gain understanding of how air can be detected based on its behavior in relation to other states of matter. They should connect this to the **anchoring phenomenon** that air has mass and volume and that its effects can be observed.

REMEDIATION If students struggle to connect the **investigative phenomenon** back to the **anchoring phenomenon,** remind them that air can expand or be compressed to fill a container because there is space in between the particles of air.

MAKING SENSE OF PHENOMENA IDEA ORGANIZER

After completing Exploration 2, students can fill in the **Idea Organizer** to summarize the connection between the behavior of matter that they observed and what causes the rocket to fly.

SOCIAL EMOTIONAL LEARNING

Remind students that being a good listener can be critical to understanding how the different activities were related. Encourage students to keep quiet when others are talking and then raise their hand to ask questions of their fellow students. They should help each other make connections between their activities.

Activity Outcome

Students should follow the activity steps in order to observe particles of air are present, even if they're invisible, and how they behave.

Performance Indicators
complete all steps of the activity and record observations
make a claim about the behavior of matter
support the claim using observations as evidence

A Matter of Particles

Activity Guide, pages 39–42

TIME ESTIMATE

INVESTIGATIVE PHENOMENON
The properties of solids, liquids, and gases can be used to explain how these forms of matter interact in a system.

Phenomenon Explained Students explore the **investigative phenomenon** by recognizing that objects (matter) can be grouped into one of the common states of matter: solids, liquids, and gases.

What Makes Up Matter?

| Everyday Phenomenon | **A glass of water holds drops of water.** |

How many drops of water could fill a glass? How big or small is a drop? Whether it's a drop of water, a glass, or an ocean, water is water. Explain to students that matter can be broken down into tiny pieces, even pieces too small to see with just our eyes, but it will still retain the qualities that make it what it is. Charcoal doesn't change, no matter how small we break it down. A speck of charcoal dust has the same basic properties as a log-size chunk of charcoal.

SOCIAL EMOTIONAL LEARNING

When working with a partner, students should listen and take turns speaking. Encourage them to write both students' ideas down as a way to evaluate ideas more objectively.

States of Matter

Everyday Phenomenon **Anything we can touch is made up of matter.**

There are three common states of matter, and they make up almost everything in our world, even the wind. Review that the particles in a solid are packed tightly together. The particles in a liquid are close together, but move freely around one another. The particles in a gas are farther apart than the particles in solids and liquids.

Gases

The particles in gases are spaced farther apart, so we usually can't see a gas. Water vapor (water that has evaporated into the air) is an example of a clear, colorless gas.
Sample answer: Most gases can't be seen. The smoke is likely made up of larger particles that are solid or liquid.

FORMATIVE ASSESSMENT

MAKING SENSE OF PHENOMENA

As they explore the **investigative phenomenon**, students gain understanding of the properties of matter and how they can interact in a system. They should connect this to the **anchoring phenomenon** that the rocket system is made up of matter in all three states interacting in ways, based on their properties, that cause the rocket to fly.

REMEDIATION If students struggle to connect the **investigative phenomenon** back to the **anchoring phenomenon**, have them review the image of the rocket and describe how each form of matter is behaving.

MAKING SENSE OF PHENOMENA IDEA ORGANIZER
After completing Exploration 3, students can fill in the **Idea Organizer** to summarize the connection between properties of matter and the behavior of the three states of matter in the rocket as it flies.

Take It Further

Engage • Explore/Explain • **Elaborate** • Evaluate

TIME ESTIMATE

45 min

These Take It Further paths may be completed to enrich and extend students' comprehension of content covered within this lesson.

ONLINE

Careers in Science and Engineering: Materials Scientists and Engineers

Students explore how many of the materials we use in everyday life were developed by materials scientists.

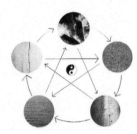

Organizing Particles

Students explore the arrangement of particles in different types of matter. (No outside research required.)

More States of Matter

Students explore the less commonly observed states of matter. (No outside research required.)

Lesson Check

Activity Guide, pages 43–45

Engage • Explore/Explain • Elaborate • **Evaluate**

Can You Explain It?

Now I know or think that . . .

Sample answer: The solid parts of the rocket don't change size or shape. The liquid in the bottom of the rocket matches its shape, but can't be squeezed into a smaller space. Air is a gas, so it can be squeezed into less space. More air can be pumped into the top of the bottle. The air forces water out the rocket nozzle. You can measure weight, length, temperature, and capacity or volume of matter.

After completing the lesson, use the **Making Sense Idea Organizer** to summarize the connections between the **investigative phenomena** and **anchoring phenomenon**.

MAKING CONNECTIONS

After students complete the lesson, they should be able to cite what they have learned about the properties and behavior of matter. They should apply this understanding to how the spray bottle works.
Sample answer: The bottle is sealed and holds water and air. I think the handle squeezes more air into the bottle. The solid bottle doesn't change and the liquid can't take up less space. So, the air pushes liquid up the tube and out the nozzle.

Checkpoints

1. Students' models should show widely spaced air particles in the flat tire and more closely spaced particles in the inflated tire.

2. solid, gas, liquid

3. **Sample answer:** The units help you understand the scale of the data and the objects. If I measure the mass of an object as 16, the unit tells me how large it is. A 16-gram object is very different from a 16-kilogram object. Changing units can make your data invalid.

4. volume—graduated cylinder; length—metric ruler; mass—balance

5. c—a chicken laying an egg; d—a container filled with milk; f—bowling pins set up on an alley

6. Matter takes up space. Feelings, etc., do not.

7. The water particles have the same spacing before and after squeezing. The squeezed air particles are closer than in the unsqueezed air.

8. Mass; the filled tire has more particles, so it should have more mass than the flat tire.

 SOCIAL EMOTIONAL LEARNING

Have students reflect on the goals they set at the beginning of the lesson. Ask them whether the goals were accomplished or if there were challenges. Have students share the factors that contributed to their success. If the goals weren't achieved, talk about what students can do to help achieve them.

02 Matter Has Many Properties

ANCHORING PHENOMENON
Sitting on a beanbag chair feels different from sitting on a typical classroom chair.

ENGAGE Can You Explain It?
Students observe and ask questions about a beanbag chair.
They answer the Can You Explain It? question to identify what they will gather evidence about in the lesson.

EVALUATE Lesson Check
Students gauge their understanding of the anchoring phenomenon.

HANDS-ON ACTIVITY

EXPLORATION 1 So Many Properties (50 min)
Investigative Phenomenon Materials have distinct properties that can be observed.

Students connect back to the **anchoring phenomenon** that the materials needed for beanbag chairs have distinct properties.

HANDS-ON ACTIVITY

EXPLORATION 2 Beat the Heat (60 min)
Investigative Phenomenon People use distinct properties of materials to design solutions.

Students connect back to the **anchoring phenomenon** that how a material interacts with heat energy could affect how it feels as a beanbag chair material.

EXPLORATION 3 What Matter Can Do (60 min)
Investigative Phenomenon Properties of materials include ways the materials interact with energy and forces.

Students connect back to the **anchoring phenomenon** that materials in beanbag chairs are flexible and may consist of a mixture (filling).

Making 3D Connections

The **anchoring phenomenon** in this lesson supports students' understanding of and application of these Next Generation Science Standards.

Building to the Performance Expectations

5-PS1-3 Make observations and measurements to identify materials based on their properties.

3–5 ETS1-1 Define a simple design problem reflecting a need or a want that includes specified criteria for success and constraints on materials, time, or cost.

3–5 ETS1-2 Generate and compare multiple possible solutions to a problem based on how well each is likely to meet the criteria and constraints of the problem.

3–5 ETS1-3 Plan and carry out fair tests in which variables are controlled and failure points are considered to identify aspects of a model or prototype that can be improved.

SEP	DCI	CCC
Using Mathematics and Computational Thinking Measure and graph quantities such as weight to address scientific and engineering questions and problems. *(Explorations 1, 2, 3)*	**PS1.A Structure and Properties of Matter** Measurements of a variety of properties can be used to identify materials. *(Explorations 1, 3)*	**Science is a Human Endeavour** Science affects everyday life. Creativity and imagination are important to science. *(Explorations 1, 2)*
Engaging in Argument from Evidence Use data to evaluate claims about cause and effect. *(Exploration 3)*	**ETS1.A Defining and Delimiting Engineering Problems** *(Explorations 1, 2)*	**Scale, Proportion, and Quantity** Natural objects exist from the very small to the immensely large. *(Explorations 1, 2, 3)*
	ETS1.B Developing Possible Solutions *(Exploration 2)*	
	ETS1.C Optimizing the Design Solution *(Exploration 2)*	

Vocabulary

Word Wall — A word wall, anchor chart, or Language Development chart can be used to support vocabulary.

mixture combination of two or more substances, or materials, that keep their identities

solution mixture that has the same composition throughout

solubility ability to dissolve

You may want to include additional academic terms such as *properties* and any other terms students might struggle with.

Language Development Prompt students to complete the chart when they come to these highlighted terms within the lesson and to add their own terms as they come across unknown science terms.

Anchor Chart As you progress through the unit, you may want to use the Language Development chart as a guide to make a vocabulary-based anchor chart that can be displayed and filled out as a whole group during each lesson.

02 Matter Has Many Properties

Activity Guide, pages 46–47

Students can engage in the Can You Explain It? content by observing the photograph or by exploring the corresponding video online.

ONLINE  View a video related to a damaged beanbag chair.

ANCHORING PHENOMENON
Sitting in a beanbag chair feels different from sitting in a typical classroom chair.

PHENOMENON EXPLAINED
From the cover to the filling, materials are carefully selected to build or repair beanbag chairs.

Lesson Objective

Students can explore properties of matter, compare substances based on their physical properties, recognize factors affecting properties of matter, identify mixtures and solutions, and relate the properties of mixtures with the properties of starting materials.

Support Discovery

The following prompts can be used to guide student-led discovery.

I notice . . .

After observing the photograph or watching the video, students should record what they noticed about the beanbag chair. If students struggle to record observations, ask them to speculate about what a beanbag chair consists of.

Sample answer: I notice it has a hole; it looks like smooth, shiny material; it's lost some filling.

I wonder . . .

After observing the photograph or watching the video, students should record what more they want to find out about beanbags.

Sample answer: What filling is comfortable? How full is it supposed to be? What cover fabric would be both comfortable and sturdy?

Can You Explain It?

In Can You Explain It?, students make an initial claim that explains the **Anchoring Phenomenon.**

Sample answer: Student responses may indicate the indefinite shape, softness, or lower weight of the beanbag compared to a typical chair.

Students will gather evidence about the materials of a beanbag chair and their properties. This will enable them to give a more complete explanation of the **Anchoring Phenomenon** at the end of the lesson.

Alternative Phenomenon

If students are unfamiliar with beanbag chairs or similar objects, use an analogous object such as a water balloon or an inflated balloon. Discuss the properties that make the balloon functional and how the states and properties of matter of the balloon, including its contents, affect how it feels.

🗨 SOCIAL EMOTIONAL LEARNING

Guide students to reflect on their goals from previous lessons and on any feedback they received from their teachers or peers. Then have each student set a personal goal for this lesson and make a plan for how to achieve the goal. Throughout the lesson, take daily breaks for students to track their progress in meeting their goals. As students move from lesson to lesson, they can continue to work toward their initial goals or set new ones. If students struggle to set goals for this lesson, share with them some of the following ideas: modeling matter, planning an investigation, participating more during activity/group work or ensuring everyone in the group has a chance to share an idea, or persevering when an activity or topic is difficult.

02

Properties Matter

WHEN TO USE

SCIENCE **30 min**

- Anchoring Phenomenon / Alternative Phenomenon
- Options for ELA Instruction
- Build on Prior Knowledge
- Preview the Phenomenon
- Read to Learn
- Support Sense Making
- Science Stretch
- Check for Comprehension

Option 1 Use before students begin the lesson in the Activity Guide to provide an engaging model to introduce the lesson's phenomenon.

Option 2 Use after students have completed the Activity Guide to reinforce students' understanding of the lesson phenomenon by exploring a related phenomenon.

ELA **20 min**

- Options for ELA Instruction
- Build on Prior Knowledge
- Read to Learn

Option 3 To use during designated ELA Reading time for independent reading, whole-class instruction, or small-group instruction, look for this icon: ELA

Plan

> ### ANCHORING PHENOMENON / ALTERNATIVE PHENOMENON
>
> The anchoring phenomenon in the Activity Guide is *Sitting on a beanbag chair feels different from sitting on a typical classroom chair.* The main example is a girl sitting on a beanbag chair that has a tear in its outer covering. The FUNomenal Reader presents a similar phenomenon *(You can identify substances using their properties)*, and the example is a boy who needs to identify five unknown cooking substances. Both present the same science concepts and cover the same standards but with different phenomena. Guide students to draw connections between the two situations and to understand the underlying principle: the properties of matter include any characteristics that can be measured, such as color, mass, volume, and temperature.

Options for ELA Instruction ELA

Choose one of the following anchor chart options below and project it or print copies. Then display and introduce the chart before reading the text. Revisit the chart after reading the text and encourage students to discuss how the skill connects to the text.

Text Structure Refer to the *Text Structure Anchor Chart* when discussing text structure in the context of this story. Guide students to an understanding of the problem-solution structure of the story. Have them identify the problem and the solution.

Visualize Use the *Visualize Anchor Chart* to help draw students into the content of the story. Have them take two minutes to close their eyes and think about what it might be like to test the five mystery substances, as Ian does in the story. Discuss what they might see, smell, and feel based on details from the text.

Learning Mindset Have student pairs study the *My Learning Mindset Anchor Chart* and then decide which of the traits describe Ian, which ones describe Eli, and which apply to both brothers. Challenge partners to give examples of where in the story the characters show these traits.

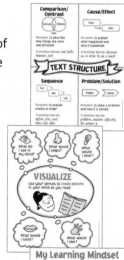

Preview

Build on Prior Knowledge Have students think about objects they come into contact with every day. Are those objects soft or hard, liquid or solid? How do they move when they are touched? Could you tell the objects apart if you were blindfolded? Have students discuss the answers to these questions as a group, drawing upon what they know about the states of matter.

Preview the Phenomenon Ask students to study the photo on pages 2–3 of the story, which shows two boys in a kitchen with unlabeled containers. Encourage students to record the first questions about this scene that come into their minds. Point out that their questions might change as they read through the story. Have them keep their questions handy and periodically check to see if any can be answered.

STANDARDS SUPPORTED

SEP

Planning and Carrying Out Investigations

Using Mathematics and Computational Thinking

Engaging in Argument from Evidence

DCI

PS1.A Structure and Properties of Matter

ETS1.A Defining and Delimiting Engineering Problems

ETS1.B Developing Possible Solutions

ETS1.C Optimizing the Design Solution

CCC

Science Is a Human Endeavor

Scale, Proportion, and Quantity

Scientific Knowledge Assumes an Order and Consistency in Natural Systems

Properties Matter (continued)

Discover

Read to Learn ELA

The **Read to Learn** suggestions inside the book's front cover encourage students to interact with the book multiple times for different purposes.

Preview Students look for unfamiliar words and share them with a partner. New terms may include *property, matter, solubility,* and *conductivity*. Have students look up words they aren't sure about and notice how they are used in the context of the story.

Skim Students skim the photos. Have them turn to a partner and share their predictions of what the story will be about.

Read As students read the story, ask them to look for connections to one of the following anchor chart skills. **Text Structure, Visualize, Learning Mindset**

Support Sense Making

Choose one or more of the following:

▶ Be sure students can identify the phenomenon presented on the opening pages of the story: Ian has poured some pantry substances into unlabeled containers and now doesn't know what they are. The story follows his efforts, with his brother's help, to figure out which substance is which. Have students name the ways Eli and Ian test the substances and tell how the tests relate to properties of matter.

▶ Have students name the five major senses (sight, smell, hearing, taste, touch) and recall how Ian used his senses as he tested the mystery substances. Why does Eli warn Ian about smelling and tasting the unknown substances? Guide students to relate Eli's warnings to safety practices in a science lab setting.

▶ Prepare a brown paper bag with two different objects for each pair of students. Objects might include small toys, balls, or blocks. Partners should take turns reaching in the bag, feeling the objects without looking, and guessing what they are. Have students tell the properties they used to identify each object.

▶ Tell students that things in nature are classified by patterns of similarities to and differences from other things. For example, an element is a primary component of matter, and the periodic table is a system for arranging the elements by their properties. Have interested students do research about the periodic table and present their findings to the class.

Extend

Science Stretch

The **Science Stretch** suggestions inside the book's back cover help students think about what they read. Students can complete one or more as time allows.

> Make a list, with examples, of properties of matter that weren't included in the story. Students may need to do research to find out properties (such as melting point and freezing point) that aren't mentioned in the story.

> Compare two objects in the room using properties of matter. **Sample answer:** My backpack and my shirt are both soft and blue, but the backpack has a rougher texture than my shirt does.

> Make up a game that uses properties of matter. Have students work in small groups to devise a guessing game like the one in the story or a different kind of game.

 SOCIAL EMOTIONAL LEARNING

How could you help someone who made a mistake feel better? **Sample answer:** I would remind them that part of being a scientist or engineer is learning from mistakes.

Check for Comprehension Have students write three things they found out in the story, two things they found interesting, and one question they still have about the properties of matter.

So Many Properties

TIME ESTIMATE

SHORT ON TIME?

This activity can be done as a whole class to save the amount of time individual groups would take to plan and conduct the investigation.

POSSIBLE MATERIALS

☐ fabric samples—rubber, denim, vinyl, sheer, wool

☐ filling samples—real beans, balls, pebbles, sponge, bubble wrap

☐ ballast samples—sand, rocks, golf balls, bearings

PREPARATION

Brainstorm possible materials for these categories with students. Encourage creative repurposing of everyday objects. Collect materials that are available and practical to distribute and use for this activity. If you have concerns of spills or allergies, provide samples in thin plastic bags so students can feel the materials' weight and other properties without making direct contact with them or being able to spill them.

INVESTIGATIVE PHENOMENON
Materials have distinct properties that can be observed.

Phenomenon Explained Students explore the **investigative phenomenon** by observing the properties of different materials to determine which ones would be the best to use to make a beanbag chair. Students gather evidence to support their explanation.

Form a Question After observing the photograph, students should form a question about making beanbag chairs. If students struggle to form a question, ask them to consider the function of a beanbag chair. **Sample answer:** What filling is comfortable? Does it need ballast (weights) on the bottom? What covering is durable? How do the cover and filling respond to forces such as stretching and squeezing?

STEP 1   Students observe sample materials and describe their physical properties. Students may mention texture, color, shape, stretchability, weight, etc.

STEP 2   Students collaborate to make a claim about the best material for a beanbag chair. **Sample answer:** The heavy cotton fabric is best. It's smooth and thick. Therefore, it will feel good and won't wear out quickly.

- **Make a Claim** Students should claim that one of the provided materials would be better than the others as part of a beanbag chair.

- **Evidence** Students' observations of the material's properties should serve as evidence to support their claims.

- **Reasoning** Students should justify their claim by showing how the material's properties align with how a beanbag chair is used.

STEP 3 Students describe how they might test one of the materials.
Sample answer: Stitch together a small model beanbag. Stress test the fabric by squeezing and dragging the model. Count squeezes or measure the distance it's dragged.

FORMATIVE ASSESSMENT

MAKING SENSE OF PHENOMENA

As they explore the **investigative phenomenon,** students gain understanding that materials have different properties that lend themselves to different uses. They should connect this to the **anchoring phenomenon** that sitting in a beanbag chair feels different from sitting in a typical classroom chair. Students should understand that a beanbag chair has a sturdy, comfortable cover and relative soft, flexible filler inside that allows the chair to take different shapes.

REMEDIATION If students struggle to connect the **investigative phenomenon** back to the **anchoring phenomenon,** have them review the properties of the materials they observed and make a T-chart of those that were or were not suitable for use in a beanbag.

MAKING SENSE OF PHENOMENA
IDEA ORGANIZER
After completing Exploration 1, students can fill in the **Idea Organizer** to summarize the connection between materials having distinct properties that can be observed and the anchoring phenomenon that sitting on a beanbag chair feels different from sitting on a typical classroom chair.

Activity Outcome

Students should record observations and draw inferences about different materials' suitability as beanbag materials based on observed properties.

Performance Indicators	
	observe and feel a variety of materials
	make a claim about the material that would work best
	describe how a material could be tested

Engineer It • Beat the Heat

Activity Guide, pages 50–53

TIME ESTIMATE

SHORT ON TIME?

You can skip or facilitate Step 1 by providing information about the insulating or conducting properties of the specific materials that you are providing.

POSSIBLE MATERIALS

- ☐ small piece of unwrapped chocolate placed in a small container with a lid
- ☐ foam cup
- ☐ tape
- ☐ glue
- ☐ aluminum foil
- ☐ aluminum trays
- ☐ wax paper
- ☐ paper cup
- ☐ cotton balls
- ☐ felt
- ☐ brown paper bag
- ☐ zip-top bag
- ☐ clock or timer

PREPARATION

In advance, prepare sets of materials that are large enough so each group can work with any of them in their design. Distribute materials to students prior to starting the activity.

INVESTIGATIVE PHENOMENON
People use distinct properties of materials to design solutions.

Phenomenon Explained Students explore the **investigative phenomenon** by designing a solution based on properties of materials. Students gather evidence to support their solution.

Form a Question After observing the photograph, students should form a question about the design challenge. If students struggle to form a question, explain that they need to design a package that will insulate chocolate from sources of heat such as warm air or direct sunlight. **Sample answer:** What type of insulation is thin but works well?

Explore

STEP 1 Students conduct research into the insulating or conducting properties of different materials. **Sample answer:** Foam works well. Foil can reflect sunlight but it does not insulate well.

STEP 2 Students identify the criteria and constraints. **Sample answer:** criteria: no melting, use minimal supplies; constraints: ≤ three times the size of the chocolate container, 15 minutes without melting.

STEP 3 Students brainstorm solutions, then assign points to each based on how well it meets the criteria and constraints. The highest-scoring solutions satisfy all constraints and do well on criteria.

Make and Test, Improve and Test

STEPS 4 and 5 Observations should lead to ideas about how solutions could be improved and evaluations of solutions based on the criteria and constraints. Diagrams should show the labeled materials used. Notes should focus on meeting criteria within the constraints.

- **Make a Claim** Identify material(s) that best insulate(s) the chocolate.
- **Evidence** Cite data about how well the chocolate was insulated.
- **Reasoning** Infer that materials that did not work well are not good at blocking (reducing the transfer of) heat energy.

FORMATIVE ASSESSMENT

MAKING SENSE OF PHENOMENA

As they explore the **investigative phenomenon,** students gain understanding that properties of materials affect their performance in design solutions. They should connect this to the **anchoring phenomenon** that sitting in a beanbag chair feels different than sitting in a typical classroom chair. Students should infer that beanbag chair materials may be limited by constraints and that insulating properties should be considered.

REMEDIATION If students struggle to connect the **investigative phenomenon** back to the **anchoring phenomenon,** set up a T-chart and work as a class to compare the criteria and constraints in this activity with the evaluation of beanbag chair materials.

Activity Outcome

Students should design a solution and test it to evaluate how well it meets the criteria and constraints.

Performance Indicators	
	evaluate the provided materials
	based on properties, identify materials to design a solution that meets criteria and constraints
	test and evaluate the solution

MAKING SENSE OF PHENOMENA IDEA ORGANIZER

After completing Exploration 2, students can fill in the **Idea Organizer** to connect using properties of materials for design solutions to the anchoring phenomenon that sitting on a beanbag chair is different than sitting on a typical classroom chair.

 SOCIAL EMOTIONAL LEARNING

Students might disagree about which materials or design to use. Model conflict-resolution skills.

- Demonstrate how two students can disagree without making things personal. Focus on the substance of the disagreement.
- Remind them to focus on the task at hand, which in this case is largely focused on meeting criteria and constraints. Arguments over proposed solutions should be focused on results, not guesses.

What Matter Can Do

Activity Guide, pages 54–58

TIME ESTIMATE

60 min

....

SHORT ON TIME?

Assemble circuits so students can focus on testing the different materials without having to worry about other variables.

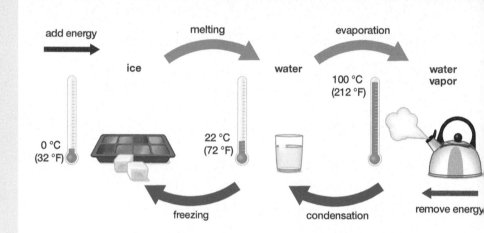

add energy · melting · evaporation

ice · water · water vapor

100 °C (212 °F)

0 °C (32 °F) · 22 °C (72 °F)

freezing · condensation · remove energy

POSSIBLE MATERIALS

- ☐ foam cups
- ☐ circuit kit (lightbulb and socket, wires with alligator clips, AA battery)
- ☐ plastic fork
- ☐ metal fork
- ☐ plastic pen
- ☐ short length of coat hanger

PREPARATION

In advance, gather parts for circuit kits or provide the materials to assemble them. Make sure all batteries have a charge.

INVESTIGATIVE PHENOMENON
Properties of materials include the ways these interact with energy and forces.

Phenomenon Explained Students explore the **investigative phenomenon** by testing how different types of matter, including mixtures, interact with different types of energy.

Challenge students to model matter and energy interactions with a line graph. Ask: If a teakettle of water is warming inside a sealed box, what would the line on a graph of the water's energy versus time look like? It would slope up to the right. What about the line on a graph of the amount of water inside the box versus time? It would be a flat line.

Everyday Phenomenon An aluminum drink can feels cold to the touch when you take it out of the refrigerator.

Students should connect the **everyday phenomenon** that aluminum is stiff and conducts heat energy to the **anchoring phenomenon** that sitting on a beanbag chair feels different from sitting in a typical classroom chair. Ask students to recall holding a cold metal drink can. Ask: Why does your hand feel cold? Heat energy passes easily through the metal conductor to the cold beverage. Then pass around foam cups. Have students each hold one for a few seconds. Ask: How did your hand feel? Why? It felt warm because the foam is an insulator. Heat energy from my hand was trapped between the cup and my hand.

Conductivity/Conductors and Insulators

Students learn about conductors and insulators, and how they interact with electricity and heat. Students can model a circuit using a small lightbulb, wires, and a battery. They can then test conductivity of materials. Students' claims about a pattern in the test results should suggest the property of conductivity can help identify whether objects are plastic or metal.

What Is a Mixture?

The term *mixture* is defined. Students work in groups to analyze the properties of a garden salad and orange juice and assess whether these foods are mixtures. They should determine that the salad is a mixture (its constituent parts can be identified); the orange juice is a solution. Ask: What part of a beanbag chair might be a mixture? the filling or stuffing How the stuffing feels is important for comfort. How should the mixture respond to heat energy and a person's weight (force)? It should conduct heat fairly well and provide a firm cushion when someone sits.

Dissolving

Students learn that solutions form when substances dissolve in a solvent, such as water. The substance may be invisible until the water is removed leaving only the particles of the substance behind. Challenge students to tell how they could identify white sand versus sugar by testing dissolving.

© Houghton Mifflin Harcourt Publishing Company • Image Credits: (tr) ©Houghton Mifflin Harcourt

---

FORMATIVE ASSESSMENT

MAKING SENSE OF PHENOMENA

As they explore the **investigative phenomenon,** students gain understanding that the ways matter interacts with types of energy are other properties of matter. They should connect this to the **anchoring phenomenon** that sitting in a beanbag chair feels different from sitting in a typical classroom chair. Students should understand that how well a beanbag case and filler conduct heat could make a beanbag chair more or less comfortable.

REMEDIATION If students struggle to connect the **investigative phenomenon** back to the **anchoring phenomenon,** have them discuss what it would mean if a beanbag chair did not conduct much heat away from a user's body.

MAKING SENSE OF PHENOMENA IDEA ORGANIZER
After completing Exploration 3, students can fill in the **Idea Organizer** to summarize the connection between how properties of materials include ways these interact with energy and forces and the anchoring phenomenon that sitting on a beanbag chair feels different from sitting on a typical classroom chair.

02

Take It Further

Engage • Explore/Explain • **Elaborate** • Evaluate

TIME ESTIMATE

45 min

These Take It Further paths may be completed to enrich and extend students' comprehension of content covered within this lesson.

ONLINE

People in Science and Engineering: Shirley Ann Jackson and Anthony Atala

In this feature, students learn about a physicist who specializes in particle movement and semiconductors and a physician who is pioneering the use of 3D printers in regenerative medicine.

Healthy Mixtures

Students will explore the mixtures of vitamins and minerals found in foods and the impact of these substances on the body and overall health. Then, students will research one specific vitamin or mineral nutrient.

People in Science and Engineering: Dr. Jani Ingram and Ciarra Greene

Students will learn about Dr. Jani Ingram's and Ciarra Greene's research into the link between environmental contaminants and cancer among Native American peoples.

Lesson Check

Activity Guide, pages 59–61

Can You Explain It?

Now I know or think that . . .

Sample answer:

- The outer fabric must be tough and flexible but feel comfortable against the skin. It should not be too good an insulator or it will feel hot. The filling needs to be lightweight, small, and a little springy. Ballast is optional. Sand is least likely to damage the covering and floor.

- It may be helpful to have fabric covering that lets air pass through without losing filling. Other properties: nonfading color, stain resistant, waterproof.

After completing the lesson, use the **Making Sense Idea Organizer** to summarize the connections between the **investigative phenomena** and **anchoring phenomenon.**

MAKING CONNECTIONS

After students complete the lesson, they should be able to answer a question about how a pencil eraser's properties affect its performance. **Sample answer:** An eraser needs to be flexible enough not to break. It can't be too rough or it will rub through the paper. If it's too soft it will be used up too fast.

Checkpoints

1. b—withstands high temperature, c—easy to replace, g—flexible, h—transparent

2. **Sample answer:** The glass withstanding high temperatures keeps fire fighters inside safer.

3. **Sample answer:** Warm a small sample until it bubbles, measure temperature, and repeat 5 times to get a pattern of data for evidence.

4. a—placing the substance in warm water; b—testing it in a circuit; c—trying to bend it

5. 3—aluminum; 4—gold

6. c—Each part keeps its own identity.

7. a—cover the container

8. **Sample answer:** Covering the container will keep any particles of water from evaporating and leaving the container, which would change the salt and water solution.

 SOCIAL EMOTIONAL LEARNING

Have students reflect on the goals they set at the beginning of the lesson. Ask them to think about whether the goals were accomplished or if there were challenges. Have students share the factors that contributed to their success. If the goals weren't achieved, talk about what students can do to help them achieve the goals.

03 Matter Can Change

ANCHORING PHENOMENON
This metal sculpture has dark and shiny areas.

ENGAGE Can You Explain It?
Students observe and ask questions about the statue and its condition. They answer the Can You Explain It? question to identify what they will gather evidence about in the lesson.

EVALUATE Lesson Check
Students gauge their understanding of the anchoring phenomenon.

HANDS-ON ACTIVITY

EXPLORATION 1 Changes in Matter 40 min

Investigative Phenomenon Substances can undergo changes in which they retain or change their identities.

Students connect back to the **anchoring phenomenon** that the dark areas of the sculpture are a new substance with a different identity.

HANDS-ON ACTIVITY

EXPLORATION 2 Which Will React? 50 min

Investigative Phenomenon Substances can be identified based on their properties.

Students connect back to the **anchoring phenomenon** that the dark substance covering the sculpture is a new substance because it looks different from the shiny area.

EXPLORATION 3 When Matter Changes 40 min

Investigative Phenomenon The properties of substances determine how they react or change when mixed.

Students connect back to the **anchoring phenomenon** that the shiny area shows that the dark coating can be removed by some interaction of substances.

EXPLORATION 4 Conservation of Matter 40 min

Investigative Phenomenon The amount of matter in a system doesn't change when two or more substances are mixed.

Students connect back to the **anchoring phenomenon** that the mass of substances before and after changes to the sculpture is the same.

Making 3D Connections

The **anchoring phenomenon** in this lesson supports students' understanding of and application of these Next Generation Science Standards.

Building to the Performance Expectations

5-PS1-2 Measure and graph quantities to provide evidence that regardless of the type of change that occurs when heating, cooling, or mixing substances, the total weight of matter is conserved.

5-PS1-4 Conduct an investigation to determine whether the mixing of two or more substances results in new substances.

SEP	DCI	CCC
Planning and Carrying Out Investigations Conduct an investigation collaboratively to produce data to serve as the basis for evidence. *(Explorations 1, 2, 4)*	**PS1.A Structure and Properties of Matter** The amount (weight) of matter is conserved when it changes form, even in transitions in which it seems to vanish. *(Explorations 1, 2, 4)*	**Cause and Effect** Cause and effect relationships are routinely identified and used to explain change. *(Explorations 1, 2, 3)*
Using Mathematics and Computational Thinking Measure and graph quantities such as weight to address scientific questions. *(Exploration 4)*	**PS1.B Chemical Reactions** When two or more different substances are mixed, a new substance with different properties may be formed. No matter what reaction or change in properties occurs, the total weight of the substances does not change. *(Explorations 2, 3, 4)*	**Systems and System Models** A system can be described in terms of its components and their interactions. *(Explorations 2, 3)*
		Scientific Knowledge Assumes and Order and Consistency in Natural Systems Science assumes consistent patterns in natural systems. *(Exploration 4)*

Vocabulary

Word Wall A word wall, anchor chart, or Language Development chart can be used to support vocabulary.

physical change change in which matter is altered but no new substances are made

chemical change change in which new matter is formed

conservation of mass the fact that the amount of matter always stays the same, regardless of physical change, phase change, or chemical change

You may want to include additional academic terms such as *identity, conservation, mixture,* or any other terms students might struggle with.

Language Development Prompt students to complete the chart when they come to these highlighted terms within the lesson and to add their own terms as they come across unknown science terms.

Anchor Chart As you progress through the unit, you may want to use the Language Development chart as a guide to make a vocabulary-based Anchor Chart that can be displayed and filled out as a whole group during each lesson.

03 Matter Can Change

Activity Guide, pages 62–63

Students can engage in the Can You Explain It? content by observing the photograph or by exploring the corresponding video online.

ONLINE  View a video related to a tarnished metal statue.

ANCHORING PHENOMENON
This metal sculpture has dark and shiny areas.

PHENOMENON EXPLAINED
Bronze sculptures develop a dark patina over time. The dog is shiny because people rub it for luck. The rubbing plus the substances in peoples' sweat gradually remove the patina.

Lesson Objective

Students can gather data to use as evidence to demonstrate that properties of matter can be used to identify substances and that no matter the type of change, matter is conserved.

Support Discovery

The following prompts can be used to guide student-led discovery.

I notice . . .

After observing the photograph or watching the video, students should record what they noticed about the sculpture. If students struggle to record observations, ask them to focus on changes in color.

Sample answers: It's made of metal. Most of it is dark and dull except for the dog, which is shiny.

I wonder . . .

After observing the photograph or watching the video, students should record what more they want to find out about the sculpture.

Sample answer: I wonder why the dog is shiny but the rest of the sculpture is dark and dull.

Can You Explain It?

In Can You Explain It?, students make an initial claim that explains the **Anchoring Phenomenon**.

Sample answer: Students may explain that the metal has undergone some change as a result of being exposed to the weather.

Students will gather evidence about properties of matter. This will enable them to give a more complete explanation of the **Anchoring Phenomenon** at the end of the lesson.

Alternative Phenomenon

If students are unfamiliar with metal objects and tarnishing, guide them to think of other examples of metals being changed by their environment, such as ferrous objects rusting, or other types of corrosion. You may want to bring one or more of these examples to class so that students can make in-person observations of how different metals are affected by other substances.

 SOCIAL EMOTIONAL LEARNING

Guide students to reflect on their goals from previous lessons and on any feedback they received from their teachers or peers. Then have each student set a personal goal for this lesson and make a plan for how to achieve the goal. Throughout the lesson, take daily breaks for students to track their progress in meeting their goals. As students move from lesson to lesson, they can continue to work toward their initial goals or set new ones. If students struggle to set goals for this lesson, share some of the following ideas: modeling matter, planning an investigation, participating more during activity/group work or ensuring everyone in the group has a chance to share an idea, or persevering when an activity or topic is difficult.

On the Nose

WHEN TO USE

SCIENCE (30 min)

- Anchoring Phenomenon / Alternative Phenomenon
- Options for ELA Instruction
- Build on Prior Knowledge
- Preview the Phenomenon
- Read to Learn
- Support Sense Making
- Science Stretch
- Check for Comprehension

Option 1 Use before students begin the lesson in the Activity Guide to provide an engaging model to introduce the lesson's phenomenon.

Option 2 Use after students have completed the Activity Guide to reinforce students' understanding of the lesson phenomenon by exploring a related phenomenon.

ELA (20 min)

- Options for ELA Instruction
- Build on Prior Knowledge
- Read to Learn

Option 3 To use during designated ELA Reading time for independent reading, whole-class instruction, or small-group instruction, look for this icon: ELA

Plan

> **ANCHORING PHENOMENON / ALTERNATIVE PHENOMENON**
>
> The anchoring phenomenon in the Activity Guide is *Some parts of the sculpture stay dark and dull even after it is rained on.* The main example is a tarnished bas-relief sculpture of a knight and dog. The FUNomenal Reader presents a similar phenomenon *(This bronze bust's nose is a different color from the rest of the head),* and the example is the bust of Abraham Lincoln at the Lincoln Tomb in Illinois. Both present the same science concepts and cover the same standards but with different phenomena. Guide students to draw connections between the two situations and to understand the underlying principle: a substance's properties of matter can change as the result of a physical or chemical change.

Options for ELA Instruction

Choose one of the following anchor chart options and project it or print copies. Then display and introduce the chart before reading the text. Revisit the chart after reading the text and encourage students to discuss how the skill connects to the text.

Following and Giving Instructions In the story, each of Ms. Reddy's lab groups makes a plan for testing materials to see which one removes tarnish from a spoon. Have students refer to the *Following and Giving Instructions Anchor Chart* to discuss what such a plan would need to include.

Narrative Nonfiction Use the *Narrative Nonfiction Anchor Chart* to discuss narrative nonfiction, which gives facts about a topic but is written like a story. Help students recognize that *On the Nose* has fictional characters presenting factual information about the Abraham Lincoln Tomb and chemical changes.

Retell Display the *Retell Anchor Chart* after reading to help gauge students' understanding of the concepts in the story. You might pair students and have them take turns retelling the story. Encourage partners to focus on the problem the main character addresses and the resolution of that problem.

Preview

ELA **Build on Prior Knowledge** Review the properties of matter with students. Have students work in groups to compare properties of solids, liquids, and gases by discussing their characteristics, such as volume and color.

Preview the Phenomenon Ask students to study the illustration on page 2 of the story, which shows a group of kids listening to a tour guide talk about a bust of Abraham Lincoln. Encourage students to record the first questions that come into their minds, including anything unusual they might notice about the bust. Point out that their questions might change as they read through the story. Have them keep their questions nearby and periodically check to see if any can be answered.

STANDARDS SUPPORTED

SEP

Analyzing and Interpreting Data

Planning and Carrying Out Investigations

Science Models, Laws, Mechanisms, and Theories Explain Natural Phenomena

Using Mathematics and Computational Thinking

DCI

PS1.A Structure and Properties of Matter

PS1.B Chemical Reactions

CCC

Cause and Effect

Structure and Function

Systems and System Models

On the Nose (continued)

Discover

Read to Learn

The **Read to Learn** suggestions inside the book's front cover encourage students to interact with the book multiple times for different purposes.

Preview Students look for unfamiliar words and share them with a partner. New terms may include *bust, tarnish,* and *chemical change.* Have students look up words they aren't sure about and notice how they are used in the context of the story.

Skim Students skim the illustrations and photos. Have them turn to a partner and share their predictions of what the story will be about.

Read As students read the story, ask them to look for connections to one of the following anchor chart skills. **Following and Giving Instructions, Narrative Nonfiction, Retell**

Support Sense Making

Choose one or more of the following:

- In the story, Ms. Reddy says, "A piece of wood burning, an iron fence rusting, and a silver spoon tarnishing are all examples of chemical changes." Ask students if they can think of other chemical changes. Remind them that during chemical changes, new substances form. Students might name the cooking of an egg, the digestion of food, and fireworks.

- Have students make a Venn diagram to compare and contrast rust and tarnish, using the information on page 8, other details from the story, and their own experience.

- Discuss the photos on pages 7 and 14–15. Can students think of any sculptures, statues, fences, or other objects they have seen that show rust or tarnish? Have them list descriptive words for each object and determine what caused it to rust or tarnish.

- Invite interested students to learn more about the Abraham Lincoln Tomb and its history and then report their findings to the class.

Extend

Science Stretch

The **Science Stretch** suggestions inside the book's back cover help students think about what they read. Students can complete one or more as time allows.

Why is the Lincoln bust's nose a different color from the rest of the face? **Sample answer:** The bust is covered with tarnish. People touch the nose. Sweat and skin oils, plus rubbing, take off the tarnish.

List adjectives to describe a rusted or tarnished object you have seen. **Sample answer:** I found an old rusted key. It was brown and had a crusty surface.

Write an argument for or against touching statues in public places. Have student consult the online *Science and Engineering Practices Handbook* for more information on writing an argument.

SOCIAL EMOTIONAL LEARNING

Can touching a statue's nose cause any harm? Discuss with a classmate. As needed, model for students how to listen respectfully while someone else is talking.

Check for Comprehension Ask students to make a visual explanation of how an object can rust or tarnish. Students can make a sketch or model to show how the object looked originally, what caused the chemical change, and how the object looked after the change. Have volunteers present their visual explanations to the class.

Changes in Matter

Activity Guide, pages 64–65

TIME ESTIMATE

40 min

....

SHORT ON TIME?

To save time, this activity can be done as a teacher-only demonstration. Alternatively, you can have each group test only one or two of the five methods.

POSSIBLE MATERIALS

- ☐ used toothbrush
- ☐ 6 tarnished pennies
- ☐ small paper plate
- ☐ 2 small plastic cups
- ☐ goggles and gloves
- ☐ paper towel
- ☐ water
- ☐ baking soda, 2 pinches
- ☐ vinegar
- ☐ table salt, pinch
- ☐ water dropper
- ☐ vinegar dropper

PREPARATION

Decide whether to distribute liquids yourself or to allow each group to manage their own droppers.

INVESTIGATIVE PHENOMENON
Substances can undergo changes in which they retain or change their identities.

Phenomenon Explained Students explore the **investigative phenomenon** by conducting a fair test to observe and record data about the effects of different cleaning methods on a tarnished penny. Students compare the different methods to explain their conclusions.

Form a Question After observing the photograph, students should form a question about how substances change when mixed. If students struggle to form a question, ask them to consider washing dishes, i.e., using soap to break up grease. **Sample answer:** Why does one cleaner interact with one type of dirt, stains, or grime and not another?

Ask students how to use the materials to create the cleaning methods described in the table. Remind students that each cleaning mix uses no more than 6 drops of liquid. **Sample answer:** Put a pinch of the correct solid powder on the penny. Add 6 drops of the liquid.

After trying to shine a tarnished penny using specific cleaning methods, students record their observations.

Cleaning method (with toothbrush)	Penny observations	Other observations
No liquid	removed some dirt	no other changes
Water	more dirt gone	no other changes
Water and baking soda	same as water	baking soda dissolved; no other change
Baking soda and vinegar	same as water	change in identity; fizzing, bubbling
Vinegar and salt	penny is now shiny	change in identity

- **Make a Claim** Claims should indicate that baking soda and vinegar react, and that a tarnish remover for a penny is a mix of vinegar and salt.

- **Evidence** Students should cite as evidence that the baking soda and vinegar fizzed, and that the interaction between vinegar, table salt, and tarnish cleaned the penny quickly.

- **Reasoning** Students should reason that the fizzing baking soda and vinegar shows a change in the substances' identity, and that tarnish changed its identity when it reacted with the salt and vinegar mix.

FORMATIVE ASSESSMENT

MAKING SENSE OF PHENOMENA

Students gain understanding of how specific substances react with each other and the tarnish as they explore the **investigative phenomenon.** They should connect this to the **anchoring phenomenon** that a metal sculpture has dark and shiny areas.

REMEDIATION If students struggle to connect the **investigative phenomenon** back to the **anchoring phenomenon,** have them compare and contrast the penny and the sculpture.

Activity Outcome

Students should observe reactions while trying to clean a tarnished penny with substances.

Performance Indicators	
	record observations about the reactions that occur when making and using the cleaning mixes
	make a claim that new substances result from baking soda plus vinegar, and from vinegar and salt plus tarnish
	support the claim using collected data as evidence

MAKING SENSE OF PHENOMENA IDEA ORGANIZER

After completing Exploration 1, students can fill in the **Idea Organizer** to summarize the connection between observable reactions between substances and whether or not those substances change or retain their identities.

 SOCIAL EMOTIONAL LEARNING

Have students reflect on how they showed respect for shared materials during the hands-on-activity. The following promote respectful handing of materials in a group setting:

- treating all materials with care
- reporting any breakage or spills immediately
- maintaining a clean workspace during the activity
- returning the materials and cleaning up according to the teacher's instruction

Which Will React?

Activity Guide, pages 66–68

TIME ESTIMATE

day 1   day 2

 40 min   **10** min

SHORT ON TIME?

This activity can be done as a whole class or each group can carry out an investigation into one of the mystery powders rather than all three.

POSSIBLE MATERIALS

- ☐ safety goggles and apron
- ☐ 3 droppers
- ☐ 3 plastic spoons
- ☐ 9 test tubes and test tube holder
- ☐ Powder 1, baking soda
- ☐ Powder 2, cream of tartar
- ☐ Powder 3, corn starch
- ☐ iodine solution
- ☐ vinegar
- ☐ water
- ☐ labels and pen
- ☐ test tube brush and soap

Materials Alert Remind students never to eat or drink anything during a lab activity. Guide students to wash their hands and safely dispose of materials when finished.

INVESTIGATIVE PHENOMENON
Substances can be identified based on their properties.

Phenomenon Explained Students explore the **investigative phenomenon** by conducting a test to identify three mystery substances based on how they react to test substances.

Form a Question After observing the photograph, students should form a question about how to identify the various white powders. If students struggle to form a question, ask them to consider how they would tell different clear solutions apart, such as water, clear vinegar, and simple syrup. **Sample answer:** How do these different kitchen ingredients change when mixed with other things? How will I get the powders to undergo a physical or chemical change?

STEPS 1–4 Have students brainstorm a few ideas in small groups on how they can determine the different powders' identities. **Sample answer:** Mix each solution with each powder for a total of nine tests.

Before they begin, emphasize the importance of carefully labeling the tubes. Remind students to put equal amounts of powder in each tube.

Results Water: no changes; Vinegar: Powder 1 fizzes; Iodine: Powder 3 turns purple. Each test tube has a powder and a liquid. The type of powder and type of liquid are different in each.

STEP 5 Students analyze their results, naming the powder containers based on the liquids that reacted with each one. **Sample answer:** Baking soda reacts with vinegar to create a gas, so A is baking soda. Cornstarch and iodine change color, so C is cornstarch. Cream of tartar does not react with water, vinegar, or iodine, so B is cream of tartar.

Did all the powders undergo a chemical change? **Sample answer:** No. B (Powder 2) showed no change.

- **Make a Claim** Claims should indicate that physical and chemical changes occurred.

- **Evidence** Evidence of chemical change includes baking soda and vinegar producing a lot of bubbles, and cornstarch and iodine producing a change in color. A physical change is powder dissolving.

- **Reasoning** The bubbles show a gas, a new substance. The color is a new property, also showing a new substance. Dissolving produces no evidence of any new substance, so it is a physical change.

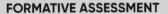

FORMATIVE ASSESSMENT

MAKING SENSE OF PHENOMENA

As they explore the **investigative phenomenon,** students gain understanding that substances can be identified based on their properties and the way they react. They should connect this to the **anchoring phenomenon** that a sculpture has dark and shiny areas.

REMEDIATION If students struggle to connect the **investigative phenomenon** back to the **anchoring phenomenon,** have them compare the color differences in the iodine and cornstarch test and the dark and shiny parts of the statue.

Activity Outcome

Students should test to identify three mystery substances.

Performance Indicators	
	record observations about physical and chemical changes
	use information about known chemical reactions to identify the mystery powders and make a claim about the chemical and physical changes that took place
	support the claim using collected data as evidence

MAKING SENSE OF PHENOMENA IDEA ORGANIZER
After completing Exploration 2, students can fill in the **Idea Organizer** to summarize how to identify mystery powders based on a comparison between observed chemical and physical changes and known chemical and physical changes.

SOCIAL EMOTIONAL LEARNING

Have students reflect on the hands-on activity they just completed. Have small groups or partners brainstorm a list of responsible actions students can take when doing hands-on activities. Then discuss their lists as a class, for example:

- Be sure to understand the purpose of the activity.
- Listen to instructions about how to use and manage any materials.

Lesson 3 • Matter Can Change   **75**

When Matter Changes

Activity Guide, pages 69–70

TIME ESTIMATE

45 min

INVESTIGATIVE PHENOMENON
The properties of substances determine how they react or change when mixed.

Phenomenon Explained Students explore the **investigative phenomenon** by gathering evidence that supports the claim that the properties of substances determine whether they retain or change their identities when mixed.

Everyday Phenomenon **At the beach, when you add sand to a bucket of water, the mixture represents a physical change. No new substance is made.**

Have students discuss **everyday phenomena** that show physical changes, such as crushing a steel can, slicing a loaf of bread, shredding or folding paper, or chopping wood.

Discuss the example of the mixture of red and blue beads. Ask students to think of other examples of mixtures that represent a physical change. If students struggle to think of examples, suggest that mixing two different types of fruit in a bowl—apples and oranges, for instance—is a type of physical change because both apples and oranges remain physically distinct, even when mixed. No change in matter takes place.

Physical changes happen when matter changes shape, size, or number. An example of this type of change would be cutting a piece of wood. In this type of change, no new matter is formed.

Before and After Are Different

Everyday Phenomenon **A chemical change takes place when you cook an egg.**

Help students distinguish between physical changes and chemical changes by pointing out that in a chemical change a new substance or substances form. Discuss clues that can be used to determine that a chemical change has taken place: the production of gas, a precipitate, or heat; the formation of a new substance that cannot be reversed. The components of the system are permanently changed.

Review the example of the glow sticks. Point out that when you snap the glow stick, you're combining substances which causes a chemical change that gives off light.

 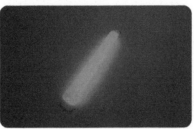

Have students recall the combination of vinegar and baking soda from Explorations 1 and 2. Remind them that when vinegar and baking soda mix, a chemical change occurs. The combination releases carbon dioxide, and the baking soda disappears, further indicating a chemical change.

FORMATIVE ASSESSMENT ■ ■ ■ □

MAKING SENSE OF PHENOMENA

As they explore the **investigative phenomenon,** students gain understanding that when types of matter mix and retain their identities, a physical change has taken place, but when types of matter mix and change their identities, a chemical change has taken place. They should connect this to the **anchoring phenomenon** that a metal sculpture has dark and shiny areas. The darkening is most likely a new substance, a new form of matter.

REMEDIATION If students struggle to connect the **investigative phenomenon** back to the **anchoring phenomenon,** have them discuss a piece of burned toast, an analogy to the tarnished statue.

SOCIAL EMOTIONAL LEARNING

Divide the class into pairs and have one student "teach" the other about physical changes, including examples; have the other student "teach" about chemical changes, including examples. Then have partners take turns completing the following sentence frames to model giving appropriate feedback:

- One thing I still don't understand about physical/chemical changes is _____. What do you think?
- One thing I liked about your description of physical/chemical changes was _____.
- I agree/disagree with you about _____ because _____.

MAKING SENSE OF PHENOMENA IDEA ORGANIZER
After completing Exploration 3, students can fill in the **Idea Organizer** to summarize the difference between a physical change and a chemical change and how to recognize signs of both.

Conservation of Matter

Activity Guide, pages 71–74

TIME ESTIMATE

INVESTIGATIVE PHENOMENON
The amount of matter in a system doesn't change when two or more substances are mixed.

Phenomenon Explained Students explore the **investigative phenomenon** by gathering evidence that supports the claim that the amount of matter remains constant before and after physical changes, phase changes, and chemical changes.

Where Does the Matter Go?
Review the examples. Ask students whether the changes shown are physical or chemical. Be sure students understand the fundamental concept, that the mass of matter does not change when a physical change takes place—such as peeling an orange and dissolving sugar in water.

Physical Changes

Everyday Phenomenon A loaf of bread has the same mass before and after it's sliced.

Explain the concept of conservation of matter as it relates to the additional examples of physical changes in this section. Ask students to provide examples of physical changes in which the amount of matter stays the same. Accept any physical change, such as melting or ripping.

Phase changes are considered <u>physical</u> changes. This means that no new substance is formed. When changing from solid to liquid form, the mass of the matter will <u>stay the same</u>. When changing from liquid to gas form, the mass will <u>stay the same</u>. This supports the conservation of matter. **Sample answer:** Student drawings should show unchanging numbers of particles as something undergoes a change of state. The amount of matter (the mass) remains constant.

Conservation in a Phase Change

Everyday Phenomenon   **A block of butter contains the same amount of matter before and after it's melted.**

Clarify for students what it means that, in a phase change, matter does not change, but energy does. For example, water vapor is warmer than ice. Also explain that, though water vapor cannot be seen with just our eyes, it still has mass.

Conservation of Matter: Chemical Change

As with water vapor, point out that during many chemical changes, some matter is released as a clear, colorless gas. Experiments that capture and weigh escaped gas prove the conservation of mass. For example, a balloon fitted over the mouth of a flask can capture gas that might otherwise escape after a chemical change.

178 g

©Houghton Mifflin Harcourt Publishing Company • Image Credits: (c) ©Houghton Mifflin Harcourt

---

SOCIAL EMOTIONAL LEARNING

Have students reflect on the concept of conservation of matter. Have pairs discuss aspects of the conservation of matter that they struggled with and how they handled the situation. Have students brainstorm ways in which they can approach and overcome a problem they have about something they're learning. The following promote perseverance and a growth mindset:

- Don't give up when faced with something difficult.
- Stop and take a breath or a break before trying again.
- Identify the source of the difficulty.
- Ask for help.

FORMATIVE ASSESSMENT   ■ ■ ■ ■

MAKING SENSE OF PHENOMENA

As they explore the **investigative phenomenon,** students gain understanding that the amount of matter in a system does not change during physical changes, phase changes, and chemical changes. They should connect this to the **anchoring phenomenon** that a metal sculpture has dark and shiny areas.

REMEDIATION If students struggle to connect the **investigative phenomenon** back to the **anchoring phenomenon,** have them consider bending the sculpture in half (physical change), melting it (phase change), and tarnishing it more (chemical change).

MAKING SENSE OF PHENOMENA IDEA ORGANIZER

After completing Exploration 4, students can fill in the **Idea Organizer** to summarize how the conservation of matter applies to physical changes including changes of state, and chemical changes.

03

Take It Further

Engage • Explore/Explain • **Elaborate** • Evaluate

TIME ESTIMATE

60 min

These Take It Further paths may be completed to enrich and extend students' comprehension of content covered within this lesson.

ONLINE

People in Science and Engineering: Antoine Lavoisier

In this feature, students read about Antoine Lavoisier, a French chemist who discovered oxygen and its roles in daily life. He was one of the first to realize that the amount of matter going into a reaction equals the amount of matter produced.

Slow Down the Spoil

Students investigate how refrigeration slows down the oxidation rate and spoilage of food.

Acids and Bases

Students learn about ways to determine how strong an acid or base a substance is.

Careers in Science and Engineering: Flavor Chemist

Students learn about the job of a flavor chemist.

Lesson Check

Activity Guide, pages 75–77

Can You Explain It?

Now I know or think that . . .

Sample answer:

- Chemical changes make new substances, for example, vinegar and baking soda form a gas. Physical changes make a new shape or texture, but the substance is unchanged.
- A thin, dark layer formed on the metal. The original metal can't be put back; a chemical change occurred. Polishing and other changes made part of it shiny again.
- Conservation of matter means new matter can't be made or destroyed during chemical and physical changes.

After completing the lesson, use the **Making Sense Idea Organizer** to summarize the connections between the **investigative phenomena** and **anchoring phenomenon.**

MAKING CONNECTIONS

After students complete the lesson, they should be able to explain how to find the best way to clean crust from a faucet. **Sample answer:** Test cleaners one at a time. Use one that changes the crust to a new material that will dissolve and wash away.

Checkpoints

1. c—fizzes with vinegar

2. a—The can had three-day-old food in it.;
   b—There was an odor.

3. **Chemical change:** energy release, odor, gas release, burning; **Physical change:** shape change, change of state, boiling

4. **Sample answer:** Conservation of matter predicts that the weight won't change. To test that, weigh the glass and ice before and after melting.

5. a—folding paper; b—breaking a window; e—building a tower of blocks; f—boiling water
   Sample answer: Folding paper is a physical change because no new substance is formed.

6. c—baking brownies; d—molding fruit; f—burning wood in a fireplace **Sample answer:** Burning wood is a chemical change because a new substance is formed and energy is released.

7. d—There would be no change

8. **Sample answer:** I would show the vinegar, baking soda, and balloon on a scale demonstration. Then, I'd draw a model of both changes and point out the similarities.

SOCIAL EMOTIONAL LEARNING

Have students reflect on the goals they set at the start of the lesson. Ask whether the goals were met or if there were challenges. Have students share what helped them succeed. If the goals weren't met, discuss what students can do next time to succeed.

The Unit Review items enable you to assess student comprehension of core ideas, as well as crosscutting concepts and science and engineering practices.

1. **DOK 3** **Sample answers:** Squeeze each bottle to show matter taking up space. Weigh the bottles to show that they have different masses.
Remind students that matter has mass and takes up space. Mass can be perceived by senses such as touch or measured using tools such as a scale. Volume can also be perceived and measured.

2. **DOK 3** Students' models should include particles of air far apart in the "empty" balloon. The filled balloon should have more closely spaced particles.
Some students might not perceive the greater pressure in the inflated balloon. Use an actual inflated balloon to allow them to feel and perceive the pressure, or ask them to recall what it felt like when they played with an inflated balloon or ball.

3. **DOK 2** air—gas; bus—solid; tea—liquid; milk—liquid; sidewalk—solid
If students are unsure of the states of the named substances, tell them that the milk and tea are in beverage form (don't say "liquid"), not the leafy or dried or frozen states.

4. **DOK 3** **Sample answer:** A good solution would hold the papers together firmly and could be removed without damaging the papers. Paperclips are rigid enough to firmly connect the papers but flexible enough to be removed.
Focus students on what makes paperclips a good solution for temporarily attaching multiple sheets of paper.

5. **DOK 3** **Sample answer:** I would test and measure the properties of the blocks to determine which materials are best for building a strong and sturdy wall. Small samples of materials have the same properties as large samples.
This question builds upon the previous one, which asked students to focus on paperclip properties. In this question students should think about investigating different properties of the bricks.

6. **DOK 2** **a.** colored pencil may be shorter than crayon, **b.** colored pencil could pass through filter at an angle, **d.** crayon could get caught
If students struggle with this question, have them consider each answer in turn, asking themselves first *Could this happen?* and then *Would this be a failure to solve the problem?*

7. **DOK 2** **b.** paper being torn, **c.** wood being chopped down, **e.** cake being cut
Sample answer: a. Paper burning is chemical change. I could measure the release of heat energy and observe properties that show new substances formed (ashes and smoke).
If students struggle with this question, take each substance one by one and discuss in detail the two things that are done to the substance. For example, wood is chopped and burned. In which case is the wood undergoing a chemical change? What is the evidence?

8. **DOK 1** **a.** metal rusting; a chemical change
If students are not familiar with what is pictured, explain that the tools all contain iron and the iron is turning to rust—a new substance.

9. **DOK 2** Sample answer: collect data about reddish material, compare it to data about the nail; if different, a chemical change took place. Heating would be a physical change.
Tell students to think about what kind of change heating the nails would cause. How could they determine what kind of change took place?

10. **DOK 3** Sample answer: The amount is the same; conservation of matter; amount of matter before a chemical change = amount of matter after a chemical change
Tell students to think about the total amount of matter before and after a chemical change, not the specific amounts or forms of matter.

3D Item Analysis	1	2	3	4	5	6	7	8	9	10
SEP Planning and Carrying Out Investigations	•				•		•		•	
SEP Developing and Using Models	•	•								
SEP Using Mathematics and Computational Thinking										•
SEP Engaging in Argument from Evidence									•	
DCI Structures and Properties of Matter	•	•	•	•	•	•		•	•	•
DCI Chemical Reactions							•	•	•	•
DCI Defining and Delimiting Engineering Problems				•	•					
DCI Developing Possible Solutions						•				
DCI Optimizing the Design Solution					•					
CCC Scale, Proportion, and Quantity		•	•		•					
CCC Cause and Effect	•	•					•	•	•	•
CCC Systems and System Models						•				•
CCC Scientific Knowledge Assumes an Order and Consistency in Natural Systems					•					
CCC Science is a Human Endeavor				•						

Unit Storyline

In Unit 2, students explored properties of matter and physical and chemical changes. They found out that during a chemical change, substances combine to form new substances with different properties. In this unit, students will explore how plants and other organisms use and transform matter and energy to live and grow. They will identify energy sources and trace the flows of energy within living systems.

LESSON 1   PE 5-LS1-1
Plants Transform and Use Energy and Matter
Activity Guide, pp. 82–95

Students explore the **anchoring phenomenon** that plants can grow in tubes without soil.

SEP Developing and Using Models; Engaging in Argument from Evidence; Using Mathematics and Computational Thinking

DCI **PS3.D** Energy in Chemical Processes and Everyday Life; **LS1.C** Organization for Matter and Energy Flow in Organisms

CCC Energy and Matter

LESSON 2   PE 5-PS3-1
Organisms Use Matter and Energy
Activity Guide, pp. 96–111

Students explore the **anchoring phenomenon** that a giant panda eats bamboo for 16 hours a day.

SEP Obtaining, Evaluating, and Communicating Information

DCI **PS3.D** Energy in Chemical Processes and Everyday Life; **LS1.C** Organization for Matter and Energy Flow in Organisms

CCC Energy and Matter

LESSON 3   PE 5-LS2-1, 5-PS3-1
Energy and Matter Move Between Organisms
Activity Guide, pp. 112–131

Students explore the **anchoring phenomenon** that when there are more plants to eat, there are more caribou in the tundra.

SEP Developing and Using Models; Science Models, Laws, Mechanisms, and Theories Explain Natural Phenomena

DCI **LS2.A** Interdependent Relationships in Ecosystems; **LS2.B** Cycles of Matter and Energy Transfer in Ecosystems

CCC Systems and System Models

Unit Review Activity Guide, pp. 132–134

03

Online-Only Resources

Supporting Unit Resources

You Solve It   SUPPORTS LESSON 1

What Do Plants Need? is a virtual lab that offers practice in support of **Performance Expectation 5-LS1-1.** Students will determine which color light allows plants to grow the tallest and will conduct an investigation to find out what plants need to grow.

SEP   Constructing Explanations and Designing Solutions
DCI   **PS3.D** Energy in Chemical Processes and Everyday Life
CCC   Energy and Matter

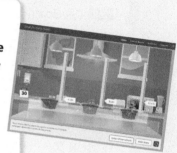

Unit Project   SUPPORTS LESSONS 1 AND 3   90 min

The Best Light provides students an opportunity to practice aspects of **Performance Expectation 5-LS1-1.** Students will conduct an investigation to see under which conditions the plants grow the best.

SEP   Asking Questions and Defining Problems; Engaging in Argument from Evidence; Planning and Carrying Out Investigations
DCI   **LS1.C** Organization for Matter and Energy Flow in Organisms
CCC   Energy and Matter

Unit Performance Task   SUPPORTS LESSONS 1 AND 3   90 min

Business Has Bean Bad provides an opportunity for students to practice or be assessed on aspects of **Performance Expectation 5-LS1-1.** Students design a water solution to help bean plants grow quickly.

SEP   Asking Questions and Defining Problems; Engaging in Argument from Evidence; Planning and Carrying Out Investigations
DCI   **LS1.C** Organization for Matter and Energy Flow in Organisms; **ETS1.B** Developing Possible Solutions
CCC   Energy and Matter

Language Development

This worksheet is used as students progress through the unit's lessons. As they come to a highlighted vocabulary term, they should come back to this chart and fill in the blanks with words or phrases.

ONLINE  We've got you covered.

Updates and additional student and teacher resources can be found online. Check back often!

Supporting Lesson Resources

 ### Do the Math!

Lesson 1 Thirsty Trees
Lesson 2 Growing Anew; Counting Krill Calories
Lesson 3 Calculate Energy Units

 ### Language SmArts

Lesson 1 Use Visual Displays
Lesson 2 Use the Internet
Lesson 3 Making Inferences; Connections

Take It Further

Lesson 1 People in Science & Engineering: Ynes Mexia; Not Only Plants!; Careers in Science & Engineering: Mycologist
Lesson 2 Careers in Science & Engineering: Animal Nutritionist; In the Water; Engineer It: Feed Me Now!
Lesson 3 Careers in Science & Engineering: Zoologist; People in Science & Engineering: Jafet Vélez-Valentín; Exploring a Desert Ecosystem

MAKING SENSE OF PHENOMENA
This idea organizer is used to make sense of the following **anchoring phenomena**:
Lesson 1—Plants can grow in tubes without soil.
Lesson 2—A giant panda eats bamboo for 16 hours a day.
Lesson 3—When there are more plants to eat, there are more caribou in the tundra.

It also connects the investigative phenomena back to the anchoring phenomenon in each lesson.

Assessment

Unit Readiness Check: Are You Ready?
Lesson Quizzes: Can You Apply It?
Unit 3 Test
Performance-Based Assessment

Assessments are available in an editable, printable format or can be administered and auto-graded online.

LESSON

01

Plants Transform and Use Energy and Matter

ANCHORING PHENOMENON
Plants can grow in tubes without soil.

ENGAGE Can You Explain It?
Students observe and ask questions about how plants grow without soil.
They answer the Can You Explain It? question to identify what they will
gather evidence about in the lesson.

EVALUATE Lesson Check
Students gauge their understanding of the anchoring phenomenon.

HANDS-ON ACTIVITY

EXPLORATION 1 A Tree in a Forest (50 min)
Investigative Phenomenon Plants need
the right amount of light to live and grow.

Students connect back to the **anchoring
phenomenon** that plants need light to live
and grow, which they get even in tubes
without soil.

HANDS-ON ACTIVITY

EXPLORATION 2 Needs for Growth (45 min)
Investigative Phenomenon Plants gain
weight and grow when able to make food.

Students connect back to the **anchoring
phenomenon** that plants absorb water,
which enables them to make food and is partly
responsible for their increase in matter (weight).

EXPLORATION 3 Plant Needs (15 min)
Investigative Phenomenon Plants
need water, nutrients, and air to grow.

Students connect back to the **anchoring
phenomenon** that hydroponic systems meet
basic plant needs, which do not include soil.

EXPLORATION 4 Making Food (20 min)
Investigative Phenomenon Plants use
energy from the sun and matter from their
environments to make food.

Students connect back to the **anchoring
phenomenon** that all basic plant needs must
be met for them to make food.

Making 3D Connections

The anchoring phenomenon in this lesson supports students' understanding of and application of these Next Generation Science Standards.

Building to the Performance Expectations

5-LS1-1 Support an argument that plants get the materials they need for growth chiefly from air and water.

SEP

Developing and Using Models Develop a model to describe phenomena. *(Exploration 1, 4)*

Engaging in Argument from Evidence Support an argument with evidence, data or a model. *(Explorations 2, 3)*

Using Mathematics and Computational Thinking Describe and graph quantities such as area and volume to address scientific questions. *(Exploration 2)*

DCI

PS3.D Energy in Chemical Processes and Everyday Life The energy released [from] food was once energy from the sun that was captured by plants in the chemical process that forms plant matter (from air and water). *(Explorations 1, 4)*

LS1.C Organization for Matter and Energy Flow in Organisms Plants acquire their material for growth chiefly from air and water. *(Explorations 2, 3)*

CCC

Energy and Matter Energy can be transferred in various ways and between objects. Matter is transported into, out of, and within systems. *(Explorations 1, 2, 3, 4)*

Vocabulary

Word Wall A word wall, anchor chart, or Language Development chart can be used to support vocabulary.

You may want to include additional academic terms such as *weight and nutrients* and other terms students might struggle with.

Language Development Prompt students to add their own terms as they come across unknown science terms in the lesson.

Anchor Chart As you progress through the unit, you may want to make a vocabulary-based anchor chart using the Language Development chart as a guide that can be displayed and filled out as a whole group during each lesson.

01 Plants Transform and Use Energy and Matter

Activity Guide, pages 82–83

nutrient return

nutrient pump

Students can engage in the Can You Explain It? content by observing the photograph or by exploring the corresponding video online.

ONLINE @Ed

View a video related to hydroponic systems.

ANCHORING PHENOMENON

Plants can grow in tubes without soil.

PHENOMENON EXPLAINED

Hydroponic systems do not include soil. In these systems, plants receive the water, light, air, and nutrients they need to survive.

Lesson Objective

Students can use evidence to support a claim that plants get energy from sunlight and materials they need for growth from air and water.

Support Discovery

The following prompts can be used to guide student-led discovery.

I notice . . .

After observing the photograph or watching the video, students should record what they noticed about the plants. If students struggle to record observations, ask them to identify what is different about these plants and where they are growing.

Sample answers: The plants look green and healthy. The plants aren't planted in the ground. They are growing without soil.

I wonder . . .

After observing the photograph or watching the video, students should record what they want to find out about what plants need to live and grow.

Sample answer: I wonder how the plants get water and how they grow indoors. I wonder how plants grow without soil and if they would grow better in soil.

Can You Explain It?

In the Can You Explain It?, students make an initial claim that explains the **Anchoring Phenomenon**.

Sample answer: The plants growing without soil must be getting everything they need to grow, including light and air. I know this is possible because orchids and similar plants also grow without soil.

Students will gather evidence about plant needs. This will enable them to give a more complete explanation of the **Anchoring Phenomenon** at the end of the lesson.

Alternative Phenomenon

If students are unfamiliar with hydroponic systems, guide them to think of other examples of plants that grow without soil, such as orchids and air plants. You may want to bring one or more of these examples to class so that students can make in-person observations of how plants grow without soil.

 SOCIAL EMOTIONAL LEARNING

Guide students to reflect on their goals from previous lessons and on any feedback they received from their teachers or peers. Then have each student set a personal goal for this lesson and make a plan for how to achieve the goal. Throughout the lesson, take daily breaks for students to track their progress in meeting their goals. As students move from lesson to lesson, they can continue to work towards their initial goals or set new ones. If students struggle setting goals for this lesson, share with them some of the following ideas: identifying plant needs, engaging in argument from evidence, and ensuring everyone in the group has a chance to share an idea.

01

Air Plants at the Airport

WHEN TO USE

SCIENCE **30 min**

- Anchoring Phenomenon / Alternative Phenomenon
- Options for ELA Instruction
- Build on Prior Knowledge
- Preview the Phenomenon
- Read to Learn
- Support Sense Making
- Science Stretch
- Check for Comprehension

Option 1 Use before students begin the lesson in the Activity Guide to provide an engaging model to introduce the lesson's phenomenon.

Option 2 Use after students have completed the Activity Guide to reinforce students' understanding of the lesson phenomenon by exploring a related phenomenon.

ELA **20 min**

- Options for ELA Instruction
- Build on Prior Knowledge
- Read to Learn

Option 3 To use during designated ELA Reading time for independent reading, whole-class instruction, or small-group instruction, look for this icon: **ELA**

Plan

ANCHORING PHENOMENON / ALTERNATIVE PHENOMENON

The anchoring phenomenon in the Activity Guide is *Plants can grow in tubes without soil*, and the main example is a hydroponic greenhouse. The FUNomenal Reader presents a similar phenomenon *(Plants can grow in air without soil)*, but the example is an aeroponic garden, in which the plants' roots are in air instead of in water or soil. Both present the same science concepts and cover the same standards but with different phenomena. Guide students to draw connections between the two situations and to understand the underlying principle: plants need light, water, air, and nutrients to grow and survive—and these needs can be met with or without soil.

Options for ELA Instruction **ELA**

Choose one of the following anchor chart options and project it or print copies. Then display and introduce the chart before reading the text. Revisit the chart after reading the text and encourage students to discuss how the skill connects to the text.

Text Structure Use the *Text Structure Anchor Chart* when discussing text structure in the context of this story. Guide students to an understanding of the problem-solution structure of the story. Have them identify the problem and the solution.

Argument Have students consult the online *Science and Engineering Practices Handbook* for more information on the claim-evidence-reasoning format Elena uses in the story. You can also use the *Parts of an Argument Anchor Chart*.

Narrative Nonfiction Use the *Narrative Nonfiction Anchor Chart* to discuss the differences between literary and informational text. Help students understand that this story has fictional characters presenting factual information about plants.

Preview

ELA **Build on Prior Knowledge** Ask for a show of hands from students who have worked with plants at school, in a garden, or on a farm. Have volunteers share their experiences with the class, including the conditions and materials that plants need to grow.

Preview the Phenomenon Ask students to study the illustration on page 2 of the story and come up with a list of questions about what they see in the background. To do so, students must think about what plants need to grow. Encourage students to record the first questions that come into their minds. Point out that their questions might change as they read through the story. Have them keep their questions handy and periodically check to see if any can be answered.

STANDARDS SUPPORTED

SEP
Developing and Using Models

Engaging in Argument from Evidence

DCI
PS3.D Energy in Chemical Processes and Everyday Life

LS1.C Organization for Matter and Energy Flow in Organisms

CCC
Energy and Matter

Air Plants at the Airport (continued)

Discover

Read to Learn

The **Read to Learn** suggestions inside the book's front cover encourage students to interact with the book multiple times for different purposes.

> **Preview** Students look for unfamiliar words and share them with a partner. New words may include *germinate* and *aeroponics*. Have students look up words they aren't sure about and notice how they are used in the context of the story.

> **Skim** Students skim the story quickly to get a general idea of what it is about. Have them turn to a partner and share their predictions of what the story will be about.

> **Read** As students read the story, ask them to look for connections to one of the following anchor chart skills. **Text Structure, Argument, Narrative Nonfiction**

Support Sense Making

Choose one or more of the following:

▶ Be sure students can identify the phenomenon presented on the opening pages of the story: Elena sees plants growing without being planted in soil. The story is about her efforts to make sense of that phenomenon.

▶ Have students make a T-chart to compare and contrast traditional soil-based farming with aeroponic gardening in the story. The chart can include both similarities and differences.

▶ Have students analyze the claim-evidence-reasoning argument Elena makes in the story. Is her claim supported by the evidence she states? Is her reasoning sound? Have them work in pairs to present their own claims, evidence, and reasoning related to the phenomenon.

▶ Encourage a student-led discussion about the advantages of growing plants without soil. Discussion points might include that farmers could grow more food in smaller areas such as greenhouses and rooftops. Food could be produced in areas where space, soil, or water is limited. Interested students might want to do online research to find out more and then share their findings with the class.

Extend

Science Stretch

The **Science Stretch** suggestions inside the book's back cover help students think about what they read. Students can complete one or more as time allows.

> How could you make a model of how plants make food?
> **Sample answer:** I could make a poster that shows a growing plant with arrows to indicate what it takes in and what it produces.

> Write a blog post from the point of view of a plant that doesn't grow in soil. Encourage students to use their imagination while also addressing the science underlying the situation.

> Make a plan for a community garden. How would you begin? **Sample answer:** I would first write to my local city council representative to ask about nearby empty lots that could be repurposed.

 SOCIAL EMOTIONAL LEARNING

What surprised you in this story? Share ideas with a classmate. Encourage self-reflection as well as the respectful and supportive sharing of ideas.

Check for Comprehension Ask students to make a visual explanation of how plants get what they need to make food. They should make a sketch that shows a plant—in soil, water, or air—receiving light, air, and water to make food (sugar) plus waste gases.

A Tree in a Forest

Activity Guide, pages 84–87

TIME ESTIMATE

day 1   day 2   day 3   day 4   day 5

 20 min   **5 min**   **5 min**   **5 min**   **15 min**

SHORT ON TIME?

This activity can be done as a whole class to save the amount of time individual groups would take to plan and conduct the investigation.

POSSIBLE MATERIALS

- ☐ 2 small potted plants
- ☐ shoebox and lid
- ☐ masking tape
- ☐ marker
- ☐ measuring cup
- ☐ water
- ☐ colored pencils

PREPARATION

In advance, gather or grow small plants of the same kind and of similar size. Plan a location where students' plants can be placed and will be left undisturbed for the duration of the activity. Distribute materials to students prior to starting the activity.

INVESTIGATIVE PHENOMENON
Plants need the right amount of light to live and grow.

Phenomenon Explained Students explore the **investigative phenomenon** by planning and conducting a fair test to explain why few young trees grow on a forest floor. Students gather evidence to support their explanation.

Form a question After observing the photograph, students should form a question about the growth of young trees on a rainforest floor to investigate. If students struggle to form a question, ask them to consider what plants need to live and grow. Sample answer: How does a rain forest affect what young trees need in order to grow?

STEP 1 Students make a plan to test how a plant grows with little to no light or with a lot of light. Sample answer: Test two plants of the same kind that are similar in size. Place both plants on or near a window, but use the shoebox and lid as a barrier to limit the amount of light one of them receives. Give both plants the same amount of water. Measure and record their height at the same time each day.

STEPS 2 and 3 Students use the recording space to organize and display their data. They may use tables and/or graphs. Prompt them to look for cause-and-effect relationships in their data. Sample answer: The plant grown in deep shade was taller, but it looks unhealthy. The plant grown in light looks healthier.

STEP 4 Remind students to look for patterns as they identify similarities and differences in the data.

- **Make a Claim** Claims should indicate that the amount of light a plant receives affects how quickly it grows.
- **Evidence** Students should cite as evidence the data from the activity that show that plants depend on light.
- **Reasoning** Students should explain their reasoning that few plants grow on the forest floor because plants need light to grow, and the adult trees block most of the sun's light.

MAKING SENSE OF PHENOMENA IDEA ORGANIZER

After completing Exploration 1, students can fill in the **Idea Organizer** to summarize the connection between plants needing the right amount of light to live and grow and the anchoring phenomenon that plants need light to live and grow and that they can get the light they need even though they are in tubes without soil.

FORMATIVE ASSESSMENT

MAKING SENSE OF PHENOMENA

Students gain understanding that plants need light to grow as they explore the **investigative phenomenon.** They should connect this to the **anchoring phenomenon** that plants need light to live and grow and can get the light they need even without soil. Students should understand plants need light (and air and water)—but not soil—to grow.

REMEDIATION If students struggle to connect the **investigative phenomenon** back to the **anchoring phenomenon,** have them discuss how plants get the light they need and how that is possible without soil.

Activity Outcome

Students should design and follow the steps of a fair test in order to observe that plants with little or no exposure to light do not grow well.

Performance Indicators
record observations about the plants' growth patterns and physical appearance
make a claim that access to light is necessary for plant growth
support the claim using collected data as evidence

 SOCIAL EMOTIONAL LEARNING

Have students discuss how they communicate with friends or family members and how they use teamwork in other aspects of their lives. The following promote effective communication and teamwork:

- actively listening to everyone
- giving others the opportunity to share their ideas
- having a judgment-free zone
- not one person dominating/doing all of the work
- building on the ideas of others

Needs for Growth

Activity Guide, pages 88–89

TIME ESTIMATE

45 min

POSSIBLE MATERIALS

☐ one-week-old seedling in pot

☐ six-week-old plant in pot

☐ pan balance or scale

PREPARATION

For each group, the seedling and the mature plant should be the same type of plant.

In order for students to rule out soil as the source of the adult plant's weight gain, minimize any difference in soil weight between seedling and adult plant. You may wish to grow the plants, using identical pots and equal weights of soil. If you start with grown plants, make sure that both pots have the same weight of soil. As an alternative to small groups, use a single class setup.

INVESTIGATIVE PHENOMENON
Plants gain weight and grow when able to make food.

Phenomenon Explained Students explore the **investigative phenomenon** that plants need the right conditions to live and grow by collecting and analyzing data to demonstrate that plants gain weight as they grow.

Form a question After observing the photograph, students should form a question about how the weight of a plant changes over time. If students struggle to form a question, ask them to consider what plants need to live and grow. **Sample answer:** How much of a plant's added weight comes from soil?

Analyze your data Students should use the data table provided to record their weight measurements. They will need to carefully separate the parts of each plant system (plant, soil, pot).

Alternatively, you may supply weight measurements for the pots and soil, so that students need only to measure the plants' weights. Confirm that students' recorded data are reasonable.

- **Make a Claim** Students' claims should indicate that the increased weight of the plant must be from air, water, or a combination of both.

- **Evidence** Students should cite as evidence the data from the activity that show that the weight of the plant increases as it grows, but the weight of the soil shows no/little change.

- **Reasoning** Students should explain their reasoning that access to soil must not be necessary for the plant to grow and increase in weight.

FORMATIVE ASSESSMENT

MAKING SENSE OF PHENOMENA

Students gain understanding that, as they grow, plants gain weight as they explore the **investigative phenomenon.** They should connect this to the **anchoring phenomenon** that plants absorb water from the soil, which allows them to make food and is one reason for their increase in matter (weight). Students should understand that the soil is not the source of the plant's weight gain.

REMEDIATION If students struggle to connect the **investigative phenomenon** back to the **anchoring phenomenon,** review and discuss their data, which indicate that plants do not get food from soil. If they did, the weight of the soil in the pot with the six-week-old plant would be considerably less than the weight of the soil in the seedling's pot. In future Explorations, students will learn that plants make their own food. This process also produces materials that plants need to build new tissue (matter). This helps explain why plants gain weight and grow when they are able to make food.

MAKING SENSE OF PHENOMENA IDEA ORGANIZER

After completing Exploration 2, students can fill in the **Idea Organizer** to summarize the connection between plants gaining weight as they grow and the anchoring phenomenon that potted plants absorb water from the soil, which is at least partially responsible for the increase in matter (weight) as they grow.

Activity Outcome

Students should understand that as plants grow they gain weight, but soil is not the source.

Performance Indicators	
	record observations about the plants' growth patterns and physical appearance
	make a claim that access to soil is not necessary for plant growth
	support a claim with evidence that the plant is growing and gaining weight without soil losing weight

Plant Needs

Activity Guide, pages 90–91

TIME ESTIMATE

15 min

Materials Alert For this exploration, have a hand lens available so that students can look at the illustrations on their Interactive Worktext pages.

You may want to have a variety of leaves and a microscope available for students to support their discovery and to teach the content of the Exploration as a Hands-On Activity.

INVESTIGATIVE PHENOMENON
Plants need water, nutrients, and air to grow.

Phenomenon Explained Students explore the **investigative phenomenon** by gathering evidence that supports the claim that plants need water, nutrients, and air to stay healthy and grow.

Drink It In

Before students read the text on the page, have them examine the two pictures of the plant. In pairs, have students discuss their ideas about why the plant on the left is wilted and what it would need to be healthy again. Encourage students to reflect on the Hands-On Activities and any everyday experiences to inform their conversation. After they read the text, have students identify information in the text that supports their initial ideas or helps them revise their ideas.

Nutrients

Students may use a model to illustrate how plants take in nutrients through their roots. Models should include how the dissolved nutrients move from the roots into the stem and then to the rest of the plant.

Sample answer: water, air, and nutrients. Students might also say sunlight. However, they should recognize that soil is not needed for growth.

In and Out

Everyday Phenomenon **The air we breathe out is different from the air we breathe in.**

To help students visualize the structures that enable plants to exchange these gases with the environment, let them use hand lenses to get a closer look at the illustrations or have a microscope and leaves available.

SOCIAL EMOTIONAL LEARNING

Before students answer the question, discuss as a class what it means to give constructive feedback. Talk about how feedback should include the positive aspects of student work as well as helping others improve upon their work without being mean or disrespectful. Provide students time to practice this with a partner or small group before answering the question.

FORMATIVE ASSESSMENT

MAKING SENSE OF PHENOMENA

Students gain understanding that water, nutrients, and air are basic plant needs as they explore the **investigative phenomenon**. They should connect this to the **anchoring phenomenon** that hydroponic systems provide plants with all their basic needs, which do not include soil. Students should understand that plants cannot be healthy without water, nutrients, and air.

REMEDIATION If students struggle to connect the **investigative phenomenon** back to the **anchoring phenomenon**, have them list all of the things that have found out in the Exploration about what plants need to stay healthy and grow (water, nutrients, and air). Review the list with students, and point out that the list does not include soil.

MAKING SENSE OF PHENOMENA IDEA ORGANIZER

After completing Exploration 3, students can fill in the **Idea Organizer** to summarize the connection between plants needing water, nutrients, and air to grow and the anchoring phenomenon that hydroponic systems provide plants with their basic needs (which do not include soil).

Making Food

Activity Guide, page 92

TIME ESTIMATE

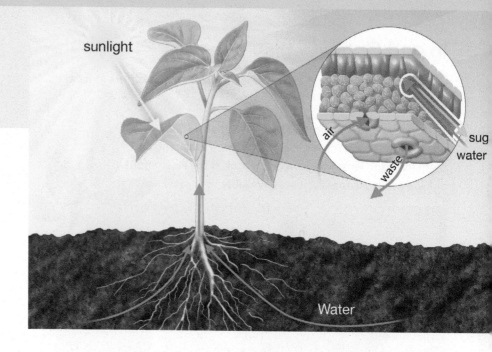

sunlight

air

sug
water

waste

Water

INVESTIGATIVE PHENOMENON
Plants use energy from the sun and matter from their environments to make food.

Phenomenon Explained Students explore the **investigative phenomenon** by observing what a plant needs to make food.

The model explains the chemical process of how plants make the food they need. Remind students that all necessary elements must be available. For example, plants cannot make food in the dark because plants need light to make food.

Have student pairs or small groups analyze the model by writing the letter of each caption next to the part(s) of the process it describes. Students can then refer to their labeled diagram as they give an overview in their own words.

Students may wish to make their own models. They can review each others' pictures and captions and provide feedback. Does each model show all the plant parts and processes involved in making food?

Everyday Phenomenon   **Plants make their own food.**

Ask students to identify and discuss examples of the **everyday phenomenon** in the classroom or on school grounds. Examples could include plants growing in the sunlight through a window or grasses growing on school grounds.

FORMATIVE ASSESSMENT

MAKING SENSE OF PHENOMENA

Students gain understanding of how plants use energy from the sun and matter from their environment as they explore the **investigative phenomenon**. They should connect this to the **anchoring phenomenon** that plants require that all their basic needs be met in order to make food.

REMEDIATION If students struggle to connect the **investigative phenomenon** back to the **anchoring phenomenon**, project the *Capturing Energy as Food* diagram on a large screen or refer students to the picture and captions in their books. Go through the steps of how plants make food, and have students point out the basic needs of plants as part of the discussion. Students should conclude that soil is not a basic need and is not needed for plants to make their own food, so plants can grow without soil.

MAKING SENSE OF PHENOMENA IDEA ORGANIZER

After completing Exploration 4, students can fill in the **Idea Organizer** to summarize the connection between plants using energy from the sun and matter from their environments to make food and the anchoring phenomenon that plants require all their basic needs to be met in order to make food, but soil is not a basic need.

Engage • Explore/Explain • **Elaborate** • Evaluate

TIME ESTIMATE

45 min

These Take It Further paths may be completed to enrich and extend students' comprehension of content covered within this lesson.

ONLINE

People in Science & Engineering: Ynes Mexia

In this feature, students read about Ynes Mexia, a Mexican-American plant collector, explorer, and botanist who lived during the early 20th century and made many contributions to the collection and study of different plants, including the discovery of new species.

Not Only Plants!

Students discover that plants are not the only organisms that can make their own food. Kelp and a strange-looking slug are among the other living things that can make their own food!

Careers in Science & Engineering: Mycologist

Students learn about mycologists, scientists who study fungi. Because of their work, scientists now know that fungi are not plants but take in food in ways similar to animals.

Lesson Check

Activity Guide, pages 93–95

Can You Explain It?

Now I know or think that . . .

Sample answer: I now think that the plants can survive because their needs for light, air, water, and nutrients are met. Soil is not a need. So, they are able to make food with air, water, and light energy.

After completing the lesson, use the **Making Sense Idea Organizer** to summarize the connections between the **investigative phenomena** and **anchoring phenomenon.**

MAKING CONNECTIONS

After students complete the lesson, they should be able to answer a question about an alternative phenomenon to explain how a potato plant growing in water from a small piece of potato is alike and different from the plants growing without soil.

Sample answer: The potato in the water is like the plants growing without soil because the potato is also growing without soil. It is different because the potato looks like it is in plain water and probably did not start growing from a seed. It looks like the plant is growing from the potato.

Checkpoints

1. air + water = sugar + waste

2. **c**—It is the effect of getting too much water.
   d—It is the effect of not getting enough water.

3. **Sample answer:** Plants use light energy, air, and water to make food. With less light, the plant will make less food. So, it will use less water and air, and release less waste.

4. **a**—sun; **b**—roots; **c**—leaves

5. **Sample answer:** The plant will weaken and may die. This is because a plant needs light, water, and air to make food (sugar). Without food, it can't carry out life processes.

6. needed to make food—air, sunlight, water; made by the plant—sugar, waste; energy—sunlight

7. **b**—soil, **e**—bacteria; **Sample answer:** All a plant requires to make food and grow are water, air, nutrients, and light.

8. **Sample answer:** Roots; the plant needs to take in as much water as it can.

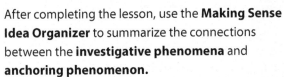 **SOCIAL EMOTIONAL LEARNING**

Have students reflect on the goals they set at the beginning of the lesson. Ask them to think about whether the goals were accomplished or if there were challenges. Have students share the factors that contributed to their success. If the goals were not achieved, talk about what students can do to help them achieve the goals.

LESSON

02 Organisms Use Matter and Energy

ANCHORING PHENOMENON
A giant panda eats bamboo for 16 hours a day.

ENGAGE Can You Explain It?
Students observe and ask questions about how organisms such as pandas acquire and use matter and energy in the form of food. They answer the Can You Explain It? question to identify what they will gather evidence about in the lesson.

EVALUATE Lesson Check
Students gauge their understanding of the anchoring phenomenon.

HANDS-ON ACTIVITY

EXPLORATION 1 A Filling Morsel (45 min)
Investigative Phenomenon Some foods provide more energy than others.

Students connect back to the **anchoring phenomenon** that animals need to eat more food if the food they are eating provides too little energy.

HANDS-ON ACTIVITY

EXPLORATION 2 Where's the Heat? (45 min)
Investigative Phenomenon The energy in food is used by many organisms to maintain body temperature.

Students connect back to the **anchoring phenomenon** that food energy is required for many life processes including maintaining warmth in warm-blooded organisms.

EXPLORATION 3 Growth, Change, and Regrowth (15 min)
Investigative Phenomenon The energy from food is used by organisms for growth, body repair, and other life processes.

Students connect back to the **anchoring phenomenon** that energy is needed daily for body growth and repair, whether visible or not. That need must be balanced with other life processes.

EXPLORATION 4 Animal Energy (15 min)
Investigative Phenomenon Some organisms use energy in ways unique to their species.

Students connect back to the **anchoring phenomenon** that some animals require more energy because of size or circumstance.

Making 3D Connections

The **anchoring phenomenon** in this lesson supports students' understanding of and application of these Next Generation Science Standards.

Building to the Performance Expectations

5-PS3-1 Use models to describe that energy in animals' food (used for body repair, growth, motion, and to maintain body warmth) was once energy from the sun.

SEP	DCI	CCC

Obtaining, Evaluating, and Communicating Information
Obtain and combine information from books and/or other reliable media to explain phenomena or solutions to a design problem.
(Explorations 1, 2, 3, 4)

LS1.C Organization for Matter and Energy Flow in Organisms
Food provides animals with the materials they need for body repair and growth and the energy they need to maintain body warmth and for motion. *(Explorations 1, 2, 3, 4)*

PS3.D Energy in Chemical Processes and Everyday Life
The energy released from food was once energy from the sun that was captured by plants in the chemical process that forms plant matter (from air and water).
(Explorations 1, 3)

Energy and Matter Energy can be transferred in various ways and between objects.
(Explorations 1, 2, 3, 4)

Vocabulary

| Word Wall | A word wall, anchor chart, or Language Development chart
can be used to support vocabulary.

consumer organism that obtains energy and matter by feeding on other organisms

producer organism that makes its own food

You may want to include additional academic terms such as *byproduct* and *Calorie* and any other terms that students might struggle with.

Language Development Prompt students to complete the chart when they come to these highlighted terms within the lesson.

Anchor Chart As you progress through the unit, you may want to make a vocabulary-based anchor chart using the Language Development chart as a guide that can be displayed and filled out as a whole group during each lesson.

02 Organisms Use Matter and Energy

Activity Guide, pages 96–97

Students can engage in the Can You Explain It? content by observing the photograph or by exploring the corresponding video online.

ONLINE  View a video related to panda feeding behavior.

ANCHORING PHENOMENON

A giant panda eats bamboo for 16 hours a day.

PHENOMENON EXPLAINED

A large organism eating food that doesn't provide a great deal of energy means that organism has to eat a lot of food, or eat all day long.

Lesson Objective

Students can describe how animals exchange matter with their environment and use the matter and energy stored in food for warmth, motion, body growth, and body repair.

Support Discovery

The following prompts can be used to guide student-led discovery.

I notice . . .

After observing the photograph or watching the video, students should record what they noticed about the panda. If students struggle to record observations, ask them to note the properties of the bamboo that the panda is feeding on.

Sample answer: The panda chews on bamboo.

I wonder . . .

After observing the photograph or watching the video, students should record what they want to find out about pandas. If students struggle to record what they want to know about the panda, encourage them to consider the panda's food choice or eating habits.

Sample answer: What else does the panda need energy to do?

Alternative Phenomenon

If students are unfamiliar with pandas, guide them to think of other animals that feed throughout the day, such as hummingbirds. You may want to bring in photographs or have students view a video of hummingbirds feeding so that they can make their own observations. Explain that hummingbirds feed on plant nectar, which is a sugary substance. These birds need a great deal of energy to sustain their incredibly fast wing beats.

Can You Explain It?

In the Can You Explain It?, students make an initial claim that explains the **Anchoring Phenomenon.** Students might write or draw their ideas about the panda's food needs and how those needs are met.

Students will gather evidence about how organisms acquire and use energy and matter from food. This will enable them to give a more complete explanation of the **Anchoring Phenomenon** at the end of the lesson.

 SOCIAL EMOTIONAL LEARNING

Guide students to reflect on their goals from previous lessons and on any feedback they received from their teachers or peers. Then, have each student set a personal goal for this lesson and make a plan for how to achieve the goal. Throughout the lesson, take daily breaks for students to track their progress in meeting their goals. As students move from lesson to lesson, they can continue to work towards their initial goals or set new ones. If students struggle setting goals for this lesson, share with them some of the following ideas: describing how animals use food for energy, developing models, and persevering through activities that are difficult.

02

FUNomenal READER

Octavius the Expanding Octopus

WHEN TO USE

SCIENCE **30 min**

- Anchoring Phenomenon / Alternative Phenomenon
- Options for ELA Instruction
- Build on Prior Knowledge
- Preview the Phenomenon
- Read to Learn
- Support Sense Making
- Science Stretch
- Check for Comprehension

Option 1 Use before students begin the lesson in the Activity Guide to provide an engaging model to introduce the lesson's phenomenon.

Option 2 Use after students have completed the Activity Guide to reinforce students' understanding of the lesson phenomenon by exploring a related phenomenon.

ELA **20 min**

- Options for ELA Instruction
- Build on Prior Knowledge
- Read to Learn

Option 3 To use during designated ELA Reading time for independent reading, whole-class instruction, or small-group instruction, look for this icon: 🔖 ELA

Plan

ANCHORING PHENOMENON / ALTERNATIVE PHENOMENON

The anchoring phenomenon in the Activity Guide is *A giant panda eats bamboo for 16 hours a day*. The main example is a panda chewing on bamboo. The FUNomenal Reader presents a similar phenomenon (*Giant Pacific octopuses grow very quickly and can more than double in size in 90 days*), and the example is an octopus in a tank at a marine life research center. Both present the same science concepts and cover the same standards but with different phenomena. Guide students to draw connections between the two situations and to understand the underlying principle: animals eat food to get the materials necessary for body growth and repair.

Options for ELA Instruction ELA

Choose one of the following anchor chart options and project it or print copies. Then display and introduce the chart before reading the text. Revisit the chart after reading the text and encourage students to discuss how the skill connects to the text.

Text Features Have students refer to the *Text Features Anchor Chart* to help them identify the various text features in this story. As they page through the story, students should notice illustrations, photos, and a chart. Guide them to understand that these visual features help explain ideas in the text.

Ask and Answer Questions Use the *Ask and Answer Questions Anchor Chart* when introducing, developing, or reviewing those skills. Have students consider how questioning helps Darius and Andrew find out more information about Octavius the octopus.

Context Clues Use the *Context Clues Anchor Chart* if students struggle to understand the meaning of some words in the story. Note that the word *crustaceans* on page 9 of the story is an example on the chart. In the story, a context clue is the phrase *such as crabs and shrimp*. This helps students deduce that crustaceans are a group of animals with shells.

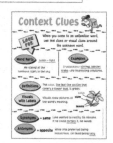

Preview

© Houghton Mifflin Harcourt Publishing Company

ELA **Build on Prior Knowledge** Ask volunteers to share what they know about octopuses. They may know that octopuses have eight arms and live in the ocean. You may want to share additional background information about octopuses. These invertebrates can squeeze into tight spaces; have a hard beak to eat prey such as shellfish; can camouflage themselves by changing color; and most can eject a thick, black ink to distract a predator. Ask students how they think an octopus gets the energy and material to do these things.

Preview the Phenomenon Ask students to study the illustration on pages 2–3 of the story, which shows people looking at an octopus in a tank. Nearby is a sign that shows how the octopus has grown since its rescue. Encourage students to record the first questions about this scene that come into their minds. Point out that their questions might change as they read through the story. Have them keep their questions handy and periodically check to see if any can be answered.

STANDARDS SUPPORTED

SEP
Developing and Using Models

DCI
LS1.C Organization for Matter and Energy Flow in Organisms

CCC
Energy and Matter

GIANT PACIFIC OCTOPUS

Octavius the Expanding Octopus (continued)

Discover

Read to Learn

The **Read to Learn** suggestions inside the book's front cover encourage students to interact with the book multiple times for different purposes.

Preview Students look for unfamiliar words and share them with a partner. New terms may include *marine biologist, prosthesis,* and *den*. Have students look up words they aren't sure about and notice how they are used in the context of the story.

Skim Students skim the illustrations and photos. Have them turn to a partner and share their predictions of what the story will be about.

Read As students read the story, ask them to look for connections to one of the following anchor chart skills. **Text Features, Ask and Answer Questions, Context Clues**

Support Sense Making

Choose one or more of the following:

▶ Be sure students can identify the phenomenon presented on the opening pages of the story: Darius and Andrew see an octopus at a research center and wonder how it could have more than doubled in size in 30 days. The story follows their efforts to learn more about octopuses and how they grow.

▶ Discuss Andrew's question on page 6 about adding water to the octopus's tank. This is a logical question because a typical fish tank in a home needs to have water added periodically due to evaporation. Point out to students that an octopus habitat in a research setting like the one in the story is a closed system, so evaporation is not an issue.

▶ Have students make a Venn diagram to compare and contrast octopuses in the wild and octopuses in a research center. They should focus on how the octopus gets food and uses energy. If they need to do more research about octopuses, provide books and approved websites for them to use.

▶ Help students understand that some animals can regenerate, or regrow, body parts—and this requires energy and matter from food. Point out that for an organism to be able to repair itself, its immune system's structures and processes must be maintained. Encourage a student-led discussion of how factors in a natural environment might affect an organism's immune system.

Extend

Science Stretch

The **Science Stretch** suggestions inside the book's back cover help students think about what they read. Students can complete one or more as time allows.

> Write a blog post about another animal and what it eats. As students research their animals, have them focus on what is unique about the way the animal uses energy.

> Make a pamphlet about a mammal and what it does with the matter and energy from its food. Provide books and approved websites for students to use in their research.

> Make a model showing how energy moves between an octopus and its food and how the octopus uses its energy. This activity works well with student pairs or small groups. The model might take the form of a diagram with labels, a clay sculpture, or a short video.

 SOCIAL EMOTIONAL LEARNING

Make a menu for a healthful meal that would provide energy and matter for someone's body. Students may need to review which foods make up a nutritious diet for humans.

Check for Comprehension Have students write a short paragraph summarizing how animals use matter in the environment to get energy.

A Filling Morsel

Activity Guide, pages 98–100

TIME ESTIMATE

SHORT ON TIME?

This activity can be done as a whole class to save the amount of time individual groups would take to plan and conduct the investigation. Divvy up the provided foods and/or nutritional information so each team researches one food and reports back to the class with their data.

POSSIBLE MATERIALS

☐ nutritional information/labels for various foods

☐ calculator

☐ balance (optional)

☐ foods (optional)

☐ gloves (optional)

PREPARATION

In advance, gather foods and/or their nutrition information. Distribute materials to students prior to starting the activity.

INVESTIGATIVE PHENOMENON
Some foods provide more energy than others.

Phenomenon Explained Students explore the **investigative phenomenon** by obtaining, evaluating, and communicating information about the energy content of different foods. Using materials provided by the teacher, students develop questions to investigate. They then make a claim about energy and types of food.

Form a question After observing the photograph, students should form a question about the energy content in different foods. If students struggle to form a question, ask them to think about what kinds of foods they or people they know typically eat before an athletic event. Sample answer: How much food by weight should a runner eat each day compared to a panda?

STEP 1 After agreeing on a small subset of questions to investigate, students make a plan to conduct their investigations. Sample answer: Find out the nutritional needs of an athlete compared to the nutritional needs of a panda. Then, analyze foods to find the weight of food for each for a day. Assume 1 cup of any food = 8 oz by weight, and 1 kg= 2.2 1bs.

STEP 2 Students should choose a way to communicate their data.
Sample answer: Giant pandas need to eat 12–38 kg of bamboo daily. An adult athlete needs a variety of foods, about 2.6 kg daily.

- **Make a Claim** Students' claims should indicate that energy content of food varies and that some organisms need more energy than others.

- **Evidence** Claims should cite the number of Calories per unit of food (e.g., per cup) as evidence of a given food's energy content and therefore its value to an athlete or other consumer.

- **Reasoning** Students should explain their reasoning that foods that are higher in Calories per unit (serving, unit of weight) make for a more efficient meal for an organism that needs a lot of energy.

FORMATIVE ASSESSMENT

MAKING SENSE OF PHENOMENA

Students gain understanding that energy content of food is measured in Calories as they explore the **investigative phenomenon.** They should connect this to the **anchoring phenomenon** that animals need to eat more food if the food they are eating provides too little energy, which explains why a giant panda spends 16 hours a day eating bamboo.

REMEDIATION If students struggle to connect the **investigative phenomenon** back to the **anchoring phenomenon,** have them discuss how much celery an athlete would need to eat before an athletic event versus how many bananas he or she would need to eat. Explain that the panda only eats one kind of food, bamboo.

MAKING SENSE OF PHENOMENA IDEA ORGANIZER

After completing Exploration 1, students can fill in the **Idea Organizer** to summarize the connection between some foods providing more energy than others and the anchoring phenomenon that animals need to eat more food if the food they are eating provides too little energy.

Activity Outcome

Students should obtain and evaluate information about the energy contents of different foods and make a claim about which food would be the best option for an athlete.

Performance Indicators	
	obtain and evaluate information about energy contents of different foods
	make a claim about one or more of the foods
	support the claim using collected data as evidence

Where's the Heat

Activity Guide, pages 101–103

TIME ESTIMATE

45 min

....

SHORT ON TIME?

To save time, refer students to a thermostat that displays the current air temperature in the room and have them measure only their skin temperatures.

POSSIBLE MATERIALS

☐ thermometer

☐ forehead thermometer strips

☐ research materials for Calorie needs, printed or devices with internet access

PREPARATION

In advance, set up some thermometers in the room away from major sources or sinks of heat (e.g., vents, windows). Demonstrate the use of forehead thermometer strips.

INVESTIGATIVE PHENOMENON
The energy in food is used by many organisms to maintain body temperature.

Phenomenon Explained Students explore the **investigative phenomenon** by observing the different temperatures of their own bodies and surrounding environments and researching the Calorie needs of people in different circumstances. Students connect Caloric intake with activity levels and the temperatures of environments.

Form a question   After observing the photograph, students should form a question about the connection between body temperature, the temperature of the environment, activity levels, and eating. If students struggle to form a question, have them discuss their daily activities and the air temperature. **Sample answer:** How do my environment and my activity level interact with my body and its energy needs?

STEPS 1–3   Students should measure and record their temperature data with consistent units (°C or °F). They should find their skin temperatures are about 10–15°C warmer than the room temperature. **Sample answer:** room temp: 25°C; skin temp: 34°C Students should find that their body temperatures are within one degree or less of each other and that all are well above the air temperature.

STEP 4   Guide students to sources of information about daily Caloric needs of different sizes/ages of people.

- **Make a Claim** Claims should indicate that body size and environmental temperature affect people's energy needs.
- **Evidence** Students should cite their data and the clear correlation between age/size, activity level, and environmental temperature and Calorie needs.
- **Reasoning** Students should explain their reasoning that adults need more Calories to maintain their body temperature, especially in colder temperatures or when moving more.

FORMATIVE ASSESSMENT

MAKING SENSE OF PHENOMENA

Students gain understanding that body size, activity, and environmental temperatures affect energy needs of organisms as they explore the **investigative phenomenon.** They should connect this to the **anchoring phenomenon** that food energy is required for many life processes including maintaining warmth in warm-blooded organisms such as pandas.

REMEDIATION If students struggle to connect the **investigative phenomenon** back to the **anchoring phenomenon,** have them discuss their research on daily Calorie needs of people and relate it to the body size, eating habits, and activity levels of pandas.

Activity Outcome

Students should find that their bodies are warmer than their environment, and people of different sizes, with different activity levels, and in different environments have different caloric needs.

Performance Indicators
measure and record temperature data
make a claim about how body size and the temperature of an environment affect caloric needs
support the claim with evidence from the investigation and sound reasoning

MAKING SENSE OF PHENOMENA IDEA ORGANIZER

After completing Exploration 2, students can fill in the **Idea Organizer** to summarize the connection between energy in food used by many organisms to maintain body temperature and the anchoring phenomenon that food energy is required for many life processes, including maintaining warmth in warm-blooded organisms such as pandas.

SOCIAL EMOTIONAL LEARNING

As students share their temperature data, emphasize there are no right or wrong data unless there is something wrong with the thermometers or there was some user error. Effective steps in sharing data are:

- listening and recording what classmates say
- holding off on questioning data until they have all been shared

If there are outliers among the data, they can be circled, and students can politely ask questions about what might explain those outliers.

Growth, Change, and Regrowth

Activity Guide, pages 104–106

TIME ESTIMATE

 15 min

INVESTIGATIVE PHENOMENON
The energy from food is used by organisms for growth, body repair, and other life processes.

Phenomenon Explained Students explore the **investigative phenomenon** by obtaining information about the flow of matter and energy from producers to consumers and from consumers to other consumers and/or the environment.

Body Building

Students should identify the following choices as needs of the foal: **a.** air, **b.** water, **d.** nutrients, **f.** food. The other distractors are things that a horse's owner or trainer could use to make a horse behave in certain ways or be useful for certain purposes such as racing, jumping, or performing tasks on a farm, but those are not requirements for a young horse reaching adulthood.

Producers to Consumers

Students should distinguish producers and consumers. Producers, such as plants, use energy from the sun or other sources to make their own food. Consumers, such as animals, eat other organisms for food. They also should understand that organisms produce wastes as byproducts of life processes.

Everyday Phenomenon **When a person falls and scrapes the skin on her knee, her body repairs itself.**

Students might think of repairs as something people choose to do on purpose, such as an automotive mechanic using her skills to repair a damaged vehicle. However, human bodies use energy and matter to repair injuries such as scrapes without people focusing on the task. Have students discuss a common minor injury like a sunburn and talk about how a person's body would get the matter and energy necessary to repair the damaged skin.

FORMATIVE ASSESSMENT

MAKING SENSE OF PHENOMENA

Students gain understanding that the energy and matter in food is used to build and repair the bodies of consumers as they explore the **investigative phenomenon.** They should connect this to the **anchoring phenomenon** that energy is needed daily for body growth and repair, whether visible or not. That need must be balanced with other life processes.

REMEDIATION If students struggle to connect the **investigative phenomenon** back to the **anchoring phenomenon,** have them make a list of the life processes that the giant panda would need to carry out using the energy and matter from its food.

SOCIAL EMOTIONAL LEARNING

As students engage in their discussions, encourage them to consider how responsible choices about when, how often, and with what food they feed a class pet would affect the pet's health. Responsible decision-making frequently requires access to information on which to base the decisions. Prompt students to consider what information they might need about an animal to make these types of decisions. Students can also discuss their emotional responses to the idea of caring well for the health and wellbeing of a class pet.

MAKING SENSE OF PHENOMENA IDEA ORGANIZER

After completing Exploration 3, students can fill in the **Idea Organizer** to summarize the connection between the energy from food used by organisms for growth, body repair, and other life processes and the anchoring phenomenon that the panda needs energy daily for body growth and repair, whether visible or not. That need must be balanced with other life processes.

Animal Energy

Activity Guide, pages 107–108

TIME ESTIMATE

15 min

PREPARATION

Consider preparing a brief slideshow of images of different animals demonstrating heat-absorbing or heat-retaining behaviors. Examples include turtles sunning themselves on a log, a snake on a stone path, a bird with feather volume maximized in winter, and swordfish swimming in warm surface waters of the ocean.

MATERIALS ALERT

The model for Brrr! It's Cold Outside! requires two small beakers that can hold 100 mL, water, two thermometers, and a sunny location.

INVESTIGATIVE PHENOMENON
Some organisms use energy in ways unique to their species.

Phenomenon Explained Students explore the **investigative phenomenon** by obtaining information about specific examples of animals capturing or generating heat for their bodies.

Brrr! It's Cold Outside!

Students should understand how an organism's size and its environment relate to how much energy the organism requires. It might be useful to set up a model ahead of time to demonstrate the role of size. For example, set up two small beakers of water on a sunlit windowsill, one with 50 mL of water and the other with 100 mL. Have students observe how long they each take to increase by 2°C. The key takeaway is that larger bodies require more energy to increase in temperature, if all other factors are the same.

Energy and Body Temperature

Students should understand that the iguana cools at night because its environment cools, drawing heat from the iguana throughout the night. Meanwhile, the iguana has a harder time keeping itself warm, unlike the other three organisms. The mammals and bird generate more heat internally, and they are more insulated with feathers, fur, and/or fat.

Everyday Phenomenon **Humans sweat when warmed by the sun.**

Address the potential misconception that humans and other warm-blooded organisms cannot be warmed by the sun or other sources of heat in the way that a cold-blooded reptile can. In fact, humans and other mammals can absorb heat from the environment just like a snake or turtle sunning itself, and because our bodies are simultaneously generating heat internally, we can overheat. Have students discuss humans sweating, dogs panting, and birds spreading their wings and adjusting feathers to regulate body temperature.

FORMATIVE ASSESSMENT

MAKING SENSE OF PHENOMENA

Students gain understanding that some organisms use energy in ways unique to their species or environments as they explore the **investigative phenomenon.** They should connect this to the **anchoring phenomenon** that some animals, such as the giant panda, require more energy because of size or circumstance.

REMEDIATION If students struggle to connect the **investigative phenomenon** back to the **anchoring phenomenon,** compare the panda to the mouse and human in the data table. Explain that the panda is also a mammal, so its body heat is stable as long as it is well fed. Fur and a layer of fat also help to conserve body warmth.

MAKING SENSE OF PHENOMENA
IDEA ORGANIZER

After completing Exploration 4, students can fill in the **Idea Organizer** to summarize the connection between how some organisms use energy in ways unique to their species and the anchoring phenomenon that food energy is required for many life processes including maintaining warmth in warm-blooded organisms such as pandas.

02 Take It Further

Engage • Explore/Explain • **Elaborate** • Evaluate

TIME ESTIMATE

45 min

These Take It Further paths may be completed to enrich and extend students' comprehension of content covered within this lesson.

ONLINE

Careers in Science & Engineering: Animal Nutritionist

In this feature, students read about the work of an animal nutritionist—a scientist who studies and develops diets for specific types of animals. Then, they will select an animal and complete research about the characteristics and appropriate diet of that animal.

In the Water

Students explore how dolphins, tuna, squid, and shrimp meet their needs for matter and energy.

Engineer It: Feed Me Now!

Students explore design and functions of automatic pet feeders and design their own pet feeder.

Lesson Check

Activity Guide, pages 109–111

Engage • Explore/Explain • Elaborate • **Evaluate**

Can You Explain It?

Now I know or think that . . .

Sample answer: Pandas need food to provide energy for growth, repairs, and other life functions, such as keeping warm. The panda gets energy from the bamboo, which used the sun's energy to make food. Bamboo provides very little nutrition, so the panda must eat each day for many hours to get the energy and matter it needs.

After completing the lesson, use the **Making Sense Idea Organizer** to summarize the connections between the **investigative phenomena** and **anchoring phenomenon.**

MAKING CONNECTIONS

After students complete the lesson, they should be able to answer a question about an alternative phenomenon to explain why the snake only eats every few weeks based on its energy and matter needs. **Sample answer:** To go for a few weeks without eating, the snake must have low energy and matter needs, eat foods that provide lots of energy and matter, or both.

Checkpoints

1. The sun; the horse is eating grass. The grass gets its energy from the sun.

2. Models should show a food web where some animals eat plants, and other animals eat them.

3. chemical process; Some; All

4. **c**—motion; **d**—body temperature

5. **Sample answer:** Animals aren't producers. They get energy and matter from prey or producers. It is producers, not animals, that take in light energy to make food. Animals are consumers that release waste matter.

6. **Sample answer:** Students' models should show that pandas are animals and consumers who take in matter and energy from producers. Pandas need the energy and matter from food to move, grow, heal, and carry out life processes.

SOCIAL EMOTIONAL LEARNING

Have students reflect on the goals they set at the beginning of the lesson. Ask them to think about whether the goals were accomplished or if there were challenges. Have students share the factors that contributed to their success. If the goals were not achieved, talk about what students can do to help them achieve the goals.

Energy and Matter Move Between Organisms

ANCHORING PHENOMENON

When there are more plants to eat, there are more caribou in the tundra.

ENGAGE **Can You Explain It?**
Students observe and ask questions about the tundra ecosystem. They answer the Can You Explain It? question to identify what they will gather evidence about in the lesson.

EVALUATE **Lesson Check**
Students gauge their understanding of the anchoring phenomenon.

HANDS-ON ACTIVITY

EXPLORATION 1 **Modeling Matter Moving Within an Ecosystem**

Investigative Phenomenon Matter moving through an ecosystem can be modeled.

Students connect back to the **anchoring phenomenon** that all organisms are important to a food chain to hold it together.

HANDS-ON ACTIVITY

EXPLORATION 2 **Break It Down**
Investigative Phenomenon
Decomposers break down plant material and recycle that matter back into the soil.

Students connect back to the **anchoring phenomenon** that decomposers are an important part of a food chain, as important as any other link in the chain as they return matter to the soil.

EXPLORATION 3 **Moving Energy and Matter**

Investigative Phenomenon Energy moves between organisms in an ecosystem through food chains.

Students connect back to the **anchoring phenomenon** that each part of a food chain contributes to its existence.

EXPLORATION 4 **Following Matter and Energy**

Investigative Phenomenon Food chains in an ecosystem overlap to form food webs.

Students connect back to the **anchoring phenomenon** that the health of an ecosystem is tied to the health of its food web.

Making 3D Connections

The **anchoring phenomenon** in this lesson supports students' understanding of and application of these Next Generation Science Standards.

Building to the Performance Expectations

5-LS2-1 Develop a model to describe the movement of matter among plants, animals, decomposers, and the environment.

5-PS3-1 Use models to describe that energy in animals' food (used for body repair, growth, motion, and to maintain body warmth) was once energy from the sun.

SEP	DCI	CCC

Developing and Using Models
Develop a model to describe phenomena. *(Explorations 1, 2, 3, 4)*

Science Models, Laws, Mechanisms, and Theories Explain Natural Phenomena
Science explanations describe the mechanisms for natural events. *(Explorations 1, 2, 3, 4)*

LS2.A Interdependent Relationships in Ecosystems
The food of almost any kind of animal can be traced back to plants. Organisms are related in food webs. Some organisms break down dead organisms. Organisms can survive only where their needs are met. *(Explorations 1, 2, 3, 4)*

LS2.B Cycles of Matter and Energy Transfer in Ecosystems
Matter cycles between the air and soil and among plants, animals, and microbes as these organisms live and die. *(Exploration 1, 3)*

Systems and System Models
A system can be described in terms of its components and their interactions. *(Explorations 1, 2, 3, 4)*

Vocabulary

Word Wall A word wall, anchor chart, or Language Development chart can be used to support vocabulary.

predator an animal that hunts, catches, and eats other animals

prey animals that are caught and eaten by predators

food chain the transfer of energy and matter from one organism to the next in an ecosystem

scavenger consumer that eats dead organisms

decomposer organism that uses chemicals called enzymes to break down the remains of organisms and animal wastes

food web a group of overlapping food chains

You may want to include additional academic terms such as *factor* and other terms students might struggle with.

Language Development Prompt students to complete the chart when they come to these highlighted terms within the lesson.

Anchor Chart As you progress through the unit, you may want to make a vocabulary-based anchor chart using the Language Development chart as a guide that can be displayed and filled out as a whole group during each lesson.

Students can engage in the Can You Explain It? content by observing the photograph or by exploring the corresponding video online.

ONLINE View a video related to the tundra ecosystem.

ANCHORING PHENOMENON
When there are more plants to eat, there are more caribou in the tundra.

PHENOMENON EXPLAINED
Producers are the basis of a food chain. If a single link in the chain is removed, the rest of the chain suffers.

Lesson Objective

Students develop models to show the flow of energy derived from the sun is transferred as matter through a food chain and food web to consumers and decomposers.

Support Discovery

The following prompts can be used to guide student-led discovery.

I notice . . .

After observing the photograph or watching the video, students should record what they noticed about the caribou's environment. If students struggle to record observations, ask them to compare the tundra landscape to other environments, such as temperate forests, wetlands, rain forests, or other heavily-vegetated habitats.

Sample answer: I notice that the tundra ecosystem has at least one large animal with antlers and lot of low-growing plants.

I wonder . . .

After observing the photograph or watching the video, students should record what they want to find out about the availability of plants and its effect on caribou and other organisms in the tundra. Some students may not be familiar with the animal in the photograph - share with them that it is a caribou.

Sample answer: I wonder how the availability of plants affects caribou and other organisms in the tundra.

Can You Explain It?

In the Can You Explain It?, students make an initial claim that explains the **Anchoring Phenomenon**. Students might write that some animals eat plants. So, fewer plants could result in starvation or less growth in consumers. Or, students might draw a system model with plants as an input.

Students will gather evidence about the movement of matter and energy among organisms. This will enable them to give a more complete explanation of the **Anchoring Phenomenon** at the end of the lesson.

Alternative Phenomenon

If students are unfamiliar with the tundra, guide them to think of other ecosystems, such as a temperate forest or marine ecosystem. You may want to show images of one or more of these systems to the class so that students can make observations of the components of these systems.

SOCIAL EMOTIONAL LEARNING

Guide students to reflect on their goals from previous lessons and on any feedback they received from their teachers or peers. Then, have each student set a personal goal for this lesson and make a plan for how to achieve the goal. Throughout the lesson, take daily breaks for students to track their progress in meeting their goals. As students move from lesson to lesson, they can continue to work towards their initial goals or set new ones. If students struggle setting goals for this lesson, share with them some of the following ideas: describing how plants affect animals in an ecosystem, developing models, and listening without interrupting when others are talking.

Gone Fishing

WHEN TO USE

SCIENCE **30 min**

- Anchoring Phenomenon / Alternative Phenomenon
- Options for ELA Instruction
- Build on Prior Knowledge
- Preview the Phenomenon
- Read to Learn
- Support Sense Making
- Science Stretch
- Check for Comprehension

Option 1 Use before students begin the lesson in the Activity Guide to provide an engaging model to introduce the lesson's phenomenon.

Option 2 Use after students have completed the Activity Guide to reinforce students' understanding of the lesson phenomenon by exploring a related phenomenon.

ELA 20 min

- Options for ELA Instruction
- Build on Prior Knowledge
- Read to Learn

Option 3 To use during designated ELA Reading time for independent reading, whole-class instruction, or small-group instruction, look for this icon: **ELA**

Plan

> **ANCHORING PHENOMENON / ALTERNATIVE PHENOMENON**
>
> The anchoring phenomenon in the Activity Guide is *When there are more plants to eat, there are more caribou in the tundra*. The main example is caribou in a tundra ecosystem. The FUNomenal Reader presents a similar phenomenon (*A lake is home to a complex food web*), and the example is a story about the complex relationships in a lake ecosystem. Both present the same science concepts and cover the same standards but with different phenomena. Guide students to draw connections between the two situations and to understand the underlying principle: matter and energy move between organisms in food webs.

Options for ELA Instruction ELA

Choose one of the following anchor chart options and project it or print copies. Then display and introduce the chart before reading the text. Revisit the chart after reading the text and encourage students to discuss how the skill connects to the text.

Learning Mindset Have student pairs study the *My Learning Mindset Anchor Chart* and then decide which of the traits describe Theo, the story's protagonist. Challenge partners to find where in the story he shows these traits. Have them consider if these are good traits for studying science.

Visualize Use the *Visualize Anchor Chart* to help draw students into the content of the story. Have them take two minutes to close their eyes and think of what it would feel like to be in a boat on a lake, as Theo and his grandfather are in the story. Discuss what they might see, smell, and hear based on details from the text.

Argument Have students consult the online *Science and Engineering Practices Handbook* for more information on the claim-evidence-reasoning format Theo uses in the story. They can also use the *Parts of an Argument Anchor Chart* as a reference.

Preview

ELA **Build on Prior Knowledge** Students should already know that animals obtain the energy and matter they need from plants or other animals. Ask volunteers to name an animal and how it gets energy and matter. They can describe an animal they are familiar with, such as a rabbit or squirrel, or an animal they have read about or seen in a TV show or movie. Can they name any predator–prey, food-chain, or food-web relationships?

Preview the Phenomenon Ask students to study the illustration on page 4 of the story, which shows a boy and his grandfather fishing from a boat. Encourage students to record the first questions that come into their minds, focusing on the lake setting. Point out that their questions might change as they read through the story. Have them keep their questions handy and periodically check to see if any can be answered.

STANDARDS SUPPORTED

SEP

Developing and Using Models

Science Models, Laws, Mechanisms, and Theories Explain Natural Phenomena

DCI

LS2.A Interdependent Relationships in Ecosystems

LS2.B Cycles of Matter and Energy Transfer in Ecosystems

CCC

Systems and System Models

Gone Fishing (continued)

Discover

Read to Learn

The **Read to Learn** suggestions inside the book's front cover encourage students to interact with the book multiple times for different purposes.

> **Preview** Students look for unfamiliar words and share them with a partner. New terms may include *decomposer, food chain,* and *food web.* Have students look up words they aren't sure about and notice how they are used in the context of the story.

> **Skim** Students skim the illustrations and photos. Have them turn to a partner and share their predictions of what the story will be about.

> **Read** As students read the story, ask them to look for connections to one of the following anchor chart skills. **Learning Mindset, Visualize, Argument**

Support Sense Making

Choose one or more of the following:

▶ Have students analyze the claim-evidence-reasoning argument Theo makes in the story. Is his claim supported by the evidence he states? Is his reasoning sound? Have them work in pairs to present their own claims, evidence, and reasoning related to the phenomenon.

▶ Encourage a student-led discussion that connects matter and energy moving through a food chain back to the law of conservation of matter and the law of conservation of energy: that matter and energy cannot be made or destroyed. Guide students to discuss what happens to matter and energy throughout a food chain.

▶ For ELD students and others, discuss the meaning of the prefix *com-*, which means "together" or "with." Explain that a decomposer is the opposite of a composer and that the prefix *de-* means "to reverse" or "opposite." Ask students to choose an example of a decomposer from the story—bacteria and fungi are mentioned—and explain how it changes matter.

▶ Have students consider the effects of introducing a new organism to an ecosystem. For example, what if an invasive species such as the lionfish or zebra mussel were introduced into the lake ecosystem in the story? Have students work in pairs to research the effects of introducing a specific organism to a new ecosystem. Groups can share what they have learned with other groups.

Extend

Science Stretch

The **Science Stretch** suggestions inside the book's back cover help students think about what they read. Students can complete one or more as time allows.

> How could you make a model of a food web in your area? Provide materials for students to use for their models, such as poster board, markers, yarn, and modeling clay.

> Write a blog post from the point of view of an animal in the middle of a food web. Provide appropriate books or a set of links to approved online sites for students to use in their research.

> Which organism, if removed from the food web, would have the greatest effect on the lake ecosystem?
> **Sample answer:** I think removing algae would have the greatest effect. Small fish eat algae, and birds and other animals eat small fish.

 SOCIAL EMOTIONAL LEARNING

What did you learn about food webs from this story? Share your thoughts with a classmate. As needed, model for students how to listen respectfully while someone else is talking.

Check for Comprehension Have students write three things they found out in the story, two things they found interesting, and one question they still have about food-web relationships in a lake ecosystem.

Modeling Matter Moving Within an Ecosystem

Activity Guide, pages 114–117

TIME ESTIMATE

50 min

SHORT ON TIME?

Provide ready-made materials such as cards or photographs that can be organized into models without additional gathering, cutting, or reshaping.

POSSIBLE MATERIALS

☐ scissors

☐ index cards

☐ markers

☐ paste

☐ string or yarn

☐ stapler

☐ other craft materials (optional)

PREPARATION

In advance, gather lists of different ecosystems and their components. Consider gathering images of those components, too. Distribute materials to students prior to starting the activity.

INVESTIGATIVE PHENOMENON
Matter moving through an ecosystem can be modeled.

Phenomenon Explained Students explore the **investigative phenomenon** by researching and modeling an ecosystem. Students connect food chains in the ecosystem to make a food web. They analyze the food web to make claims about energy movement within the ecosystem.

Form a question After observing the photograph, students should form a question about how energy and matter move between organisms in a food chain. If students struggle to form a question, ask them to consider which animal is eating the other or how the two are interacting. Sample answer: How can you make a model to show how matter moves among organisms?

STEPS 1 and 2 Students select an ecosystem to research. They fill out a data table to categorize the different organisms in the system. Share with students the list of materials you make available so they can consider this when designing their models. Sample answer: I'll use pictures to show organisms. Strings connecting pictures will show how energy moves from organism to organism.

STEPS 3–5 Students make and analyze their models. Tell students that piecing different chains together into a food web is easier if pieces that are involved in multiple chains are placed in the center of the web. Students should predict the effects of removing an organism. Sample answer: Removing one organism affected the organisms that relied on it as a food source. **Students consider if their food web is a system.** Sample answer: Yes, it has inputs, outputs, and components that interact.

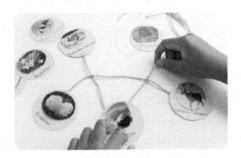

- **Make a Claim** Claims should indicate that energy and matter move from plants to animals and then to other animals.

- **Evidence** Students should cite as evidence the interactions among organisms in their models.

- **Reasoning** Students should explain their reasoning that the consumption that occurs among the different food chains involves movements of matter and energy.

FORMATIVE ASSESSMENT

MAKING SENSE OF PHENOMENA

Students gain understanding that matter moves among organisms as they explore the **investigative phenomenon.** They should connect this to the **anchoring phenomenon** that all organisms are important to a food chain to hold it together.

REMEDIATION If students struggle to connect the **investigative phenomenon** back to the **anchoring phenomenon,** have them discuss what would happen to the movement of matter and the stability of their ecosystem if the producer was removed.

Activity Outcome

Students should develop and use a model of an ecosystem to show a food web, which is made of different, interconnected food chains.

Performance Indicators	
	research an ecosystem, and organize the data
	build a model of the ecosystem by assembling food chains into a food web
	make inferences and predictions about the modeled system

MAKING SENSE OF PHENOMENA IDEA ORGANIZER
After completing Exploration 1, students can fill in the **Idea Organizer** to summarize the connection between how matter moving through an ecosystem can be modeled and the anchoring phenomenon that when there are more plants to eat, there are more caribou in the tundra.

 SOCIAL EMOTIONAL LEARNING

Have students discuss how they helped each other design and build their models. Some guidelines include:

- actively listening to each suggestion

- repeating suggestions back to each other to confirm that they were heard

- being aware of biases that students might have and doing their best to avoid letting such biases affect how they judge suggestions or ideas

Break It Down

TIME ESTIMATE

45 min

SHORT ON TIME?

Use one bucket of soil and select one or two students to act as diggers. Provide an average apple slice weight before burial. Let different groups observe their own dug-up apple slices.

POSSIBLE MATERIALS

☐ gloves

☐ flower pots, labeled A–F

☐ plastic spoon

☐ small brush

☐ pan balance

☐ hand lens

☐ camera (optional)

PREPARATION

Two weeks in advance, set up six different pots or plastic buckets with relatively equal amounts of moist soil. Slice an apple into six pieces. Weigh each slice, record its weight on the label of a pot, and bury the slice in the soil. Keep the pots at room temperature or warmer. Distribute materials to students prior to starting the activity. Slice a fresh apple to show students what the wedges looked like before burial. You may choose to provide cameras for students to record observations with photos.

INVESTIGATIVE PHENOMENON

Decomposers break down plant material and recycle that matter back into the soil.

Phenomenon Explained Students explore the **investigative phenomenon** by observing how an apple slice changes after two weeks buried in soil. Students gather evidence to support their explanations.

Form a question After observing the photograph, students should form a question about what happens to a fallen tree or discarded piece of fruit. If students struggle to form a question, ask them to think about an example from their own lives and discuss it with others. **Sample answer:** How long does it take for the fruit to disappear completely? Does it last longer in summer or fall?

STEPS 1–3 Students dig up the buried apple slice and make observations. They organize their data, such as the apple slice's initial weight (provided by you) and its weight now. **Sample answer:** The slice of apple turned brown and mushy, and it lost weight. The fresh apple slice looks and feels firm, full, and juicy.

Students make inferences about what happened to the slice of apple. Students may not know the term *decomposer* for bacteria and fungi yet, as it will be introduced in later Explorations. They may use other everyday terms like *germ* to refer to what they think caused the changes to the buried apple slice. **Sample answer:** Air and water made the apple turn brown. Germs (bacteria, fungi) made it mushy.

- **Make a Claim** Claims should indicate factors that caused the apple wedge to change.

- **Evidence** Students should cite their observations of both the apple wedge (before and after) and the soil in which the wedge was buried.

- **Reasoning** Students should explain their reasoning for how their evidence supports their claim about the factors they identified.

FORMATIVE ASSESSMENT

MAKING SENSE OF PHENOMENA

Students gain understanding that decomposers help the remains of organisms break down as they explore the **investigative phenomenon.** They should connect this to the **anchoring phenomenon** that decomposers are an important part of a food chain, as important as any other link in the chain as they return matter to the soil. Students should understand that the soil in which the apple wedges were buried is itself made in part of broken-down parts of dead organisms.

REMEDIATION If students struggle to connect the **investigative phenomenon** back to the **anchoring phenomenon,** have them discuss what happened to the matter the apple slice lost while it was in the soil. Then, have them consider how that matter would help a plant potted in that same soil.

MAKING SENSE OF PHENOMENA IDEA ORGANIZER

After completing Exploration 2, students can fill in the **Idea Organizer** to summarize the connection between how decomposers break down material and recycle that matter back into the soil and the anchoring phenomenon that when there are more plants to eat, there are more caribou in the tundra.

Activity Outcome

Students should understand that the remains of organisms will decompose or break down, and the rate of decomposition depends on the conditions of the environment.

Performance Indicators	
	observe wedges of apples that are fresh and those retrieved from two weeks of burial in soil
	organize observations, including the relative before-and-after weights of apple wedges
	make a claim about what happened to the buried apple wedge
	come up with an idea to test a specific factor that might affect the rate of the apple's changes

Moving Energy and Matter

TIME ESTIMATE

INVESTIGATIVE PHENOMENON
Energy moves between organisms in an
ecosystem through food chains.

Phenomenon Explained Students explore the **investigative
phenomenon** by modeling the movements of energy and matter
in the tundra ecosystem. Students learn more about the breakdown
of organisms' remains, including the roles played by scavengers and
decomposers.

Energy and Matter Flow

Students should briefly discuss their ideas about how energy moves
through food chains. Most should know from the other Explorations that
energy moves through food chains stored in matter, namely as food that
is eaten at different links of a food chain. Students read about the sun,
grasses, rabbits, and owls to place them in the correct sequence in the
incomplete food chain. sun ⟶ grasses ⟶ rabbits ⟶ owls

Explore the Tundra

Students identify resources in the tundra used by all organisms. The sun is the primary source of energy. Its light is used by plants to grow, which provides matter and energy for the food chain.

Modeling Matter and Energy Movement

Students should place organisms into the incomplete food chain based on descriptions of those organisms and their roles on the previous page. Students should explain their reasoning. sun → reindeer moss → caribou → wolves **Sample answer:** I did not include the Arctic gull, the bacteria, or the fungi in my food chain. The Arctic gull, bacteria, and fungi will feed on dead organisms at any point in the chain.

Scavengers and Decomposers Are Important

Students should understand the roles that scavengers and decomposers play in the cycling of matter. They can revisit the previous food chain model and consider how the raven, bacteria, and fungi would exchange matter and energy with the other organisms.

SOCIAL EMOTIONAL LEARNING

Discuss as a class what it means to give constructive feedback. Talk about how feedback should include the positive aspects of student work as well as helping others improve upon their work without being mean or disrespectful. Provide students time to practice this with a partner or small group before answering the question.

FORMATIVE ASSESSMENT

MAKING SENSE OF PHENOMENA

Students gain understanding that matter and energy cycle through ecosystems as they explore the **investigative phenomenon.** They should connect this to the **anchoring phenomenon** that each part of a food chain contributes to its existence.

REMEDIATION If students struggle to connect the **investigative phenomenon** back to the **anchoring phenomenon,** have them discuss what the caribou needs and how those needs are met by the movement of energy and matter, starting with the sun.

MAKING SENSE OF PHENOMENA IDEA ORGANIZER

After completing Exploration 3, students can fill in the **Idea Organizer** to summarize the connection between how energy moves between organisms in an ecosystem through food chains and the anchoring phenomenon that when there are more plants to eat, there are more caribou in the tundra.

Following Matter and Energy

TIME ESTIMATE

INVESTIGATIVE PHENOMENON
Food chains in an ecosystem overlap to form food webs.

Phenomenon Explained Students explore the **investigative phenomenon** by using models to explore the tundra ecosystem, as well as the movements of energy and matter within the ecosystem.

Tundra Ecosystem

Students should assign roles to the organisms in the illustration.
a. consumer (caribou), **b.** producer (reindeer moss),
c. decomposer (fungi), **d.** consumer (Arctic hare),
e. scavenger (Arctic gulls), **f.** consumer (lemming), **g.** consumer (hawk),
h. producers (Arctic wildflowers)

Connecting Food Chains

Students infer what it means if a food web shows an organism with many lines leading away from it. They should understand that food chains in an entire ecosystem usually overlap. **Sample answer:** That organism is important. It supports several other organisms in the food web.

Adding Connections to the Tundra

Everyday Phenomenon   Removing hawks from a park food web can disrupt the ecosystem.

Have students come up with their own examples from another ecosystem where factors such as food, space, water, and predators limit the number of organisms of a certain kind.

If students struggle to complete the food web, have them start by labeling the circles as producers, consumers who eat producers, and consumers who eat consumers. Arrows go from the organism being eaten to the organism eating. Then students can use the information in the Exploration about the organisms to place them in the food web.

FORMATIVE ASSESSMENT

MAKING SENSE OF PHENOMENA

Students gain understanding that interactions among organisms and food chains are complex as they explore the **investigative phenomenon.** They should connect this to the **anchoring phenomenon** that the movements of energy and matter maintain food chains, food webs, and ecosystems.

REMEDIATION If students struggle to connect the **investigative phenomenon** back to the **anchoring phenomenon,** have them consider how a change in the number of producer organisms would affect the number of caribou in the tundra, based on the food web.

MAKING SENSE OF PHENOMENA
IDEA ORGANIZER

After completing Exploration 4, students can fill in the **Idea Organizer** to summarize the connection between how food chains overlap in an ecosystem to form food webs and the anchoring phenomenon that when there are more plants to eat, there are more caribou in the tundra.

03

Take It Further

Engage • Explore/Explain • **Elaborate** • Evaluate

TIME ESTIMATE

45 min

These Take It Further paths may be completed to enrich and extend students' comprehension of content covered within this lesson.

ONLINE

Careers in Science and Engineering: Zoologist

Students script their own interview questions for a specific type of zoologist.

People in Science and Engineering: Jafet Vélez-Valentín

Students meet a conservationist who has worked to save animals from extinction.

Exploring a Desert Ecosystem

Students explore the feeding relationships in a complex desert ecosystem.

Can You Explain It?

Now I know or think that . . .

Sample answer: Plants and other producers are the energy source for the tundra ecosystem. Plant die-offs could cause hunger for the animals that feed on them. Decomposers break down waste from plants and animals. This restores vital materials to the soil.

After completing the lesson, use the **Making Sense Idea Organizer** to summarize the connections between the **investigative phenomena** and **anchoring phenomenon.**

MAKING CONNECTIONS

After students complete the lesson, they should be able to answer a question about an alternative phenomenon to describe a food chain composed of the organisms shown in the city park ecosystem and predict what would happen if one of the organisms left. **Sample answer:** Insects eat the plants, and the birds eat the plants and insects. If the insects were to leave or die off, the birds would have less food, and fewer of them might survive.

Checkpoints

1. sun → corn → mouse → hawk; Corn is a producer; the mouse and hawk are consumers.

2. **a**—Animals that use the trees for food or shelter might die off.; **c**—Animals that use the trees for food or shelter may have to move to a new location.

3. sun → tomato → you; sun → lettuce → you; sun → grass → cow → you; **Sample answer:** The food chains need to start with an energy source, have a producer next, and end with a consumer.

4. Models should show a food web that identifies relationships among the organisms and labels the inputs and outputs of matter and energy.

5. **Sample answer:** Waste would pile up. Plants that depend on what decomposers restore to the soil would die. Other organisms would die or leave.

 SOCIAL EMOTIONAL LEARNING

Have students reflect on the goals they set at the beginning of the lesson. Ask them to think about whether the goals were accomplished or if there were challenges. Have students share the factors that contributed to their success. If the goals were not achieved, talk about what students can do to help them achieve the goals.

The Unit Review items enable you to assess student comprehension of core ideas as well as crosscutting concepts and science and engineering practices.

1. **DOK 3** Students' drawings should have a simple plant with roots, a stem, and visible leaves and the sun. Students should use some mechanism to show that plants use energy from the sun to change matter that isn't food into matter that is food. **Sample answer:** A plant takes in water from its roots and air from structures in its leaves. It uses energy from the sun to change the water and air from matter that is not food into sugar, matter that is food.

   If students struggle with the question, have them identify the different parts of a plant and explain the function of each part.

2. **DOK 3** **Sample answer:** The weight should stay about the same. The plant does not use soil to add weight as it grows.

   If students struggle with the question, have them write a model of how the plant makes food and consider whether soil is part of that process.

3. **DOK 1** **a**—water; **d**—light; **e**—air

   If students choose c, encourage them to think about the plants growing in tubes and what they needed and did not need to live and grow.

4. **DOK 2** matter and energy, longer

   Some students may list only matter or energy, not both. Accept those answers. If students struggle to answer the question, discuss with them that growth and repair require energy that is released when food matter is broken down.

5. **DOK 3** **Sample answer:** Matter from food goes to building new bone to heal a broken arm. The

body uses energy from food for life processes, including healing injuries.

   If students struggle to answer the question, have them think about the life processes that animals need energy and matter to carry out. Then, they should determine which life process is relevant to the image.

6. **DOK 2** **c.** The bird eats the raspberry bushes, and the fox eats the bird.

   If students choose a, b, or d, encourage them to focus on the arrows in the diagram and interpret what each arrow is representing.

7. **DOK 2** **a.** They can make their own food.; **b.** They use energy from the sun to make food.

   If students choose c or d, help them realize that the question is asking what is true of producers and that c is referring to consumers and d, decomposers.

8. **DOK 3** **Sample answer:** More energy; Olympic swimmers swim hours a day and need a lot of energy to move through water and keep their bodies warm.

   If students struggle to answer the question, encourage them to compare the energy needs of an Olympic swimmer and an ordinary person in the course of a single day.

9. **DOK 1** **L:** releasing waste, taking in air; **G:** making food; **R:** taking in water, taking in nutrients

   If students struggle to answer the question, remind them that nutrients are materials from the environment that help the plant grow and that they are found in water or soil. Have students identify the parts of the plant in the image and label them according to their functions.

10. **DOK 3** **Sample answer:** Claim: In winter time, it may take longer for dead organisms and waste to be broken down. Evidence: At home, food that is stored in the refrigerator lasts longer than food that is left on the counter. Reasoning: Cold, freezing weather is like a refrigerator; it takes longer for decomposers to break down matter in cold temperatures.

If students struggle to answer the question, have them identify the season in which environments will have similar characteristics to the inside of a refrigerator. Guide them to consider how organisms carry out their life processes in environments at different temperatures.

3D Item Analysis	1	2	3	4	5	6	7	8	9	10
SEP Developing and Using Models	●					●	●		●	
SEP Engaging in Argument from Evidence		●			●			●		●
SEP Obtaining, Evaluating, and Communicating Information	●									●
SEP Science Models, Laws, Mechanisms, and Theories Explain Natural Phenomena	●				●					
DCI Organization for Matter and Energy Flow in Organisms	●	●	●	●	●			●	●	
DCI Interdependent Relationships in Ecosystems						●	●			●
DCI Cycles of Matter and Energy Transfers in Ecosystems									●	●
DCI Energy in Chemical Processes and Everyday Life	●		●				●			
CCC Systems and System Models	●					●	●		●	
CCC Energy and Matter	●	●	●	●	●	●	●	●	●	●

04 Energy and Matter in Ecosystems

Activity Guide, page 135

Unit Storyline

In Unit 3, students explored how matter and energy move between organisms, with plants and other producers using light energy, air, water, and nutrients to make chemical energy in the form of food. Students found out that the food made by producers to feed themselves serves as the base of many food chains, and multiple food chains form food webs that help shape ecosystems. In this unit, students will use models to explore how organisms interact in ecosystems and how these interactions can change environments.

Before starting Unit 4, you may want to administer the Mid-Year Test found online. A Modified Mid-Year Test is also available.

LESSON 1   PE 5-LS2-1

Organisms Interact in Ecosystems

Activity Guide, pages 136–153

Students explore the **anchoring phenomenon** that many different types of organisms live together and interact in the African savanna.

SEP Developing and Using Models; Science Models, Laws, Mechanisms, and Theories Explain Natural Phenomena

DCI **LS2.A** Interdependent Relationships in Ecosystems; **LS2.B** Cycles of Matter and Energy Transfer in Ecosystems; **ESS2.A** Earth Materials and Systems

CCC Systems and System Models

LESSON 2   PE 5-LS2-1

Organisms Change Their Ecosystems

Activity Guide, pp. 154–169

Students explore the **anchoring phenomenon** that kudzu grows quickly, climbing over native plants and blocking their access to sunlight.

SEP Developing and Using Models; Science Models, Laws, Mechanisms, and Theories Explain Natural Phenomena

DCI **LS2.A** Interdependent Relationships in Ecosystems; **ETS1.B** Developing Possible Solutions

CCC Systems and System Models

Unit Review Activity Guide, pp. 170–172

Online-Only Resources

Supporting Unit Resources

You Solve It SUPPORTS LESSON 1

Build an Ecosystem is a virtual lab that offers practice in support of **Performance Expectation 5-LS2-1.** Students design a model to observe and describe the movement of matter in an ecosystem.

- **SEP** Developing and Using Models
- **DCI** **LS2.A** Interdependent Relationships in Ecosystems; **LS2.B** Cycles of Matter and Energy Transfer in Ecosystems
- **CCC** Systems and System Models

Unit Project SUPPORTS LESSON 1 **90 min**

Self-Contained Ecosystem provides students an opportunity to practice aspects of **Performance Expectation 5-LS2-1.** Students research and develop a self-contained ecosystem model that shows how organisms interact through matter and energy in the environment.

- **SEP** Developing and Using Models; Engaging in Argument from Evidence
- **DCI** **LS2.A** Interdependent Relationships in Ecosystems
- **CCC** Systems and System Models

Unit Performance Task SUPPORTS LESSON 1 **90 min**

Design an Ecosystem provides an opportunity for students to practice or be assessed on aspects of **Performance Expectation 5-LS2-1.** Students obtain information and use it to design a self-contained system as a habitat for an animal.

- **SEP** Obtaining, Evaluating, and Communicating Information; Constructing Explanations and Designing Solutions
- **DCI** **LS2.A** Interdependent Relationships in Ecosystems
- **CCC** Systems and System Models

Language Development

This worksheet is used as students progress through the unit's lessons. As they come to a highlighted vocabulary term, they should come back to this chart and fill in the blanks with words or phrases.

ONLINE **We've got you covered.**

Updates and additional student and teacher resources can be found online. Check back often!

Supporting Lesson Resources

 ## Do the Math!

Lesson 1 Calculate Available Land
Lesson 2 Pig Populations

 ## Language SmArts

Lesson 1 Making Connections; Using Signal Words
Lesson 2 Multiple Resources

Take It Further

Lesson 1 People in Science & Engineering: Alejandro E. Almario; People in Science & Engineering: Dr. John Weishampel & Dr. Tanya Berger-Wolf; Exploring a Deep Sea Ecosystem
Lesson 2 Careers in Science & Engineering: Entomologist; It's News to Me!; Careers in Science & Engineering: U.S. Army Corps of Engineers; Fantastic Field Guides

MAKING SENSE OF PHENOMENA

This idea organizer is used to make sense of the following **anchoring phenomena**:
Lesson 1—Many different types of organisms live together and interact in the African savanna.
Lesson 2—Kudzu grows quickly, climbing over native plants and blocking their access to sunlight.

It also connects the investigative phenomena back to the anchoring phenomenon in each lesson.

Assessment

Unit Readiness Check: Are You Ready?
Lesson Quizzes: Can You Apply It?
Unit 4 Test
Performance-Based Assessment

Assessments are available in an editable, printable format or can be administered and auto-graded online.

Organisms Interact in Ecosystems

ANCHORING PHENOMENON
Many different types of organisms live together and interact in the African savanna.

ENGAGE Can You Explain It?
Students observe and ask questions about why different organisms live together and interact in the African savanna. They answer the Can You Explain It? question to identify what they will gather evidence about in the lesson.

EVALUATE Lesson Check
Students gauge their understanding of the anchoring phenomenon.

HANDS-ON ACTIVITY

EXPLORATION 1 What's Out There? **65 min**
Investigative Phenomenon Living and nonliving things make up ecosystems.

Students connect back to the **anchoring phenomenon** that ecosystems such as the African savanna are made up of many living and nonliving things.

HANDS-ON ACTIVITY

EXPLORATION 2 Environment Matters **45 min**
Investigative Phenomenon Organisms survive in environments where their needs are met.

Students connect back to the **anchoring phenomenon** that organisms that live in the African savanna can get what they need in that environment.

EXPLORATION 3 Living Things and Their Environment **45 min**
Investigative Phenomenon Organisms interact with each other and with the nonliving parts of the environment.

Students connect back to the **anchoring phenomenon** that organisms in the African savanna use and exchange matter with their ecosystems.

EXPLORATION 4 Competition in Ecosystems **45 min**
Investigative Phenomenon Food, water, and space are scarce in some ecosystems.

Students connect back to the **anchoring phenomenon** that the availability of resources in the African savanna affects the number and different types of organisms that can live there.

Making 3D Connections

The **anchoring phenomenon** in this lesson supports students' understanding of and application of these Next Generation Science Standards.

Building to the Performance Expectations

5-LS2-1 Develop a model to describe the movement of matter among plants, animals, decomposers, and the environment.

SEP	DCI	CCC

SEP

Developing and Using Models
Develop a model to describe phenomena. *(Explorations 1, 2, 3)*

Science Models, Laws, Mechanisms, and Theories Explain Natural Phenomena
Science explanations describe the mechanisms for natural events. *(Exploration 1, 2, 4)*

DCI

LS2.A Interdependent Relationships in Ecosystems Organisms are related in food webs. Organisms can survive only in environments in which their particular needs are met. A healthy ecosystem is one in which multiple species of different types are each able to meet their needs. *(Explorations 1, 2, 3, 4)*

LS2.B Cycles of Matter and Energy Transfer in Ecosystems Organisms obtain gases and water from the environment, and release waste matter (gas, liquid, or solid) back into the environment. *(Exploration 3)*

ESS2.A Earth Materials and Systems Earth's major systems interact in multiple ways. *(Exploration 3)*

CCC

System and System Models
A system can be described in terms of its components and their interactions. *(Explorations 1, 2 , 3, 4)*

Vocabulary

Word Wall A word wall, anchor chart, or Language Development chart can be used to support vocabulary.

ecosystem system in which organisms interact and exchange matter and energy.

environment all the living and nonliving systems that surround and affect an organism

biosphere system that includes all living things

You may want to include additional academic terms such as *system* and *interaction* and any other terms students might struggle with.

Language Development Prompt students to complete the chart when they come to these highlighted terms within the lesson.

Anchor Chart As you progress through the unit, you may want to make a vocabulary-based anchor chart using the Language Development chart as a guide that can be displayed and filled out as a whole group during each lesson.

01 Organisms Interact in Ecosystems

Activity Guide, pages 136–137

Students can engage in the Can You Explain It? content by observing the photograph or by exploring the corresponding video online.

ONLINE **Ed** View a video related to organisms in the African savanna.

ANCHORING PHENOMENON

Many different types of organisms live together and interact in the African savanna.

PHENOMENON EXPLAINED

The African savanna is an ecosystem whose conditions and resources allow a wide variety of organisms to meet their needs and survive there.

Lesson Objective

Students develop and use models to explore how organisms interact and survive in ecosystems consisting of environments where their needs are met.

Support Discovery

The following prompts can be used to guide student-led discovery.

I notice . . .

After observing the photograph or watching the video, students should record what they noticed about the savanna. If students struggle to record observations, ask them to focus on one type of organism or one interaction at a time.

Sample answers: I notice different types of animals close together. I notice that the animals are different sizes. I notice that there are more zebras than elephants in the photo.

I wonder . . .

After observing the photograph or watching the video, students should record what they wonder about the savanna. If students struggle, ask them to sort the interactions they observed as *expected* and *surprising* to spark questions.

Sample answer: I wonder if the animals interact peacefully or if they fight. I wonder if some of these animals eat the others. I wonder if the animals mostly interact with others of their same type or if different animals interact with each other.

Can You Explain It?

In the Can You Explain It?, students make an initial claim that explains the **Anchoring Phenomenon**. Students might draw a model of relationships between the organisms or write a sentence about how the animals interact.

Students will gather evidence about interactions in an ecosystem. This will enable them to give a more complete explanation of the **Anchoring Phenomenon** at the end of the lesson.

Alternative Phenomenon

If the savanna ecosystem seems overwhelmingly far away, guide students to think of local examples such as temperate forests, wetlands, prairies, or a coastal marine ecosystem. You might want to assemble a slideshow or series of videos so that students can further observe the organisms in the system and how they interact.

 SOCIAL EMOTIONAL LEARNING

Guide students to reflect on their goals from previous lessons and on any feedback they received from their teachers or peers. Then have each student set a personal goal for this lesson and make a plan for how to achieve the goal. Throughout the lesson, take daily breaks for students to track their progress in meeting their goals. As students move from lesson to lesson, they can continue to work towards their initial goals or set new ones. If students struggle setting goals for this lesson, share with them some of the following ideas: identifying how and why organisms interact in ecosystems, participating more during group work, or ensuring everyone in the group has a chance to share.

The Wolves and Moose of Isle Royale

WHEN TO USE

SCIENCE (30 min)

- Anchoring Phenomenon / Alternative Phenomenon
- Options for ELA Instruction
- Build on Prior Knowledge
- Preview the Phenomenon
- Read to Learn
- Support Sense Making
- Science Stretch
- Check for Comprehension

Option 1 Use before students begin the lesson in the Activity Guide to provide an engaging model to introduce the lesson's phenomenon.

Option 2 Use after students have completed the Activity Guide to reinforce students' understanding of the lesson phenomenon by exploring a related phenomenon.

ELA (20 min)

- Options for ELA Instruction
- Build on Prior Knowledge
- Read to Learn

Option 3 To use during designated ELA Reading time for independent reading, whole-class instruction, or small-group instruction, look for this icon: ELA

Plan

> ### ANCHORING PHENOMENON / ALTERNATIVE PHENOMENON
>
> The anchoring phenomenon in the Activity Guide is *Many different types of organisms live together and interact in the African savanna,* and the main example is a group of zebras, elephants, and other animals at a watering hole. The FUNomenal Reader presents a similar phenomenon *(The conditions on Isle Royale are ideal for studying interactions between organisms in an ecosystem),* and the example is the interdependence between populations of wolves and moose on Isle Royale in Lake Superior. Both present the same science concepts and cover the same standards but with different phenomena. Guide students to draw connections between the two situations and to understand the underlying principle: organisms interact and survive in environments where their needs are met.

Options for ELA Instruction ELA

Choose one of the following anchor chart options and project it or print copies. Then display and introduce the chart before reading the text. Revisit the chart after reading the text and encourage students to discuss how the skill connects to the text.

Informational Text Use the *Informational Text Anchor Chart* to discuss the difference between informational text and narrative nonfiction. Help students understand that this nonfiction selection presents factual information without the use of characters and dialogue.

Text Features Refer to the *Text Features Anchor Chart* to help students identify the various text features in this story. Students should notice a map, graphs, photos, and illustrations. Guide them to understand that these visual features help explain ideas in the text.

Point of View Use the *Point of View Anchor Chart* to discuss first-person vs. third-person point of view. In this selection, the narrator gives information but did not experience the events firsthand.

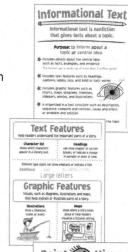

Preview

ELA **Build on Prior Knowledge** Discuss the word *population* as used in life science and in daily usage. Explain that a population is a group of the same type of organisms. The members live and interact with one another. The term *population* can also describe the number of people who live in a city or area. Invite volunteers to find out the population of their area or a nearby city. Have students discuss how members of the population work together for the good of the population.

Preview the Phenomenon Ask students to study the map on p. 2 of the story, which depicts parts of the United States and Canada, with an inset showing the location of Isle Royale in Lake Superior. Encourage students to record the first questions that come into their minds about what types of organisms might live in such a location. Point out that their questions might change as they read through the selection. Have them keep their questions on hand and periodically check to see if any can be answered.

STANDARDS SUPPORTED

SEP
Developing and Using Models

Science Models, Laws, Mechanisms, and Theories Explain Natural Phenomena

DCI
LS2.A Interdependent Relationships in Ecosystems

LS2.B Cycles of Matter and Energy Transfer in Ecosystems

ESS2.A Earth Materials and Systems

CCC
Systems and System Models

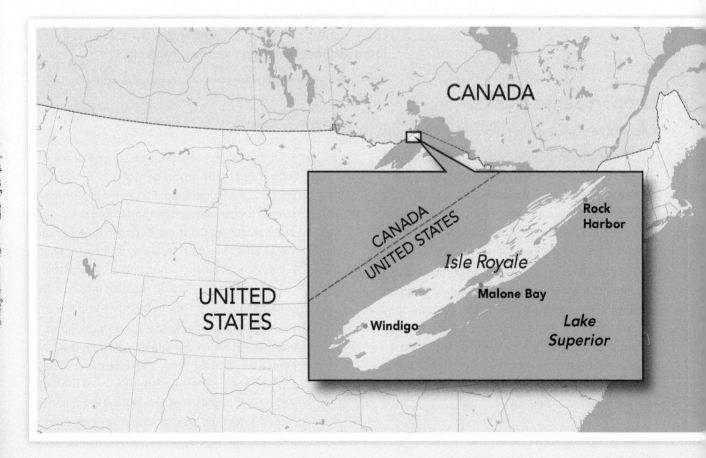

The Wolves and Moose of Isle Royale (continued)

Discover

Read to Learn ELA

The **Read to Learn** suggestions inside the book's front cover encourage students to interact with the book multiple times for different purposes.

> **Preview** Students look for unfamiliar words and share them with a partner. New terms may include *population, predator,* and *prey.* Have students look up words they aren't sure about and notice how they are used in the context of the story.

> **Skim** Students skim the photos, illustrations, map, and graphs. Have them turn to a partner and share their predictions of what the story will be about.

> **Read** As students read the story, ask them to look for connections to one of the following anchor chart skills.
> **Informational Text, Text Features, Point of View**

Support Sense Making

Choose one or more of the following:

▶ Be sure students can identify the phenomenon presented on the opening pages of the reader: the wolf population on Isle Royale reached a high of 50 in 1980 but dropped to just 2 in 2016. The remaining pages describe what led to this decline and what scientists are doing to address the issue.

▶ Have students make a T-chart to compare and contrast the wolf and moose populations on Isle Royale. Facts might include when and how they arrived on the island, what they eat, body size, and if they are solitary or live in groups. Help students relate the information in their charts to this statement: *When wolf numbers are high, moose numbers tend to be lower.*

▶ Scientists placed GPS radio collars on wolves introduced to Isle Royale between 2018 and 2019. Encourage a student-led discussion about what scientists hope to learn by monitoring the progress of these wolves. Do students feel that GPS collars are an effective and ethical way to monitor animals' behavior, movements, and survival? Interested students might want to do research into how these collars are used and report back to the class.

▶ Have student pairs act out a short TV or online interview in which one student portrays the interviewer and the other a science expert. The topic should be the interdependence of the wolf and moose populations on Isle Royale. Students should write their script and then act out their interview for the class.

Extend

Science Stretch

The **Science Stretch** suggestions inside the book's back cover help students think about what they read. Students can complete one or more as time allows.

> Make a food web that includes at least five other species on Isle Royale. Refer students to the list of other species on p. 3. Provide books and approved websites for students to use in their research.

> Draw a model of the Isle Royale ecosystem. Identify the living and nonliving parts. You may need to review the nonliving parts of an ecosystem, such as air, water, light, and nutrients.

> What are the pros and cons of reintroducing wolves on Isle Royale? **Sample answer:** Pro—More wolves will keep the moose from eating all the plants. Con—The moose population will decrease.

SOCIAL EMOTIONAL LEARNING

Why is communicating results an important part of scientific research? **Sample answer:** Scientists need to know what other scientists have done so they can learn from their results.

Check for Comprehension Have students write a paragraph explaining the interdependence of wolves and moose on Isle Royale. They should use details from the text to support their conclusions.

What's Out There?

Activity Guide, pages 138–141

TIME ESTIMATE

65 min

POSSIBLE MATERIALS

- ☐ gloves
- ☐ string
- ☐ wooden dowels
- ☐ hand lens
- ☐ field guides for the local environment
- ☐ other objects students may need to complete their plans
- ☐ camera (optional)

PREPARATION

Some students may select an area on or off the school grounds to investigate. Select a safe area outside in which each group can survey a one square meter section without bumping into each other. Areas with some shade and rocks, leaves, or twigs are ideal because insects may live under these items. Look for areas where the ground is soft enough for students to push their dowels into it. Review rules for field investigations. Remind students to wear gloves, and caution them not to handle living things without your approval. You may want to provide cameras for documenting observations.

INVESTIGATIVE PHENOMENON
Living and nonliving things make up ecosystems.

Phenomenon Explained Students explore the **investigative phenomenon** by planning and conducting an investigation to explain the health of a local ecosystem. Students gather evidence to support their explanation.

Form a Question After observing the photograph, students should form a question about living things around the school. If students struggle to form a question, ask them to consider spots near the school and any living things they've noticed there. Sample question: How many different kinds of living things can I find around my school?

STEP 1   As a class, develop questions about local ecosystems. Initiate a discussion about which questions are the most important. Sample answer: How many different living things can I find in an area the size of a piece of paper? How many of each kind of living thing are in that area?

STEP 2   Students plan their investigations. Review student plans to check for safety concerns. Student plans should specify what they plan to do, what materials they will need, and what information they will collect.

STEP 3 Students conduct their investigations. Remind them to record their results and display them with a table, graph, or graphic organizer.

- **Make a Claim** Claims should describe the ecosystem as healthy if it supports many types of organisms or unhealthy if it supports very few.

- **Evidence** Students should cite as evidence observations they made and data they collected about the number and types of organisms.

- **Reasoning** Students should explain their reasoning by clearly connecting their evidence to their claim about the ecosystem's health.

FORMATIVE ASSESSMENT ▪ ▫ ▫ ▫

MAKING SENSE OF PHENOMENA

Students gain understanding that living and nonliving things make up ecosystems as they explore the **investigative phenomenon.** They should connect this to the **anchoring phenomenon** that the African savanna is an example of an ecosystem made up of living and nonliving things.

REMEDIATION If students struggle to connect the **investigative phenomenon** back to the **anchoring phenomenon,** have them discuss how the living things in the African savanna are similar to the living things in the school ecosystem in how they share living and nonliving resources, such as air, water, food, and shelter.

MAKING SENSE OF PHENOMENA IDEA ORGANIZER

After completing Exploration 1, students can fill in the **Idea Organizer** to summarize the connection between the idea that living and nonliving things make up an ecosystem and the anchoring phenomenon that many different types of organisms live together and interact with each other and with nonliving things in the African savanna ecosystem.

Activity Outcome

Students should plan and carry out a field investigation in order to observe the diversity of living things in a local environment.

Performance Indicators
design an investigation of a local ecosystem
record results and use presentation tools to display results
make a claim about the health of a local ecosystem
support the claim using the results of the investigation as evidence

SOCIAL EMOTIONAL LEARNING

As a class, create a list of rules for field investigations of living things and their environments. The following promote responsible treatment of living things:

- wearing gloves
- following teacher instructions and precautions
- demonstrating patience when observing living things
- taking care not to hurt any organisms

Environment Matters

Activity Guide, pages 142–143

TIME ESTIMATE

day 1   day 2   day 3   day 4   day 5

15 min 5 min   5 min   5 min   15 min

SHORT ON TIME?

Consider setting up the investigation ahead of time, having students responsible for the daily observations only.

POSSIBLE MATERIALS

- ☐ container, clear, large
- ☐ plants, herbaceous, live, cilantro is recommended
- ☐ water
- ☐ weights, washers or rocks

PREPARATION

In advance, gather or grow plants of the same kind and similar size. Cilantro is especially responsive to the environment. The activity uses a control plant and a test plant. A class could share a control plant or a set of plants to save on materials. Multiple groups can share a container. Plan a location where plants can be left undisturbed. Fill a tall container, tub, or pitcher with enough water to cover a plant including stems and leaves. Depending on plant species and size, changes may take more than three days.

INVESTIGATIVE PHENOMENON
Organisms survive in environments where their needs are met.

Phenomenon Explained Students explore the **investigative phenomenon** by conducting an investigation to explain which environment meets the needs of a plant. Students make observations and gather evidence to support their conclusions.

Form a Question After observing the photograph, students should form a question about the environments where plants can live. If students struggle to form a question, ask them to consider the places and environments where they usually see plants growing. Sample question: What do plants need to be able to live? Can all plants live in all environments?

STEP 1   Students water and make initial observations about the two plants. Direct students to pay particular attention to color when making all observations.

STEP 2   Students submerge one plant in the container of water, with weights on the soil to keep it under water. They position the second plant next to the container.

STEP 3 Students observe the two plants over several days. Discuss the kinds of qualitative and quantitative observations most useful to this activity. Students should use a data table or other tool to organize their data. Data may include observations, measurements, or sketches.

- **Make a Claim** Claims should indicate which environment was better for the type of plant in the investigation and connect the better environment with the fact that it included air.

- **Evidence** Students should cite data from the activity that the plant underwater started to die, while the plant on the countertop survived.

- **Reasoning** Students should explain their reasoning that the better environment for the type of plant used in the investigation included air. Therefore, this type of plant must need air.

FORMATIVE ASSESSMENT ■ ■ ▢ ▢

MAKING SENSE OF PHENOMENA

Students gain understanding that organisms have different environmental needs that must be met for them to live and grow as they explore the **investigative phenomenon.** They should connect this to the **anchoring phenomenon** that organisms that live in the African savanna can get their needs met in environment.

REMEDIATION If students struggle to connect the **investigative phenomenon** back to the **anchoring phenomenon,** have them return to the photo of the African savanna and identify what resources organisms could find there.

MAKING SENSE OF PHENOMENA
IDEA ORGANIZER
After completing Exploration 2, students can fill in the **Idea Organizer** to summarize the connection between the needs of specific plants and the anchoring phenomenon that specific organisms can live together and interact in the African savanna because the African savanna is an environment that meets these organisms' needs.

Activity Outcome

Students should carry out an investigation to determine the type of environment a specific plant needs to live.

Performance Indicators
carry out specific steps to set up an investigation
record observations about the plants' growth and physical appearance
make a claim that air is a necessary part of the environment for this type of plant to survive
support the claim using collected data as evidence

Living Things and Their Environment

Activity Guide, pages 144–147

TIME ESTIMATE

45 min

Materials Alert Depending on time considerations, you may wish to provide materials such as colored pencils or markers so that students can add detail to their models of interactions between living things and between living and nonliving things.

INVESTIGATIVE PHENOMENON
Organisms interact with each other and with the nonliving parts of the environment.

Phenomenon Explained Students explore the **investigative phenomenon** by examining interactions of living things and the flow of matter and energy between living and nonliving things in an ecosystem.

It's Alive!

If students struggle to understand interactions with living and nonliving things, have them reflect on their experience arriving at the classroom that morning. List things they interacted with, and sort those things based on whether they are Living or Nonliving.

Living Partnerships

Remind students that an environment includes both living and nonliving things. Encourage them to include at least one interaction between living things and one interaction between a living and a nonliving thing in their models. You can refer back to this conversation later in the activity when reviewing the model under Waste Matter.

Animal Groups

Everyday Phenomenon **Many birds live and interact in flocks.**

Birds in rural, urban, and suburban areas where students live are often seen in flocks. To help students understand animal groups, brainstorm reasons that a population of animals might live together and interact. Focus on the idea that animals of the same type have shared needs.

System Connections

Review the different systems with students. Make sure students understand a system that includes all living things is called a biosphere. Then have students refer back to the image of the forest ecosystem, make a list of nonliving natural things, and put them into specific systems.

Waste Matter

Have students give examples of producers, consumers, and decomposers. Explain the importance of decomposers in the flow of matter and energy in the biosphere. If students struggle to understand the model, have them trace paths through the model with their finger following the arrows. Give examples of everyday phenomena that could be modeled by that path. For instance, when squirrels eat nuts from trees or cattle eat grass, energy and matter flow from producers to consumers.

SOCIAL EMOTIONAL LEARNING

Small group discussions allow students to practice collaboration skills. Have students evaluate their own role in a group. Ask:

- Name a good thing you bring to every team.
- Do you listen to everyone?
- Do you give others an opportunity to share their ideas?
- What are your strengths as a team member?
- What are your weaknesses as a team member?

Then initiate a class discussion to review the characteristics of a good team member.

FORMATIVE ASSESSMENT

MAKING SENSE OF PHENOMENA

Students gain understanding that organisms interact with each other and with the environment as they explore the **investigative phenomenon.** They should connect this to the **anchoring phenomenon** that organisms in the African savanna use and exchange matter with their ecosystem.

REMEDIATION If students struggle to connect the **investigative phenomenon** back to the **anchoring phenomenon,** have them discuss what nonliving things in the African savanna must be shared by organisms and how these nonliving things make it possible for organisms to survive.

MAKING SENSE OF PHENOMENA IDEA ORGANIZER

After completing Exploration 3, students can fill in the **Idea Organizer** to summarize the connection between the idea that organisms interact with each other and with nonliving things and the anchoring phenomenon that these types of interactions occur in the African savanna.

Competition in Ecosystems

TIME ESTIMATE

45 min

> **INVESTIGATIVE PHENOMENON**
> Food, water, and space are scarce in some ecosystems.

Phenomenon Explained Students explore the **investigative phenomenon** by investigating how organisms compete for limited resources to meet their needs within an ecosystem.

Battling for Survival

Everyday Phenomenon **Hikers carry water with them.**

Drinking water is a limited resource on short nature walks and long hikes. To help students understand limited resources, have small groups make packing lists with resources hikers would need for an all-day hike. Discuss what might happen if hikers forgot something or didn't pack enough.

Limited Supply

Present an example of competition for resources that applies to your local area. For instance, raccoons and feral cats compete for resources in areas where garbage cans are their primary food source.

Habitat Factors

Students can research the habitats and needs of local animals to determine which animals are most likely to survive a change in the ecosystem and which animals are most likely to struggle.

The Difference Is Night and Day

Students compare the red-shouldered hawk and the barred owl, two animals that share habitats and also roles as hunters, though one hunts in the day and one at night. Have students discuss how the different times of day the animals hunt affects their competition for resources. Encourage students to consider how each animal's hunting behavior affects the resources available to the other animal.

Case Study

In exploring the case study, discuss the relationship between predator and prey. Students can discuss possible causes of bears' interest in garbage cans such as changes in the availability of their natural prey. If students struggle to order the causes and effects, have them describe the issue in their own words to think about what came first. They could also consider which issue, if resolved, would make the others irrelevant.

FORMATIVE ASSESSMENT

MAKING SENSE OF PHENOMENA

Students gain understanding that the scarcity of food, water, and space in some ecosystems causes competition between organisms as they explore the **investigative phenomenon.** They should connect this to the **anchoring phenomenon** that the availability of resources in the African savanna affects the number and different types of organisms that can live there and how they interact.

REMEDIATION If students struggle to connect the **investigative phenomenon** back to the **anchoring phenomenon,** have them discuss how a sudden drought might affect a variety of organisms in the African savanna.

MAKING SENSE OF PHENOMENA
IDEA ORGANIZER

After completing Exploration 4, students can fill in the **Idea Organizer** to summarize the connection between the ways that organisms compete for scarce resources within an ecosystem and the anchoring phenomenon that some of the interactions between organisms on the African savanna include competing for resources.

01

Take It Further

TIME ESTIMATE

45 min

These Take It Further paths may be completed to enrich and extend students' comprehension of content covered within this lesson.

ONLINE

People in Science & Engineering: Alejandro E. Almario

In this feature, students learn about the work of Alejandro E. Almario, who researches how human behavior and products affect marine ecosystems in the Gulf of Mexico. As an employee of the U.S. government, it is Mr. Almario's job to help solve the problems that can kill off wildlife in the Gulf.

People in Science & Engineering: Dr. John Weishampel and Dr. Tanya Berger-Wolf

Students study the work of two scientists who use modern technology to explore issues facing natural habitats.

Exploring a Deep Sea Ecosystem

Students explore the flow of energy among organisms in a deep-ocean ecosystem, where certain types of bacteria use energy derived from chemicals released by volcanic vents to produce food.

Lesson Check

Activity Guide, pages 151–153

Engage • Explore/Explain • Elaborate • **Evaluate**

Can You Explain It?

Now I know or think that . . .

Sample answer: Now I know or think that different types of organisms in the African savanna can live there because their needs are met. Animals have their needs for water and air met by the nonliving parts of their environment. They have their need for food met by plants or other animals as living parts of their environment. If organisms cannot meet their needs with the resources in the environment, they will compete. This will cause some animals to leave and try to find a new habitat. Other animals may die.

After completing the lesson, use the **Making Sense Idea Organizer** to summarize the connections between the **investigative phenomena** and **anchoring phenomenon.**

MAKING CONNECTIONS

After students complete the lesson, they should be able to answer a question about an alternative phenomenon to explain how bears and fish live together and interact in a forest ecosystem. Sample answer: Bears and fish interact in this ecosystem when the bears eat the fish.

Checkpoints

1. **Sample answer:** The bear drinks from the pond to meet its need for water.

2. d—all of the above

3. 1—Decomposers leave nutrients in the soil; 2—Producers take in nutrients from the soil; 3—Consumers get nutrients from eating producers.

4. **Sample answer:** When two or more arrows point away from an organism, that means at least two organisms eat the same food source.

5. **Sample answer:** Students should show a food resource that is 1) limited and 2) relied on by two or more competing species.

6. **Sample answer:** rain falls → soaks into soil → plant roots take in water → animal eats plant → waste soaks into soil

 SOCIAL EMOTIONAL LEARNING

Have students reflect on the goals they set at the beginning of the lesson. Ask them to think about whether the goals were accomplished or if there were challenges. Have students share the factors that contributed to their success. If the goals were not achieved, talk about what students can do to help them achieve the goals.

02 Organisms Change Their Ecosystems

ANCHORING PHENOMENON
Kudzu grows quickly, climbing over native plants and blocking their access to sunlight.

ENGAGE Can You Explain It?
Students observe and ask questions about how kudzu vines can affect an entire ecosystem. They answer the Can You Explain It? question to identify what they will gather evidence about in the lesson.

EVALUATE Lesson Check
Students gauge their understanding of the anchoring phenomenon.

HANDS-ON ACTIVITY

EXPLORATION 1 Invasion!   **60 min**
Investigative Phenomenon Native organisms are often at a disadvantage when interacting with invasive species.

Students connect back to the **anchoring phenomenon** that native organisms often cannot get what they need when kudzu causes changes to an ecosystem.

HANDS-ON ACTIVITY

EXPLORATION 2 Balance Restored   **40 min**
Investigative Phenomenon Humans develop solutions to protect the environment from invasive species.

Students connect back to the **anchoring phenomenon** that people attempt to remove invasive organisms like kudzu from ecosystems in order to limit the damage they might cause.

EXPLORATION 3 Introduced and Invasive Species   **40 min**
Investigative Phenomenon Newly introduced organisms can alter ecosystems as they use and consume resources.

Students connect back to the **anchoring phenomenon** that the effects of the kudzu vine extend to the entire web of life, beyond the immediate parts of the environment with which they interact.

Making 3D Connections

The **anchoring phenomenon** in this lesson supports students' understanding of and application of these Next Generation Science Standards.

Building to the Performance Expectations

5-LS2-1 Develop a model to describe the movement of matter among plants, animals, decomposers, and the environment.

SEP

Developing and Using Models
Develop a model to describe phenomena. *(Explorations 1, 2, 3)*

Science Models, Laws, Mechanisms, and Theories Explain Natural Phenomena
Science explanations describe the mechanisms for natural events. *(Explorations 1, 3)*

DCI

LS2.A Interdependent Relationships in Ecosystems
Organisms are related in food webs. Organisms can survive only in environments in which their particular needs are met. Newly introduced species can damage the balance of an ecosystem. *(Explorations 1, 2, 3)*

ETS1.B Developing Possible Solutions At whatever stage, communicating with peers about proposed solutions is an important part of the design process. *(Exploration 2)*

CCC

System and System Models
A system can be described in terms of its components and their interactions. *(Explorations 1, 2, 3)*

Vocabulary

Word Wall A word wall, anchor chart, or Language Development chart can be used to support vocabulary.

invasive species nonnative species that competes for resources better than existing species in the ecosystem

You may want to include additional academic terms such as *native* and *resource* and any other terms students might struggle with.

Language Development Prompt students to complete the chart when they come to these highlighted terms within the lesson.

Anchor Chart As you progress through the unit, you may want to make a vocabulary-based anchor chart using the Language Development chart as a guide that can be displayed and filled out as a whole group during each lesson.

02 Organisms Change Their Ecosystems

Activity Guide, pages 154–155

Students can engage in the Can You Explain It? content by observing the photograph or by exploring the corresponding video online.

ONLINE  View a video related to kudzu.

ANCHORING PHENOMENON
Kudzu grows quickly, climbing over native plants and blocking their access to sunlight.

PHENOMENON EXPLAINED
Kudzu is an invasive species that can prevent native organisms from getting what they need and affects the entire ecosystem.

Lesson Objective

Students use models to describe how organisms, including newly introduced species, affect ecosystems.

Support Discovery

The following prompts can be used to guide student-led discovery.

I notice . . .

After observing the photograph or watching the video, students should record what they noticed about kudzu. If students struggle to record observations, ask them to look closely at the images and try to count the number of different plants.

Sample answers: I notice that these vines cover all of the other plants in the picture.

I wonder . . .

After observing the photograph or watching the video, students should record what they wonder about kudzu.

Sample answer: I wonder whether being covered by the vines harms the other plants.

Can You Explain It?

In the Can You Explain It?, students make an initial claim that explains the **Anchoring Phenomenon**. Students might draw a model of how kudzu vines affect other parts of the ecosystem or write a sentence about how the kudzu vines affect how other organisms in the ecosystem meet their needs.

Students will gather evidence about how invasive species cause changes in ecosystems. This will enable them to give a more complete explanation of the **Anchoring Phenomenon** at the end of the lesson.

Alternative Phenomenon

If students are unfamiliar with kudzu vines, guide them to think of other examples of species introduced to a new environment and cause changes. You may want to show students pictures of an invasive species that is causing problems in your state, or you could also invite a local wildlife expert to speak to your class.

 SOCIAL EMOTIONAL LEARNING

Guide students to reflect on their goals from previous lessons and on any feedback they received from their teachers or peers. Then have each student set a personal goal for this lesson and make a plan for how to achieve the goal. Throughout the lesson, take daily breaks for students to track their progress in meeting their goals. As students move from lesson to lesson, they can continue to work towards their initial goals or set new ones. If students struggle setting goals for this lesson, share with them some of the following ideas: identifying how organisms change ecosystems, describing cause-and-effect relationships, or persevering when an activity or topic is difficult.

02

Case of the Missing Bobcats

WHEN TO USE

SCIENCE **30** min

- Anchoring Phenomenon / Alternative Phenomenon
- Options for ELA Instruction
- Build on Prior Knowledge
- Preview the Phenomenon
- Read to Learn
- Support Sense Making
- Science Stretch
- Check for Comprehension

Option 1 Use before students begin the lesson in the Activity Guide to provide an engaging model to introduce the lesson's phenomenon.

Option 2 Use after students have completed the Activity Guide to reinforce students' understanding of the lesson phenomenon by exploring a related phenomenon.

ELA **20** min

- Options for ELA Instruction
- Build on Prior Knowledge
- Read to Learn

Option 3 To use during designated ELA Reading time for independent reading, whole-class instruction, or small-group instruction, look for this icon: ELA

Plan

ANCHORING PHENOMENON / ALTERNATIVE PHENOMENON

The anchoring phenomenon in the Activity Guide is *Kudzu grows quickly, climbing over native plants and blocking their access to sunlight.* The main example is an outdoor scene in which invasive kudzu vines cover all the other plants. The FUNomenal Reader presents a similar phenomenon (*Bobcats are not being found in the Everglades*), and the example is a story about reduced numbers of certain animals in Florida's Everglades. Both present the same science concepts and cover the same standards but with different phenomena. Guide students to draw connections between the two situations and to understand the underlying principle: organisms, including newly introduced species, affect ecosystems.

Options for ELA Instruction ELA

Choose one of the following anchor chart options and project it or print copies. Then display and introduce the chart before reading the text. Revisit the chart after reading the text and encourage students to discuss how the skill connects to the text.

Visualize Use the *Visualize Anchor Chart* to help draw students into the content of the story. Have them take two minutes to close their eyes and think of what it would feel like to be in the Everglades, as Sophia and her mother are at the beginning of the story. Discuss what they might see, smell, and hear based on details from the text.

Make Inferences Display the *Make Inferences Anchor Chart* to discuss how learning about invasive species helps Sophia make an inference about what might be causing the decline in bobcats. She combines what she knows about the problem with what she reads to come up with a new understanding of the problem.

Learning Mindset Have student pairs study the *My Learning Mindset Anchor Chart* and then decide which of the traits describe Sophia, the story's protagonist. Partners can discuss if these traits are good for solving any problem.

Extend

Science Stretch

The **Science Stretch** suggestions inside the book's back cover help students think about what they read. Students can complete one or more as time allows.

> Make a booklet about invasive species in the area where you live. Provide books and approved websites for students to use in their research.

> Design a model of an ecosystem that shows the effects of an invasive species. This activity works well with student pairs or small groups. The model might take the form of a diagram with labels, a clay sculpture, or a short video.

> Model a way an invasive species could be trapped and removed. Student models can take many forms, including posters, diagrams, videos, or devices.

 SOCIAL EMOTIONAL LEARNING

Sophia helped solve the Case of the Missing Bobcats. How can you help your community?

Sample answer: I notice that many trees were uprooted by a recent storm. I can see if my class can help plant new trees.

Check for Comprehension Have students write a short paragraph about what it means to "bring back balance to the Everglades." They should use details from the story to support their conclusions.

Invasion!

Activity Guide, pages 156–160

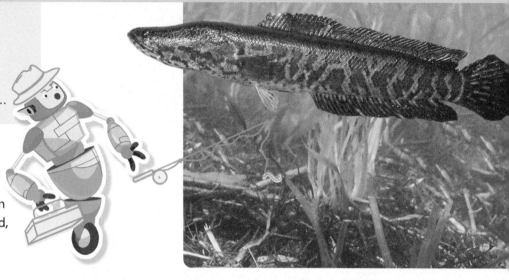

TIME ESTIMATE

60 min

POSSIBLE MATERIALS

☐ 4 index cards

☐ small squares of construction paper (10 squares each of red, blue, and yellow paper)

☐ paper clips

PREPARATION

In advance, set up bundles of materials for each group. Distribute materials to students prior to starting the activity. Have devices with Internet access or printed fact sheets about northern snakehead fish ready for students to do their research in Step 1.

INVESTIGATIVE PHENOMENON
Native organisms are often at a disadvantage when interacting with invasive species.

Phenomenon Explained Students explore the **investigative phenomenon** by modeling interactions in an ecosystem before and after an invasive organism is introduced to explain how invasive species affect native organisms. Students gather evidence to support their explanation.

Form a Question After observing the photograph, students should form a question about how the northern snakehead fish affect other species. If students struggle to form a question, ask them to think about what this fish might eat compared to other fish in the ecosystem. **Sample question:** How much do northern snakeheads eat?

STEP 1 Students will need internet access or printed fact sheets about northern snakehead fish to research three species that are affected by northern snakeheads. Tell students to make sure their selections live in areas where the northern snakehead fish is invasive. **Sample answer:** largemouth bass, white perch, bullhead catfish

STEPS 2 and 3 Assigning fish species to food requirements can be arbitrary for this model. Confirm that students are correctly pairing sets of food squares with the index cards. **Sample answer:** Yes, there was enough food to go around so that all three species could eat.

STEP 4 Make sure students are rearranging the squares correctly so the results are not skewed. The first round with only the native species counts as one of the three rounds students should model. Students should observe the snakehead depriving the other species of their food through the rounds of feeding. Round 1: native fish only, all survive; Round 2: introduce snakeheads, two fish cannot eat; Round 3: no fish can fully eat

- **Make a Claim** Claims should state that invasive species damage the balance in ecosystems.

- **Evidence** Students should cite evidence from the data tables, such as decline in food availability for the native fish species.

- **Reasoning** Students should cite the cause-and-effect connection between the introduction of the northern snakehead fish and the decline of the native species due to competition for food.

FORMATIVE ASSESSMENT

MAKING SENSE OF PHENOMENA

Students gain understanding that invasive species change ecosystems and often have negative effects on native species as they explore the **investigative phenomenon.** They should connect this to the **anchoring phenomenon** that native organisms often cannot get what they need when an invasive organism like the kudzu causes changes to an ecosystem.

REMEDIATION If students struggle to connect the **investigative phenomenon** back to the **anchoring phenomenon,** have them discuss what kinds of resources organisms compete for in ecosystems. Plants need sunlight and space, among other things, and kudzu competes with native plants for these resources.

Activity Outcome

Students model how the northern snakehead fish affect native fish when competing for food. In the model, two species can't get enough food.

Performance Indicators	
	research three fish species that are affected by the snakehead
	use a model to understand the effects of the invasive species
	make and support a claim about how the invasive northern snakehead affects other species in the ecosystem

MAKING SENSE OF PHENOMENA IDEA ORGANIZER

After completing Exploration 1, students can fill in the **Idea Organizer** to summarize the connection between native organisms often being at a disadvantage when interacting with invasive species and the anchoring phenomenon that native plants often cannot get what they need when the invasive kudzu vine causes changes to the ecosystem.

SOCIAL EMOTIONAL LEARNING

Provide students with an example of paraphrasing. For example, describe using a broom to clean dirt off of the floor. Ask them to paraphrase your description. *You swept the floor.* They can practice paraphrasing by listening to each other's claims and then providing summaries of what they heard to check for understanding.

Engineer It • Balance Restored

Activity Guide, pages 161–162

TIME ESTIMATE

45 min

POSSIBLE MATERIALS

☐ paper, white or construction

☐ colored pencils, crayons, or markers

PREPARATION

Consider finding documentaries, news articles, or other reference materials about the cane toads as invasive organisms in Florida and Australia. You may provide these additional resources to help students understand and define the problem.

Discuss with students the seriousness of the cane toad problem in Australia. Ask them to describe what might be the impact of the cane toads on existing populations. The impact of the cane toad has been devastating — they have no natural enemies, and can live in a variety of habitats. As they eat almost anything that will fit in their mouths, they leave little food for the native frogs. Cane toads destroy the balance of ecosystems. In order to battle the problem, a number of solutions must be used together, including containment, collection, and removal. However, there is still no combination of solutions that have eradicated the cane toad problem.

INVESTIGATIVE PHENOMENON
Humans develop solutions to protect the environment from invasive species.

Phenomenon Explained Students explore the **investigative phenomenon** by using an engineering design process to model a device to trap invasive organisms affecting a local environment.

Define the Problem After observing the photograph and reading the text about cane toads, students should identify the problem they are trying to solve, the criteria for a good solution, and constraints that limit possible solutions. If students struggle, have them read the introduction one sentence at a time. They can underline text about features engineers want in a good solution and circle text about rules or other factors that limit solutions. **Sample answer:** Problem: Cane toads can damage ecosystems. We need to design a trap to help control the cane toad population. Criteria: The trap must be easy to set and retrieve, and it must be durable enough to re-use. Constraint: The trap cannot harm the toads.

STEP 1 Students draw a model of their possible solution. Students should describe how one or two features of their possible solution address the criteria and constraints of the problem.

STEPS 2 and 3 Students posters and discussions should focus on meeting the criteria within the constraints. Encourage students to discuss how they used the background information about cane toads to design their solutions.

- **Make a Claim** Students claims should identify at least one important consideration engineers should keep in mind when designing solutions to protect the environment from invasive species.

- **Evidence** Students should cite evidence which may include the criteria and constraints of the problem and other environmental and ethical considerations from the Turn and Talk activity.

- **Reasoning** Students should explain their reasoning that the factor they identified helps lessen the effects of invasive species.

FORMATIVE ASSESSMENT

MAKING SENSE OF PHENOMENA

Students gain understanding that humans work to protect the environment from invasive species as they explore the **investigative phenomenon.** They should connect this to the **anchoring phenomenon** that people attempt to remove invasive kudzu from ecosystems in order to limit the damage it might cause.

REMEDIATION If students struggle to connect the **investigative phenomenon** back to the **anchoring phenomenon,** review specific examples of invasive species, and have them identify how the invasive species damage the balance of ecosystems and what attempts humans made to limit or stop the damage.

MAKING SENSE OF PHENOMENA IDEA ORGANIZER

After completing Exploration 2, students can fill in the **Idea Organizer** to summarize the connection between humans developing solutions to protect the environment from invasive species and the anchoring phenomenon that people attempt to remove invasive organisms like kudzu from ecosystems to limit the damage they might cause.

Activity Outcome

Students should develop and model a trap solution for the cane toad problem based on the criteria and constraints.

Performance Indicators	
	define the problem using information from the Activity Guide
	develop and model a solution and share it with classmates
	make and support a claim about factors engineers should consider when working on invasive species problems

SOCIAL EMOTIONAL LEARNING

Discuss intended and unintended effects of everyday decisions. For instance, sharpening a pencil has the intended effect that the pencil is sharp for writing. It might have the unintended effect of making a mess with shavings. Have students share examples from their own lives of factors they have to consider when making decisions.

Introduced and Invasive Species

Activity Guide, pages 163–166

TIME ESTIMATE

45 min

> **INVESTIGATIVE PHENOMENON**
> Newly introduced organisms can alter ecosystems as they use and consume resources.

Phenomenon Explained Students explore the **investigative phenomenon** by learning about cases of nonnative species affecting ecosystems by using resources and interacting with native species.

New in Town

Everyday Phenomenon **Alligator weed, Burmese pythons, and lionfish are three examples of invasive species in the U.S.**

Tell students that cane toads are destroying the balance of ecosystems in Australia. Identify an invasive species causing problems in your state to use as a running example. Have students research how the species was introduced and how it affects the environment and human society.

Losing Balance

Four plants are described: two aquatic, two terrestrial. Explain to students that in both environments organisms compete for space and sunlight, but aquatic organisms also compete for dissolved oxygen. The atmosphere is more stable in terms of oxygen available to organisms.

Animal Invasion

Encourage students to use a graphic organizer to summarize the similarities and differences between how invasive plants and animals affect native species. You may choose to present a variety of organizer types or allow students to design their own.

SOCIAL EMOTIONAL LEARNING

Encourage students to role-play a debate about introducing an animal to their local environment. As a class, list the characteristics of the animal and brainstorm the pros and cons of introducing the species. Tell students to:

- consider how the species' effects on the environment might be perceived differently by different groups of people

- model a civil debate by sticking to rules such as taking turns and responding to the other group's evidence and reasoning rather than their personal traits

Pig Populations

One way invasive organisms can alter ecosystems is by reproducing rapidly, especially if few predators are present. To continue this conversation, provide students with information about the reproduction rate of the invasive species in your state.

FORMATIVE ASSESSMENT

MAKING SENSE OF PHENOMENA

Students gain understanding that newly introduced species affect the balance of ecosystems as they explore the **investigative phenomenon.** They should connect this to the **anchoring phenomenon** that the effects of invasive organisms, such as the kudzu vine, extend beyond the immediate parts of the environment they interact with, affecting the entire web of life.

REMEDIATION If students struggle to connect the **investigative phenomenon** back to the **anchoring phenomenon,** have them review a specific example from this activity of a nonnative plant species that affected other organisms, focusing on how kudzu affected its ecosystem in similar and different ways as that plant.

MAKING SENSE OF PHENOMENA IDEA ORGANIZER

After completing Exploration 3, students can fill in the **Idea Organizer** to summarize the connection between newly introduced species changing ecosystems and the anchoring phenomenon that kudzu affects the organisms it interacts with directly and the resources available to all organisms.

02

Take It Further

TIME ESTIMATE

These Take It Further paths may be completed to enrich and extend students' comprehension of content covered within this lesson.

ONLINE

Careers in Science & Engineering: Entomologist

In this feature, students read about USDA scientist Richard Mankin and other entomologists study.

It's News to Me!

Students explore something they did not know about invasive or nonnative species.

Careers in Science & Engineering: U.S. Army Corps of Engineers

Students learn about the U.S. Army Corps of Engineers, a part of the U.S. Army that is dedicated to protecting ecosystems, among other things.

Fantastic Field Guides

Students research science careers that specialize in designing technology to guide scientific studies in the field (in the environment or wilderness).

Lesson Check

Can You Explain It?

Now I know or think that . . .

Sample answer: Now I know or think that kudzu is an invasive species that grows over native plant species and covers them. This can cause native plants to die because they cannot get the sunlight they need. Kudzu vines can damage the broader ecosystem because if native plants die, then other organisms that rely on those native plants for food or shelter would also be harmed. The ecosystem would become out of balance.

After completing the lesson, use the **Making Sense Idea Organizer** to summarize the connections between the **investigative phenomena** and **anchoring phenomenon.**

MAKING CONNECTIONS

After students complete the lesson, they should be able to answer a question about an alternative phenomenon to explain how crazy ants affect native species and the ecosystem. **Sample answer:** Crazy ants may compete with native ant species for space or food. If native ants die, then organisms that feed on native ants could be affected.

Checkpoints

1. a—using too much air

2. a, d, e

3. a—crowds out other plants; d—blocks sunlight from plants that live deeper in the water.

4. **Sample answer:** Brazilian *elodea* crowds out other plants, harming native plants and the organisms that rely on them. To prevent this, a new law should require safe disposal of *elodea*.

5. Models should show a chain of causes and effects. Example: Invasive insects can kill plants. Animals that rely on the plant can't eat. This is negative because the ecosystem is unbalanced.

6. **Sample answer:** Test the trap in the wild. Show how it holds the animal. Measure the population of the animal to show it is dropping and balance is returning.

7. **Sample answer:** If we don't control this invasive species, native fish will die. Sport fishing for the native fish will end. Our data shows the trap works. Use it to reduce the invasive population.

SOCIAL EMOTIONAL LEARNING

Have students reflect on the goals they set at the beginning of the lesson. Ask them to think about whether the goals were accomplished or if there were challenges. Have students share the factors that contributed to their success. If the goals were not achieved, talk about what students can do to help them achieve the goals.

The Unit Review items enable you to assess student comprehension of core ideas, as well as crosscutting concepts and science and engineering practices.

1. **DOK 2** **Sample answer:** Without water to drink and air to breathe, I would die. Sunlight keeps producers alive, and I need food energy from them to live.

    Students should be able to answer this question by thinking about their basic needs. If students struggle, brainstorm a list of nonliving things.

2. **DOK 2** Accept local examples. **Sample answer:** Raccoons can live in many places and eat many kinds of foods. Salmon can only live in certain places and eat certain foods. So, raccoons are more likely to adapt to a change in the ecosystem.

    Students can review the concept of habitat. If they are still having trouble, provide examples of local organisms.

3. **DOK 2** **a**—They are typically harmful to their new environment; **b**—They can limit resources available to other plants.

    Have students think about the word "invasive" and what it means to "invade" something.

4. **DOK 1** **a**—producers; **c**—consumers; **d**—decomposers

    If students struggle, have them review their model to understand how matter and energy flow in ecosystems.

5. **DOK 1** **Sample answer:** Models may show oak trees in a forest have food (acorns), nesting spots for birds and squirrels, and places for moss to grow. The ecosystem is healthy because this community of organisms can live and grow.

    Students should recall that a population is a group of organisms of the same kind in an ecosystem, and a community is a group of all of the populations that live and interact in an area.

6. **DOK 2** **c**—A cow uses a tree for shade; **d**—A ladybug lays eggs on a leaf.

    Suggest students work on one answer choice at a time. Discuss the different systems and review what things make up a biosphere.

7. **DOK 2** **c**—Plants use nutrients from the soil to make food; **d**—Deer drink water from a pond.

    For this question, students should work on one answer choice at a time. Make sure that students understand that the question is asking for them to identify the interactions between living and nonliving things. Two answer choices depict living things, and two answer choices depict living and nonliving things.

8. **DOK 2** All effects can be *P* or *N* depending on viewpoint. Responses should show students' reasoning. **Sample answer:** Floods are *P* because they move soil for plants.

    Effects are positive or negative for the other living and nonliving things in the ecosystem. During review, discuss each effect, in turn.

9. **DOK 1** **b.** another engineer who does computer modeling; **c.** a legal expert on environmental protection rules; **d.** a scientific expert on ecosystems and invasive species

Students should consider which professionals would need or be able to provide information and ideas for solving the problem. Students may find it helpful to reflect on their experiences with engineering design processes.

10. **DOK 3** **Sample answer:** Students may choose a food web or a simple cause and effect model to show that native mussel species may die out. So may consumers that eat those native mussels. We should stop the spread of nonnative mussels so the ecosystem won't become out of balance.

Students should review previous models that show the impacts of invasive species on an ecosystem.

3D Item Analysis	1	2	3	4	5	6	7	8	9	10
SEP Developing and Using Models								•	•	•
SEP Science Models, Laws, Mechanisms, and Theories Explain Natural Phenomena	•	•			•			•		
DCI Interdependent Relationships in Ecosystems		•	•	•	•	•	•	•	•	•
DCI Cycles of Matter and Energy Transfer in Ecosystems	•				•			•		
DCI Earth Materials and Systems						•	•			
DCI Developing Possible Solutions									•	
CCC Systems and System Models		•	•	•	•	•	•	•	•	•

05 Earth Interactions and Resources

Activity Guide, page 173

Unit Storyline

In Unit 4, students explored how energy and matter move through ecosystems. They used models to see how organisms interact and survive in environments where their needs are met, and how native and nonnative species affect ecosystems. In this unit, students will explore interactions of Earth's systems, and how humans affect those systems and the resources they contain. They will identify ways that humans can conserve environments and resources, including the use of specific technologies.

LESSON 1   PE 5-ESS2-1

Earth's Systems Interact

Activity Guide, pp. 174–191

Students explore the **anchoring phenomenon** that a volcanic eruption can affect all of Earth's systems.

> **SEP** Developing and Using Models
> **DCI** **ESS2.A** Earth Materials and Systems
> **CCC** Systems and System Models

LESSON 2   PE 5-ESS2-1, 5-ESS2-2

Water in Earth's Systems

Activity Guide, pp. 192–207

Students explore the **anchoring phenomenon** that plants are more abundant on one side of this mountain.

> **SEP** Using Mathematics and Computational Thinking
> **DCI** **ESS2.A** Earth Materials and Systems; **ESS2.C** The Roles of Water in Earth's Surface Processes
> **CCC** Systems and System Models; Scale, Proportion, and Quantity

LESSON 3   PE 5-ESS3-1

Resource Use Affects the Environment

Activity Guide, pp. 208–225

Students explore the **anchoring phenomenon** that in order to meet people's need for water, an artificial river through the desert was designed and built.

> **SEP** Obtaining, Evaluating, and Communicating Information
> **DCI** **ETS1.C** Optimizing the Design Solution; **ESS3.C** Human Impacts on Earth Systems
> **CCC** Systems and System Models; Science Addresses Questions About the World

LESSON 4   PE 5-ESS3-1

People Can Protect the Environment

Activity Guide, pp. 226–243

Students explore the **anchoring phenomenon** that people planted trees and other plants on these roofs.

> **SEP** Obtaining, Evaluating, and Communicating Information; Engaging in Argument from Evidence; Using Mathematics and Computational Thinking
> **DCI** **ETS1.B** Developing Possible Solutions; **ESS3.C** Human Impacts on Earth Systems
> **CCC** Systems and System Models; Science Addresses Questions About the World

Unit Review   Activity Guide, pp. 244–246

05 Online-Only Resources

Supporting Unit Resources

You Solve It   SUPPORTS LESSON 1

Earth's Systems is a virtual lab that offers practice in support of **Performance Expectation 5-ESS2-1**. Students explore a simulation of an event and analyze data to obtain information about how Earth's spheres interact and are affected.

- **SEP** Obtaining, Evaluating, and Communicating Information
- **DCI** **ESS3.C** Human Impacts on Earth Systems
- **CCC** Systems and System Models

Unit Project   SUPPORTS LESSONS 3 AND 4

(90 min)

My Environmental Impact provides students an opportunity to practice aspects of **Performance Expectation 5-ESS3-1.** Students will analyze data to estimate the total amount of recyclable materials they will use in their lifetimes.

- **SEP** Analyzing and Interpreting Data
- **DCI** **ESS3.C** Human Impacts on Earth Systems
- **CCC** Patterns

Unit Performance Task   SUPPORTS LESSONS 3 AND 4

(90 min)

Protecting a Sphere provides an opportunity for students to practice or be assessed on aspects of **Performance Expectation 5-ESS3-1.** Students design a way in which people can work together to protect one of Earth's systems.

- **SEP** Constructing Explanations and Designing Solutions
- **DCI** **ESS3.C** Human Impacts on Earth Systems
- **CCC** Systems and System Models; Cause and Effect

Language Development

This worksheet is used as students progress through the unit's lessons. As they come to a highlighted vocabulary term, they should come back to this chart and fill in the blanks with words or phrases.

ONLINE

Updates and additional student and teacher resources can be found online. Check back often!

Supporting Lesson Resources

Do the Math!

Lesson 1 Rating the Rain
Lesson 2 Water Footprint; Precipitation Comparison
Lesson 3 Calculate Energy Units
Lesson 4 Saving Trees

Language SmArts

Lesson 1 Making Connections; Using Evidence
Lesson 2 Making a Claim
Lesson 3 Main Idea and Details; Drawing Inferences
Lesson 4 Informative Paragraph; Make an Argument

Take It Further

Lesson 1 The Coldest Summer; Measuring Weather Across the Spheres; Monsoons; Careers in Science & Engineering: Agricultural Engineering
Lesson 2 People in Science & Engineering: Kang Hu; Engineer It! Rainwater Harvest; Gray Water
Lesson 3 Careers in Science & Engineering: Marine Biologist & Ecologist; Sustainable Forests; Overfishing
Lesson 4 People in Science & Engineering: Dr. Mario Molina; Landfills: How Long until It's Gone?; Can All Plastics Be Recycled?; Careers in Science & Engineering: Sustainability Specialist

MAKING SENSE OF PHENOMENA

This idea organizer is used to make sense of the following **anchoring phenomena**:
Lesson 1—A volcanic eruption can affect all of Earth's systems.
Lesson 2—Plants are more abundant on one side of this mountain.
Lesson 3—In order to meet people's need for water, an artificial river through the desert was designed and built.
Lesson 4—People planted trees and other plants on these roofs.

It also connects the investigative phenomena back to the anchoring phenomenon in each lesson.

Assessment

Unit Readiness Check: Are You Ready?
Lesson Quizzes: Can You Apply It?
Unit 5 Test
Performance-Based Assessment

Assessments are available in an editable, printable format or can be administered and auto-graded online.

01

Earth's Systems Interact

ANCHORING PHENOMENON
A volcanic eruption can affect all of Earth's systems.

ENGAGE Can You Explain It?
Students observe and ask questions about how lava interacts with air, water, land, and living things. They answer the Can You Explain It? question to identify what they will gather evidence about in the lesson.

EVALUATE Lesson Check
Students gauge their understanding of the anchoring phenomenon.

HANDS-ON ACTIVITY

EXPLORATION 1 Earth's Materials Form Systems **40 min**

Investigative Phenomenon Air, water, rock, and living things are components, or parts, of the Earth system.

Students connect back to the **anchoring phenomenon** that a volcanic eruption is one of many ways Earth materials, classified into systems, interact.

HANDS-ON ACTIVITY

EXPLORATION 2 Interactions of Systems Shape Landforms **40 min**

Investigative Phenomenon Some landforms are the result of changes to rock caused by water.

Students connect back to the **anchoring phenomenon** that systems like the hydrosphere and geosphere interact to affect landforms including water and lava interacting in a volcanic eruption.

EXPLORATION 3 Earth's Major Systems **20 min**

Investigative Phenomenon Earth's different systems have unique characteristics.

Students connect back to the **anchoring phenomenon** that the characteristics of Earth's different systems relates to how they interact in a volcanic eruption.

EXPLORATION 4 Natural Events Connect Systems **40 min**

Investigative Phenomenon Through energy and matter, a natural event that begins within a system can affect many others.

Students connect back to the **anchoring phenomenon** that Earth's systems interact in a volcanic eruption to affect surface materials and processes.

Making 3D Connections

The **anchoring phenomenon** in this lesson supports students' understanding of an application of these Next Generation Science Standards.

Building to the Performance Expectations

5-ESS2-1 Develop a model using an example to describe the ways the geosphere, biosphere, hydrosphere, and/or atmosphere interact.

SEP	DCI	CCC
Developing and Using Models Develop a model using an example to describe a scientific principle. *(Explorations 2, 3, 4)*	**ESS2.A Earth Materials and Systems** Earth's major systems are the geosphere (solid and molten rock, soil, and sediments), the hydrosphere (water and ice), the atmosphere (air), and the biosphere (living things, including humans). These systems interact in multiple ways to affect Earth's surface materials and processes. The ocean supports a variety of ecosystems and organisms, shapes landforms, and influences climate. Winds and clouds in the atmosphere interact with the landforms to determine patterns of weather. *(Explorations 1, 2, 3, 4)*	**Systems and System Models** A system can be described in terms of its components and their interactions. *(Explorations 1, 2, 3, 4)*

Vocabulary

Word Wall A word wall, anchor chart, or Language Development chart can be used to support vocabulary

atmosphere system made up of air that surrounds Earth

geosphere solid part of Earth

hydrosphere system that includes all of Earth's water in all three states

biosphere system that includes all living things, or life, on Earth

You may want to include additional academic terms such as *system* and any other terms students might struggle with.

Language Development Prompt students to complete the chart when they come to these highlighted terms within the lesson and to add their own terms as they come across unknown science terms.

Anchor Chart As you progress through the unit, you may want to make a vocabulary-based anchor chart using the Language Development chart as a guide that can be displayed and filled out as a whole group during each lesson.

01

Earth's Systems Interact

Activity Guide, pages 174–191

© Houghton Mifflin Harcourt Publishing Company ○ Image Credits: (c) ©USGS/Alamy

Students can engage in the Can You Explain It? content by observing the photograph or by exploring the corresponding video online.

View a video related to volcanic landforms.

ANCHORING PHENOMENON
A volcanic eruption can affect all of Earth's systems.

PHENOMENON EXPLAINED
Volcanic eruptions impact local environments the most. Some eruptions can affect the whole planet.

Lesson Objective

Students develop and use models to describe how Earth's systems interact and explore how those systems change and shape Earth's surface.

Support Discovery

The following prompts can be used to guide student-led discovery.

I notice . . .

After observing the photograph or watching the video, students should record what they noticed about the lava's interactions with the ocean. If students struggle to record observations, ask them to think about what happens when a warm liquid encounters a much colder substance or environment.

Sample answer: I see clouds where it meets the ocean; on land, it killed plants and other living things that couldn't move away.

I wonder . . .

After observing the photograph or watching the video, students should record what they want to find out more about volcanic eruptions.

Sample answer: I wonder how soil is changed by volcanic ash or contact with lava.

Can You Explain It?

In the Can You Explain It?, students make an initial claim that explains the **Anchoring Phenomenon**.

Sample answer: Volcanoes can heat the ocean, form new land, harm living things, and add gas and dust to the air.

Students will gather evidence about Earth's systems, also known as spheres. This will enable them to give a more complete explanation of the **Anchoring Phenomenon** at the end of the lesson.

Alternative Phenomenon

If students are unfamiliar with volcanoes, guide them to think of an interaction between spheres that is one to one. For example, discuss what happens to the solid geosphere of a sandy beach when a hurricane pummels it with waves and a storm surge for six hours. You may want to show a video of this type of event.

 SOCIAL EMOTIONAL LEARNING

Guide students to reflect on their goals from previous lessons and on any feedback they received from their teachers or peers. Then have each student set a personal goal for this lesson and make a plan for how to achieve the goal. Throughout the lesson, take daily breaks for students to track their progress in meeting their goals. As students move from lesson to lesson, they can continue to work towards their initial goals or set new ones. If students struggle setting goals for this lesson, share the following ideas: identifying Earth's systems, using models to explain how those systems interact, and ensuring everyone gets to share an idea during group work.

Ghost Forest

WHEN TO USE

SCIENCE **30** min

- Anchoring Phenomenon / Alternative Phenomenon
- Options for ELA Instruction
- Build on Prior Knowledge
- Preview the Phenomenon
- Read to Learn
- Support Sense Making
- Science Stretch
- Check for Comprehension

Option 1 Use before students begin the lesson in the Activity Guide to provide an engaging model to introduce the lesson's phenomenon.

Option 2 Use after students have completed the Activity Guide to reinforce students' understanding of the lesson phenomenon by exploring a related phenomenon.

ELA **20** min

- Options for ELA Instruction
- Build on Prior Knowledge
- Read to Learn

Option 3 To use during designated ELA Reading time for independent reading, whole-class instruction, or small-group instruction, look for this icon:  ELA

Plan

ANCHORING PHENOMENON / ALTERNATIVE PHENOMENON

The anchoring phenomenon in the Activity Guide is *A volcanic eruption can affect all of Earth's systems*. The main example is lava from a volcanic eruption that has reached the edge of the ocean. The FUNomenal Reader presents a similar phenomenon *(Certain groups of dead trees in the Northwest are evidence of a long-ago natural disaster)*, and the example is a "ghost forest" of dead cedar trees. Both present the same science concepts and cover the same standards but with different phenomena. Guide students to draw connections between the two situations and to understand the underlying principle: Earth's interacting systems change and shape Earth's surface.

Options for ELA Instruction ELA

Choose one of the following anchor chart options and project it or print copies. Then display and introduce the chart before reading the text. Revisit the chart after reading the text and encourage students to discuss how the skill connects to the text.

Point of View Use the *Point of View Anchor Chart* as you discuss point of view in the context of this story. Ask students who is telling the story (Jason). How do they think the story might be different if it were told from his grandmother's point of view?

Argument In the story, Jason gathers evidence to explain what happened to the cedar forest. Have students consult the online *Science and Engineering Practices Handbook* for more information on the claim-evidence-reasoning format. They can also use the *Parts of an Argument Anchor Chart* as a reference.

Text Features Have students refer to the *Text Features Anchor Chart* to help them identify the various text features in this story. As they page through the story, students should notice diagrams, a table, photos, and illustrations. Guide them to understand that these visual features help explain ideas in the text.

Preview

Build on Prior Knowledge As needed, review or introduce the names of Earth's main systems: atmosphere, hydrosphere, geosphere, biosphere. Have students discuss what kinds of things they notice about Earth's systems in their everyday lives. For example, they know that they need air to breathe, but they may not know how air interacts with Earth's other systems.

Preview the Phenomenon Ask students to study the illustration on page 2 of the story, which shows a boy taking a photo from a boat. Tree trunks are jutting out of the water around the boat. Encourage students to record the first questions that come into their minds about what might be happening. Point out that their questions might change as they read through the selection. Have them keep their questions at hand and periodically check to see if any can be answered.

STANDARDS SUPPORTED

SEP
Developing and Using Models

DCI
ESS2.A Earth Materials and Systems

CCC
Systems and System Models

Ghost Forest (continued)

Discover

Read to Learn

The **Read to Learn** suggestions inside the book's front cover encourage students to interact with the book multiple times for different purposes.

> **Preview** Students look for unfamiliar words and share them with a partner. New terms may include *sediment, tsunami,* and *subduction zone*. Have students look up words they aren't sure about and notice how they are used in the context of the story.

> **Skim** Students skim the illustrations and photos. Have them turn to a partner and share their predictions of what the story will be about.

> **Read** As students read the story, ask them to look for connections to one of the following anchor chart skills. **Point of View, Argument, Text Features**

Support Sense Making

Choose one or more of the following:

▶ Make sure students can identify the phenomenon presented on the opening pages of the story: Jason sees a forest of dead cedar-tree trunks submerged in water. The story is about his efforts to find out what killed the trees and when it happened. The steps he takes include talking to his grandmother, experimenting with plants, asking questions of a geologist, and doing online research.

▶ Encourage a student-led discussion of what Jason learned from his plant experiment. How did the results provide evidence to help him figure out what caused the "ghost forest"?

▶ Have interested students learn more about tsunamis and report their findings to the class. Discuss which of Earth's systems interact before a tsunami occurs. What are some effects on people, land, and buildings?

▶ Jason's grandmother makes a distinction between myth and oral history. Help students understand that a myth is a traditional story of unknown authorship that attempts to explain why or how something came to be. For example, a myth explains the dead forest as the result of a battle between Whale and Thunderbird, animals that represent water and storms. Discuss how the oral history Jason's grandmother shares is both similar to and different from the myth.

Extend

Science Stretch

The **Science Stretch** suggestions inside the book's back cover help students think about what they read. Students can complete one or more as time allows.

> Model an interaction among Earth's four major systems that takes place near you. **Sample answer:** My diagram shows how ocean currents (hydrosphere) in my area affect the air temperature (atmosphere).

> What strategies besides testing did Jason use to get evidence? **Sample answer:** Jason asked questions and did research.

> Find out how you should prepare for a natural disaster in your community. Have students work in small groups to find out what natural disasters are mostly likely and then make a list of the supplies they would keep on hand.

 SOCIAL EMOTIONAL LEARNING

Jason decided to ask about the family's emergency plan. How is that an example of responsible decision making? **Sample answer:** Responsible decision making involves identifying a problem, analyzing it, and finding a solution. Jason realized that an emergency could be a problem for his family and asked if they already had a solution like a plan.

Check for Comprehension Have students write three things they found out in this story, two things they found particularly interesting, and one question they still have about Earth's systems and how interactions among those systems led to the "ghost forest."

Earth Materials Form Systems

Activity Guide, pages 176–177

TIME ESTIMATE

40 min

....

SHORT ON TIME?

To save time, assign students two ecosystems to study and provide photos of those ecosystems.

POSSIBLE MATERIALS

☐ nature magazines

PREPARATION

Gather nature magazines or print images of ecosystems from the internet.

INVESTIGATIVE PHENOMENON
Air, water, rock, and living things are components, or parts, of the Earth system.

Phenomenon Explained Students explore the **investigative phenomenon** by comparing ecosystems and developing a way to classify Earth materials. They state a claim about how Earth systems interact and use evidence to support it.

Form a Question After viewing images of a reef and a forest, students should form a question about the how things found in very different environments are related. If students struggle to form a question, ask them to think about how the two environments pictured are related. **Sample answer:** What do these environments have in common?

STEP 1 Students choose and study two different ecosystems. They make a table and use it to sort the things they see into two categories. **Sample answers:** Categories might include living and nonliving things, or living things and resources.

STEP 2 Students identify things that are part of both ecosystems and describe how they interact. **Sample answer:** water and living things; Living things take in water to survive.

Discuss with students the **everyday phenomenon** of patterns in nature. Emphasize to students that categorizing parts of an ecosystem involves careful observation and analysis of patterns. Discuss patterns students observe every day that help them categorize things. Help students connect the patterns in natural systems around them to the **anchoring phenomenon** that a volcanic eruption is one of many ways Earth systems interact to affect surface materials.

- **Make a Claim** Claims should be about systems or features found in different environments, such as water, rocks, air, and living things.

- **Evidence** Students should cite evidence from the activity that supports their claim, such as their ecosystem research.

- **Reasoning** Students should explain their reasoning, such as similar systems must occur all over Earth.

FORMATIVE ASSESSMENT

MAKING SENSE OF PHENOMENA

Students gain understanding that air, water, rock, and living things are parts, or subsystems, of Earth as they explore the **investigative phenomenon.** They should connect this to the **anchoring phenomenon** that volcanic eruptions are a way Earth system interactions affect materials and organisms. Students should understand that classifying helps show patterns such as common items across ecosystems—air, water, rocks, and living things.

REMEDIATION If students struggle to connect the **investigative phenomenon** back to the **anchoring phenomenon,** have a class discussion in which students share what they learned about ecosystems in this activity.

MAKING SENSE OF PHENOMENA
IDEA ORGANIZER
After completing Exploration 1, students can fill in the **Idea Organizer** to summarize the connection between how air, water, rock, and living things are parts, or subsystems, of the Earth system and the anchoring phenomenon that a volcanic eruption affects many Earth systems.

Activity Outcome

Students should compare ecosystems to develop a way to classify Earth materials. They should also state a claim about how Earth systems interact and use evidence to support it.

Performance Indicators
compare ecosystems and classify Earth materials
make a claim about how Earth systems interact
support the claim using observations as evidence

Interactions of Systems Shape Landforms

Activity Guide, pages 178–181

TIME ESTIMATE

40 min

SHORT ON TIME?

As a class, generate a list of questions, then have small groups choose which one to investigate.

POSSIBLE MATERIALS

☐ plastic tray or box

☐ 20 sugar cubes

☐ modeling clay

☐ water and spray bottle

☐ book (about 4 cm thick)

☐ effervescent tablet

☐ paper towels

☐ goggles

Materials Alert This activity uses nontoxic, edible materials. To foster good safety practices, do not allow students to eat or lick the sugar cubes or effervescent tablets. Plastic trays may be borrowed from the lunch room with permission.

PREPARATION

Although the materials listed are a starting point for this activity, make sure there are enough materials to go around for each group to conduct their investigations.

INVESTIGATIVE PHENOMENON

Some landforms are the result of changes to rock caused by water.

Phenomenon Explained Students explore the **investigative phenomenon** by planning and conducting an investigation to model how the hydrosphere shapes landforms.

Form a Question After reading about the importance of water, students should form a question about modeling the effects of water on Earth's surface materials. If students struggle to form a question, ask them to think about effects of water they have observed. **Sample answer:** How does flowing water change landforms?

STEPS 1 and 2 Students choose a question and make a plan to investigate their question, write a summary, and get your approval. Make sure the plans support the materials that students identify they need. **Sample answer:** We'll model rock layers with sugar cubes and modeling clay. Then we'll pour water over them to see how they are affected. An effervescent tablet will represent a volcano eruption.

STEP 3 Students carry out their plan and record their data, which they display using a table, graphs, or poster. Help students identify the best way to present their data.

Students identify what the materials in their model represent, describe the changes they observe, and explain how the changes relate to the interactions between solid Earth materials and Earth's water.

Sample answer: Water washed away the sugar cubes, which represent weaker rock. The clay representing solid rock fell over when the weaker rock below it was removed. This model is a good representation of what I would expect to observe.

- **Make a Claim** Claims should relate to real world solid Earth materials and water, such as, water can affect solid Earth materials differently.

- **Evidence** Students should cite data from the activity as evidence, such as water "eroded" weaker sugar cubes, then layers above collapsed.

- **Reasoning** Students should reason that since their models represent real Earth materials and water, similar real world changes happen.

FORMATIVE ASSESSMENT

MAKING SENSE OF PHENOMENA

Students gain understanding that some landforms are the result of changes to rock caused by water as they explore the **investigative phenomenon.** They should connect this to the **anchoring phenomenon** that systems interact to affect surface materials and processes. Students should understand erosion by water represents one way that water and solid Earth interact, but this interaction can affect many Earth systems as it does when a volcano erupts.

REMEDIATION If students struggle to connect the **investigative phenomenon** back to the **anchoring phenomenon,** have them review the photo of the volcanic eruption and compare the changes occurring with those they modeled in the Exploration.

MAKING SENSE OF PHENOMENA IDEA ORGANIZER

After completing Exploration 2, students can fill in the **Idea Organizer** to summarize the connection between some landforms being the result of changes to rock caused by water and the anchoring phenomenon that systems interact to affect surface materials and processes.

Activity Outcome

Students plan and conduct an investigation to model how the hydrosphere shapes landforms. They also state a claim about solid Earth materials and water and use their data as evidence to support it.

 SOCIAL EMOTIONAL LEARNING

Encourage students to share with the class their strategies for making sure everyone's ideas were heard. List their ideas on the board. Invite volunteers to role-play group work situations and model how to use the strategies in those situations.

Performance Indicators	
	plan and conduct an investigation to model how the hydrosphere shapes landforms
	make a claim about how water affects solid Earth materials
	support the claim using collected data as evidence

Earth's Major Systems

Activity Guide, pages 182–183

TIME ESTIMATE

 20 min

INVESTIGATIVE PHENOMENON
Earth's different systems have unique characteristics.

Phenomenon Explained Students explore the **investigative phenomenon** by exploring the characteristics of each of Earth's major systems.

Systems on Earth

To help them understand what systems are, tell students that a system is a set of connected parts that interact to form a whole. Give them examples of other types of systems, such as the circulatory system in the body or a computer system in a business. Then have them name other examples of systems.

Atmosphere, Hydrosphere, Geosphere, & Biosphere

Students examine images and read descriptions of Earth's systems. They explain why Earth is both a single system and a system of other systems. **Sample answer:** The atmosphere, hydrosphere, geosphere, and biosphere are each made up of parts that interact. For example, producers and consumers are interacting components in the biosphere. Earth is one system in which four spheres interact. For example, matter from organisms cycles among the geosphere, atmosphere, and hydrosphere as organisms live and die.

Have students form pairs and study the pictures on these pages. Have them talk about a picture and discuss why it may have been chosen to represent, or model, that particular system. Ask students to name other images that could work to illustrate the same systems (for example, a blue sky for the atmosphere and a river for the hydrosphere).

FORMATIVE ASSESSMENT

MAKING SENSE OF PHENOMENA

Students gain understanding that Earth's different systems have unique characteristics as they explore the **investigative phenomenon.** They should connect this to the **anchoring phenomenon** that a volcanic eruption is one of many ways Earth systems interact to affect surface materials and processes. Students should understand that discussing systems (spheres) within the larger Earth system makes it easier to think about the many smaller interactions in a single larger event, such as a volcanic eruption.

REMEDIATION If students struggle to connect the **investigative phenomenon** back to the **anchoring phenomenon,** have them discuss with a partner the Earth systems represented by the photo of the volcanic eruption earlier in the lesson.

MAKING SENSE OF PHENOMENA
IDEA ORGANIZER
After completing Exploration 3, students can fill in the **Idea Organizer** to summarize the connection between Earth's different systems having unique characteristics and the anchoring phenomenon that a volcanic eruption is one of many ways Earth systems interact to affect surface materials and processes.

Natural Events Connect Systems

Activity Guide, pages 184–188

TIME ESTIMATE

40 min

INVESTIGATIVE PHENOMENON
Through energy and matter, a natural event that begins within a system can affect many others.

Phenomenon Explained Students explore the **investigative phenomenon** by exploring how a volcanic eruption can affect Earth's systems.

One Event, Many Systems

Students make a model that shows how the Pinatubo eruption interacted with living things, water, and the atmosphere. **Sample answer:** Models can show living things such as trees and animals (biosphere) killed by hot ash and gases; rain (hydrosphere) soaking ash and mudflows that likely polluted streams; and ash and grit blown high into the air (atmosphere).

Students identify the change that caused the lake to form and the Earth systems that interacted, and describe how they know. **Sample answer:** A stream was blocked by a large landslide, so the geosphere and hydrosphere interacted.

Students describe which system is most affected by a volcanic eruption, sharing their evidence and reasoning. **Sample answer:** The atmosphere is most affected. Ash is blown high and can circle the globe. The atmosphere is most affected because the area that is changed is huge.

Adding to the Atmosphere

Students describe events or processes that can cause matter and energy to flow into the atmosphere from other Earth systems. **Sample answer:** Volcanic eruptions add particles and gases to the atmosphere. Increased plant growth releases more waste gases into the air.

No Stopping the Biosphere

Show students an image of Earth from space and emphasize the expanse of green-covered land masses to illustrate the extent of living things on the planet. Then have students form groups to discuss how a sudden change in an Earth system may affect the biosphere.

Students identify claims about change and stability in the biosphere that can be supported using the Mount St. Helens pictures as evidence. **Sample answer:** Claims a. In time, a damaged environment can recover. and b. Ash and other volcanic matter are harmful to the environment.

SOCIAL EMOTIONAL LEARNING

After students discuss with a partner two events or processes that add matter or energy to the atmosphere, ask: How did talking with a partner help you? Give them an opportunity to share their experiences and look for other ways to provide them with opportunities to develop and practice positive communication skills.

A Home for the Hydrosphere

Students observe parts of the hydrosphere and identify two that might receive input due to a volcanic eruption. **Sample answer:** Students should circle "surface" due to possible melted glacier flows; and "air and clouds" due to possible water vapor from the eruption.

FORMATIVE ASSESSMENT ■ ■ ■ ■

MAKING SENSE OF PHENOMENA

Students gain understanding that through energy and matter, a natural event that begins within one system can affect others as they explore the **investigative phenomenon.** They should connect this to the **anchoring phenomenon** that Earth's systems interact to affect surface materials and processes. Students should understand that an eruption in the geosphere involves matter and energy that affect the atmosphere, biosphere, and hydrosphere.

REMEDIATION If students struggle to connect the **investigative phenomenon** back to the **anchoring phenomenon,** have them review the images and reread the captions in the Exploration.

MAKING SENSE OF PHENOMENA IDEA ORGANIZER
After completing Exploration 4, students can fill in the **Idea Organizer** to summarize the connection between how through energy and matter, a natural event that begins within a system can affect many others and the anchoring phenomenon that Earth's systems interact to affect surface materials and processes.

01

Take It Further

Engage • **Explore/Explain** • **Elaborate** • Evaluate

TIME ESTIMATE

60 min

....

These Take It Further paths may be completed to enrich and extend students' comprehension of content covered within this lesson.

ONLINE

The Coldest Summer

In this feature, students read about volcanic eruptions and explore how they serve as examples of interactions between the geosphere and other Earth systems.

Measuring Weather Across the Spheres

Students learn about different ways that scientists measure weather in different locations and ecosystems.

Monsoons

Students research and report on monsoons and how they are caused by the interactions of all Earth's spheres.

Careers in Science & Engineering: Agricultural Engineering

Students examine all the ways that agricultural engineers help to make farming sustainable, safe, and environmentally friendly.

Lesson Check

Can You Explain It?

Now I know or think that . . .

Sample answer: biosphere: living things; geosphere: lava, rock; hydrosphere: ocean, fog droplets; atmosphere: (invisible) air. Lava in the geosphere is killing organisms and heating the ocean. The ocean in the hydrosphere is cooling lava to form rock. The atmosphere has ash and dust from volcano eruption and is warmer and wetter from water boiling.

After completing the lesson, use the **Making Sense Idea Organizer** to summarize the connections between the **investigative phenomena** and the **anchoring phenomenon.**

Checkpoints

1. d—geosphere and atmosphere

2. atmosphere; hydrosphere

3. biosphere-plants, hydrosphere-ocean, geosphere-rock, atmosphere-air

4. c—Rainwater is used by plants and animals on the land.

5. hurricane: hydrosphere, atmosphere
    volcanic eruption: geosphere, atmosphere
    plant leaves: biosphere, atmosphere

6. Models should show exchanges of matter and energy such as ash, gases, and heat released from the volcano into the atmosphere; hot lava interacting with ocean water to harden into rock and produce steam; organisms being buried and burned by hot lava or flowing ash; and lava losing heat to the atmosphere.

MAKING CONNECTIONS

After students complete the lesson, they should be able to answer a question about an alternative phenomenon to identify the systems interacting in the photo of two rivers joining and explain how they know. **Sample answer:** hydrosphere and geosphere; The color of one river looks like lots of dirt is mixed in the water.

 SOCIAL EMOTIONAL LEARNING

Have students reflect on the concepts they have explored about Earth's systems and their interactions. Have students write a paragraph about what they enjoyed most during the lesson. Then with a partner, have them discuss something they were surprised to learn during the various explorations. Invite volunteers to share their responses.

02 Water in Earth's Systems

ANCHORING PHENOMENON
Plants are more abundant on one side of this mountain.

ENGAGE Can You Explain It?
Students observe and ask questions about the contrasting colors from one side of the island mountain range to the other. They answer the Can You Explain It? question to identify what they will gather evidence about in the lesson.

EVALUATE Lesson Check
Students gauge their understanding of the anchoring phenomenon.

HANDS-ON ACTIVITY

EXPLORATION 1 Water Moves Among Earth's Systems

Investigative Phenomenon Water moves among Earth's systems through natural processes.

Students connect back to the **anchoring phenomenon** that interactions between the atmosphere and the hydrosphere result in patterns of precipitation on the island mountain range.

HANDS-ON ACTIVITY

EXPLORATION 2 Water Stores Heat

Investigative Phenomenon Water can store and transport thermal energy.

Students connect back to the **anchoring phenomenon** that the interactions among Earth's systems, including those that caused the color pattern on the island mountain range, often involve transfers of energy and matter.

EXPLORATION 3 Earth's Water Sources

Investigative Phenomenon Water is not evenly distributed on Earth's surface.

Students connect back to the **anchoring phenomenon** that water availability on land is a factor in patterns of plant growth such as the patterns of green plant life on the island mountain range.

EXPLORATION 4 Water and the Environment

Investigative Phenomenon Water supports and shapes the environment.

Students connect back to the **anchoring phenomenon** that the hydrosphere interacts with other Earth systems and supports diverse ecosystems including those in the mountain range.

Making 3D Connections

The **anchoring phenomenon** in this lesson supports students' understanding of an application of these Next Generation Science Standards.

Building to the Performance Expectations

5-ESS2-1 Develop a model using an example to describe ways the geosphere, biosphere, hydrosphere, and/or atmosphere interact.

5-ESS2-2 Describe and graph the amounts and percentages of water and fresh water in various reservoirs to provide evidence about the distribution of water on Earth.

SEP

Using Mathematics and Computational Thinking
Describe and graph quantities such as area and volume to address scientific questions.
(Exploration 3)

DCI

ESS2.A Earth Materials and Systems Earth's major systems are the geosphere, the hydrosphere, the atmosphere, and the biosphere. These systems interact to affect Earth's surface materials and processes. The ocean supports a variety of ecosystems and organisms, shapes landforms, and influences climate. Winds and clouds in the atmosphere interact with the landforms to determine weather.
(Explorations 1, 2, 3, 4)

ESS2.C The Roles of Water in Earth's Surface Processes Nearly all of Earth's available water is in the ocean. Most fresh water is in glaciers or underground; only a tiny fraction is in streams, lakes, wetlands, and the atmosphere. *(Explorations 1, 3)*

CCC

Systems and System Models
A system can be described in terms of its components and their interactions.
(Explorations 1, 2, 3, 4)

Scale, Proportion, and Quantity
Natural objects exist from the very small to the immensely large.
(Exploration 3)

Vocabulary

| Word Wall | A word wall, anchor chart, or Language Development chart can be used to support vocabulary.

You may want to include additional academic terms such as *dissolve* and *current* and any other terms students might struggle with.

Language Development Prompt students to complete the chart when they come to these highlighted terms within the lesson and to add their own terms as they come across unknown science terms.

Anchor Chart As you progress through the unit, you may want to make a vocabulary-based anchor chart using the Language Development chart as a guide that can be displayed and filled out as a whole group during each lesson.

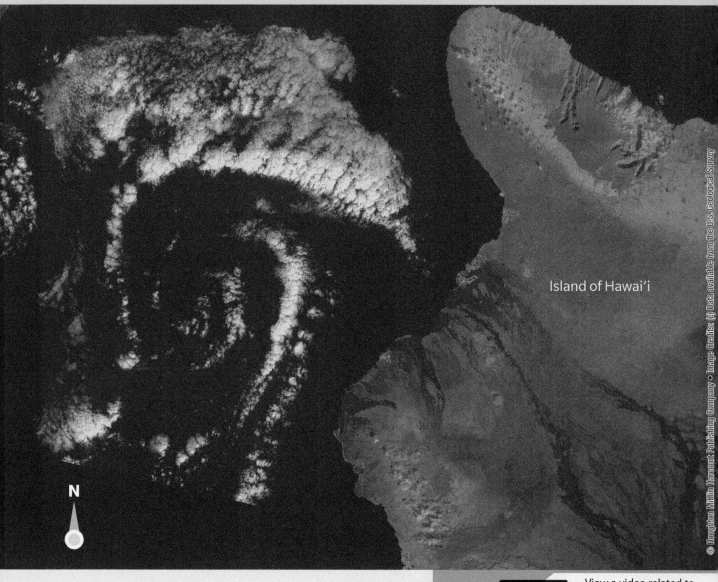

Island of Hawai'i

© Houghton Mifflin Harcourt Publishing Company • Image Credits: (j) Data available from the U.S. Geological Survey

Students can engage in the Can You Explain It? content by observing the photograph or by exploring the corresponding video online.

ONLINE

View a video related to patterns of vegetation and precipitation on the Hawaiian Islands.

ANCHORING PHENOMENON

Plants are more abundant on one side of this mountain.

PHENOMENON EXPLAINED

Wind patterns in the atmosphere and the elevation and orientation of the land cause more precipitation to fall on one side of the mountain. Plants are more abundant on the side with higher precipitation.

Lesson Objective

Students can use models and mathematical thinking to explore the distribution of water on Earth's surface and how the hydrosphere interacts with other Earth systems.

Support Discovery

The following prompts can be used to guide student-led discovery.

I notice . . .

After observing the photograph or watching the video, students should record what they noticed about the vegetation on either side of the Hawaiian mountain. If students struggle to record observations, point out the sides of the island.

Sample answer: I notice that one side of the mountain is dark green and the other side is mostly brown with only a few spots of green.

I wonder . . .

After observing the photograph or watching the video, students should record what they want to find out more about the processes that shape and color the land in places like Hawaii with volcanoes.

Sample answer: I wonder why the two sides look so different when they're so close together. Maybe the volcanoes are responsible for the different environments.

Can You Explain It?

In the Can You Explain It?, students make an initial claim that explains the **Anchoring Phenomenon**.
Sample answer: The weather patterns caused by the mountain produce more rain on one side than the other and claim that the rainy side has more plant growth.

Students will gather evidence about how water interacts with Earth systems. This will enable them to give a more complete explanation of the **Anchoring Phenomenon** at the end of the lesson.

Alternative Phenomenon

If students are unfamiliar with volcanic islands or the rain shadow effect, guide them to think about the lake effect on snowfall, coastal areas that receive fog or heavier precipitation than inland areas, or other examples of water evaporating from a large body of water and then falling on a nearby landmass.

SOCIAL EMOTIONAL LEARNING

Guide students to reflect on their goals from previous lessons and on any feedback they received from their teachers or peers. Then have each student set a personal goal for this lesson and make a plan for how to achieve the goal. Throughout the lesson, take daily breaks for students to track their progress in meeting their goals. As students move from lesson to lesson, they can continue to work towards their initial goals or set new ones. If students struggle setting goals for this lesson, share the following ideas: identify weather patterns caused by system interactions, using mathematical thinking to understand the distribution of water on Earth, and leading discussions on problem solving.

FUNomenal READER

Lost at Sea

SCIENCE 30 min

- Anchoring Phenomenon / Alternative Phenomenon
- Options for ELA Instruction
- Build on Prior Knowledge
- Preview the Phenomenon
- Read to Learn
- Support Sense Making
- Science Stretch
- Check for Comprehension

Option 1 Use before students begin the lesson in the Activity Guide to provide an engaging model to introduce the lesson's phenomenon.

Option 2 Use after students have completed the Activity Guide to reinforce students' understanding of the lesson phenomenon by exploring a related phenomenon.

ELA 20 min

- Options for ELA Instruction
- Build on Prior Knowledge
- Read to Learn

Option 3 To use during designated ELA Reading time for independent reading, whole-class instruction, or small-group instruction, look for this icon: ELA

Plan

ANCHORING PHENOMENON / ALTERNATIVE PHENOMENON

The anchoring phenomenon in the Activity Guide is *Plants are more abundant on one side of this mountain*. The main example is an aerial view of a Hawaiian mountain that has lush vegetation on one side and very little vegetation on the other side. The FUNomenal Reader presents a similar phenomenon (*Rubber ducks lost at sea traveled by ocean currents around the world*), and the example is a story about a girl who finds a rubber duck on a beach in Maine. Both present the same science concepts and cover the same standards but with different phenomena. Guide students to draw connections between the two situations and to understand the underlying principle: Earth's materials and systems interact with the hydrosphere in a variety of ways.

Options for ELA Instruction ELA

Choose one of the following anchor chart options and project it or print copies. Then display and introduce the chart before reading the text. Revisit the chart after reading the text and encourage students to discuss how the skill connects to the text.

Text Features Have students refer to the *Text Features Anchor Chart* to help them identify the various text features in this story. As they page through the story, students should notice maps, diagrams, and illustrations. Guide them to understand that these visual features help explain ideas in the text.

Learning Mindset Have student pairs study the *My Learning Mindset Anchor Chart* and then decide which of the traits describe Sage, the story's main character. Challenge partners to find where in the story she shows these traits. Have them consider if these are good traits for finding an answer to any question, not just one related to science.

Context Clues Use the *Context Clues Anchor Chart* if students struggle to understand the meaning of some words or terms in the story. Remind them to look for familiar word parts. For example, *gyre* has the same beginning as *gyrate*, which means "to revolve around a fixed point" or "to move in a spiral."

Preview

ELA **Build on Prior Knowledge** Most students will be familiar with the conveyor belts found at grocery-store checkouts. Help them relate that continuous, moving strip for transporting materials or packages from one place to another to the ocean conveyor belt, which is a constantly moving system of deep-ocean currents that moves water around the globe.

Preview the Phenomenon Ask students to study the illustration on pages 2–3 of the story, which shows a girl finding a rubber duck on a beach. Encourage students to record the first questions about this scene that come into their minds, focusing on how the toy might have ended up on the beach. Point out that their questions might change as they read through the story. Have them keep their questions handy and periodically check to see if any can be answered.

STANDARDS SUPPORTED

SEP

Developing and Using Models

Using Mathematics and Computational Thinking

DCI

ESS2.A Earth Materials and Systems

ESS2.C The Roles of Water in Earth's Surface Processes

CCC

Systems and System Models

Scale, Proportion, and Quantity

Lost at Sea (continued)

Discover

Read to Learn

The **Read to Learn** suggestions inside the book's front cover encourage students to interact with the book multiple times for different purposes.

> **Preview** Students look for unfamiliar words and share them with a partner. New terms may include *ocean current*, *gyre*, and *ocean conveyor belt*. Have students look up words they aren't sure about and notice how they are used in the context of the story.

> **Skim** Students skim the illustrations. Have them turn to a partner and share their predictions of what the story will be about.

> **Read** As students read the story, ask them to look for connections to one of the following anchor chart skills.
> **Text Features, Learning Mindset, Context Clues**

Support Sense Making

Choose one or more of the following:

▶ Be sure students can identify the phenomenon presented on the opening pages of the story: Sage finds a battered rubber duck on a beach. The story follows Sage's efforts to learn more about how the duck ended up on the beach. The steps she takes include doing online research and research in books, viewing museum displays, and asking questions of a museum guide.

▶ If feasible, bring a rubber duck to class and pass it around for students to examine. Discuss which physical properties of the object could have helped it survive an extended ocean journey, including size, mass, and buoyancy.

▶ Encourage students to think about ocean currents in terms of causes and effects. They may know that surface currents are caused by wind but not realize that slower ocean currents move heat energy from place to place. Help them understand that ocean currents interact with land and that the ocean conveyor belt moves heat energy from warm areas in the tropics toward the cooler areas at the poles.

▶ At the museum, Sage reads that oceanographers dropped "drift bottles" in the ocean with messages for people who found them. Encourage a student-led discussion of how those bottles were used to track ocean currents.

Extend

Science Stretch

The **Science Stretch** suggestions inside the book's back cover help students think about what they read. Students can complete one or more as time allows.

> Write a report about what might happen if the ocean conveyor belt stopped moving. You might want to have students write their reports in claim-evidence-reasoning format.

> Make a plan to model an ocean gyre. This activity works well with student pairs or small groups. The model might take the form of a diagram with labels, a demonstration, or a short skit.

> Conduct research to find other examples of times scientists followed objects lost at sea. Provide books and approved webpages for students to use in their research.

 SOCIAL EMOTIONAL LEARNING

Identify two ways that communication played an important role in the story. **Sample answer:** Sage asked questions and received answers, plus scientists communicated their findings to fishing boats to help them navigate.

Check for Comprehension Have students pause to think about ocean currents and then respond to the following prompts: *I became more aware of . . ., I didn't realize that . . ., I still don't understand . . .* Ask volunteers to share their responses with the class.

Water Moves Among Earth's Systems

Activity Guide, pages 194–196

TIME ESTIMATE

(50 min)

SHORT ON TIME?

Encourage students to divide up the different tasks in the activity, such as building the models and add the water, or to take turns conducting the steps.

POSSIBLE MATERIALS

- ☐ 2 plastic containers
- ☐ modeling clay
- ☐ measuring spoons
- ☐ measuring cup
- ☐ salt
- ☐ water
- ☐ dropper
- ☐ plastic wrap
- ☐ 2 rubber bands
- ☐ 2 small weights
- ☐ markers and tape

PREPARATION

In advance, gather the materials and distribute them to students prior to starting the activity. If possible, provide a variety of colors of modeling clay.

INVESTIGATIVE PHENOMENON
Water moves among Earth's systems through natural processes.

Phenomenon Explained Students explore the **investigative phenomenon** by modeling how water moves across Earth's systems. They state a claim about their models and use evidence to support it.

Form a Question After students read about rain and fresh water, they should form a question about movement of water and Earth's systems. If students struggle to form a question, ask them to recall their experiences with rain and moving water. **Sample answer:** Why isn't rain salty?

STEP 1 Students make two clay landforms models that include a lake. They infer why the models need to be identical. **Sample answer:** The landforms are identical so you can compare results fairly.

STEP 2 Explain to students that ¾ of Model A represents the ocean, but that area of Model B is empty. The remaining ¼ models land, a clay landform and lake. Students build their models, add water, and compare the water in the model lakes and oceans. **Sample answer:** The water in the model lakes is fresh and it's salty in the model ocean.

STEP 3 Students add plastic wrap and a weight to their models and place them in sunlight. After two hours, they record their observations and infer the importance of the plastic wrap. **Sample answer:** The plastic wrap provides a surface on which water droplets can form.

STEPS 4 and 5   Students compare the amounts of moisture under the plastic in the models and explain the cause. Sample answer: Model A had more drops on the plastic and water was deeper because the weight on top directed condensation to "rain" into the lake.

STEP 6   Students make and support a claim.

- **Make a Claim** Claims should indicate water evaporates, condenses, and falls as rain through the atmosphere onto the geosphere.

- **Evidence** Students should cite their observations as evidence, such as water condensed on the plastic wrap and fell over the clay.

- **Reasoning** Students should explain their reasoning that water moves in Earth's systems.

FORMATIVE ASSESSMENT

MAKING SENSE OF PHENOMENA

Students gain understanding that water moves among Earth's systems through natural processes as they explore the **investigative phenomenon.** They should connect this to the **anchoring phenomenon** that interactions between the atmosphere and the hydrosphere result in patterns of rain. Students should understand that, if water in the model evaporated from an ocean and then condensed and fell as rain nearby, similar processes might cause more rain on parts of the Hawaiian island.

REMEDIATION If students struggle to connect the **investigative phenomenon** back to the **anchoring phenomenon,** have them review what they learned in Lesson 1 about interactions between the atmosphere and the hydrosphere.

Activity Outcome

Students should make models in order to infer how water moves among Earth's systems and relate it back to the Hawaiian islands.

Performance Indicators		
	model how water moves among Earth's systems	
	make a claim about how water moves among systems	
	support the claim using observations as evidence	

MAKING SENSE OF PHENOMENA IDEA ORGANIZER

After completing Exploration 1, students can fill in the **Idea Organizer** to summarize the connection between water moving among Earth's systems through natural processes and the anchoring phenomenon that interactions between the atmosphere and the hydrosphere result in patterns of precipitation.

 SOCIAL EMOTIONAL LEARNING

Have a class discussion about the ways in which group members shared tasks so that everyone contributed equally. As volunteers share their strategies, encourage them to reflect on how effective the strategy was and ways it could be improved. As they share their reflections, remind students that each collaborative experience is an opportunity to self-assess and grow their skills.

Water Stores Heat

Activity Guide, pages 197–198

TIME ESTIMATE

45 min

SHORT ON TIME?

To save time, the collection of temperature data in this activity can be done by the whole class or as a teacher demonstration. Individual groups should record data, conduct the research, and answer the questions.

POSSIBLE MATERIALS

- ☐ 2 small plastic cups
- ☐ water
- ☐ soil
- ☐ heat lamp
- ☐ 2 thermometers
- ☐ timer or clock
- ☐ information resources - printed articles, reference books, digital devices with Internet access

Materials Alert Foster good safety habits by teaching students about how heat lamps work and cautioning them to not touch them.

PREPARATION

Students should wear gloves when handling the soil.

INVESTIGATIVE PHENOMENON
Water can store and transport heat energy.

Phenomenon Explained Students explore the **investigative phenomenon** by collecting data on the capacity of water and soil to store heat energy. They state a claim and use their collected data as evidence to support it.

Form a Question After reading about heat energy, students should form a question about heat energy, land, and water. If students struggle to form a question, suggest they consider asking a question about heat energy's effect on Earth systems. **Sample answer:** How does energy from the sun affect the temperatures of land and water each day?

STEPS 1 and 2 Students fill a plastic cup with water and another with soil. They place the cups under a heat lamp with a thermometer in each cup.

STEP 3 Students record the temperature of each after 20 minutes. Remind students not to touch the bulbs on the heat lamps. Then students turn off the lamp, wait 10 minutes, and record the temperatures.

Students research land breezes and sea breezes, and summarize their causes and effects. **Sample answer:** Land and sea breezes move air masses and trigger weather, including different forms of precipitation.

Have students discuss with their group members which Earth material heated up and cooled off faster.

- **Make a Claim** Claims should reflect interactions between heat energy, land, and water cause weather patterns.

- **Evidence** Students should cite as evidence the data from the activity that shows that the temperature of the soil increased and decreased faster than that of the water.

- **Reasoning** Students should explain their reasoning, such as that, like the soil and water in the cups, land must get warmer and cool faster than the ocean.

FORMATIVE ASSESSMENT ■ ■ ◻ ◻

MAKING SENSE OF PHENOMENA

Students gain understanding that the hydrosphere and geosphere can store heat energy as they explore the **investigative phenomenon.** They should connect to the **anchoring phenomenon** that the interactions among Earth's systems involve transfers of energy and matter. Students suggest uneven heating plus the Hawaiian island's interaction with the ocean and atmosphere as possibly causing a pattern of wet and dry areas.

REMEDIATION If students struggle to connect the **investigative phenomenon** back to the **anchoring phenomenon,** have them discuss with a partner which parts of the model or events in this activity represent land, oceans, and the transfer of heat energy.

MAKING SENSE OF PHENOMENA
IDEA ORGANIZER
After completing Exploration 2, students can fill in the **Idea Organizer** to summarize the connection between how water can store and transfer heat energy and the anchoring phenomenon that a Hawaiian island has color differences.

Activity Outcome

Students should collect data on the capacity of water and soil to store heat energy in order to state a claim about land and sea breezes. They should use their collected data as evidence to support their claim.

Performance Indicators
collect data on temperature changes of water and soil
make a claim that heat energy, land, and water cause weather patterns
support the claim using collected data as evidence

Earth's Water Sources

TIME ESTIMATE

Materials Alert Provide students with reference materials or Internet access to conduct research and colored pencils to complete the fresh water grid and key.

INVESTIGATIVE PHENOMENON
Water is not evenly distributed on Earth's surface.

Phenomenon Explained Students explore the **investigative phenomenon** by researching and modeling the distribution of water on Earth's surface.

Where on Earth Is The Water?

Everyday Phenomenon **Water makes up the hydrosphere.**

Discuss with students the **everyday phenomenon** of water making up the hydrosphere. Have students give examples of parts of the hydrosphere they have personally experienced in some way (oceans, seas, lakes, rivers, ponds, and so on). Remind students about what they learned in the previous lesson regarding ice and it being a part of the hydrosphere, too. Discuss where students think plants get the water they need to help students connect this topic to the **anchoring phenomenon** that plants are more abundant on one side of a Hawaiian island causing a color difference.

Water Distribution on Earth

Have students work in pairs to research the percentages of Earth's salt and fresh water. Then have them use math to complete the model showing all of Earth's water. Point out that the diagram shows 100% or all of the water found on Earth. The three light blue squares show $\frac{3}{100}$ to represent the fresh water found on Earth. The remainder is all salt water.

Have pairs work to complete the freshwater math. Lead students to understand this model shows the breakdown of the 3% of Earth's total water.

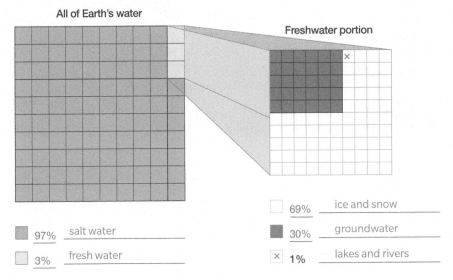

All of Earth's water

Freshwater portion

	97%	salt water
	3%	fresh water

	69%	ice and snow
	30%	groundwater
	1%	lakes and rivers

Misconception Alert Students may ask about the relationship between the water cycle and the amount of fresh and salt water on Earth. Runoff from precipitation contributes to the salinity in oceans. These minerals remain when water evaporates. The saltiest parts of the ocean occur where evaporation is highest and the amount of water is largest. Have students research the relationship between salinity and the size of the oceans. Encourage them to use math and computational thinking to graph the data and share with the class.

Explain to students that competition occurs between organisms that need the same limited resource to survive. Then have students describe how they could use math to show competition for a limited resource. **Sample answer:** Add a graph that compares fresh water available and fresh water needed by different desert animals.

FORMATIVE ASSESSMENT

MAKING SENSE OF PHENOMENA

Students gain understanding that water is not evenly distributed on Earth's surface as they explore the **investigative phenomenon.** They should connect this to the **anchoring phenomenon** that plants are more abundant on one side of the mountain. Students should infer that the difference in the Hawaiian island's color is related to differences in the amount of fresh water falling and adding to surface water and groundwater.

REMEDIATION If students struggle to connect the **investigative phenomenon** back to the **anchoring phenomenon,** suggest they consider how uneven amounts of water on the Hawaiian island would affect plants.

MAKING SENSE OF PHENOMENA IDEA ORGANIZER

After completing Exploration 3, students can fill in the **Idea Organizer** to summarize the connection between water not being evenly distributed on Earth's surface and the anchoring phenomenon that water availability on land is a factor in patterns of plant growth on a Hawaiian island.

Water and Earth's Surface

Activity Guide, pages 201–204

TIME ESTIMATE

45 min

Materials Alert You may wish to have a globe or world map available to aid students in understanding the movement of ocean currents and in locating regions likely to have rain shadows.

> **INVESTIGATIVE PHENOMENON**
> Water supports and shapes the environment.

Phenomenon Explained Students explore the **investigative phenomenon** by exploring how water affects the geosphere and biosphere and analyzing how the interaction of the atmosphere, hydrosphere, biosphere, and geosphere results in the rain shadow effect.

Water Shaping Land

Students read about how water affects Earth's systems and summarize a change caused by water. Then they make an argument for a community to control or stop the change. **Sample answer:** Currents along the ocean shore damage sandy beaches. Our tourism-dependent community needs to preserve the beach as a site for recreation.

Heat Energy, Water, and Wind

Students share what they know about how the ocean affects weather and climate with a partner.

Help students as needed to interpret the map of ocean currents. Ask them to identify the equator on the map and note where the north and south poles would be in relation to the equator. Have them describe what the arrows indicate about the water temperature. Clarify that the hottest water is closest to the equator, and the water cools down as it moves north.

Then have students describe how they think air flowing from over the ocean to over the land affects the weather on land. **Sample answer:** The air cools or warms what it passes over land. Moist, warm air can cause rain to fall on land.

Students discuss how the geosphere affects winds and rain cloud motion. Then they analyze a rain shadow effect diagram and explain how the atmosphere, geosphere, and hydrosphere interact, providing evidence and reasoning in their answer. **Sample answer:** The hydrosphere adds water to the atmosphere. Air interacting with the geosphere causes water vapor to condense and fall as rain on the ocean-facing side of a mountain. This allows plants (biosphere) to flourish. The air is drier as it moves down the other side, so there's little or no rain. Fewer plants grow.

SOCIAL EMOTIONAL LEARNING

Challenge students to identify a water-caused change in their own community and look for ways to control or stop that change. Discuss the relationship between how scientists and engineers argue and how students think about arguing in everyday life. Effective scientific arguments are communicated respectfully, supported by evidence, and revised as new evidence becomes available.

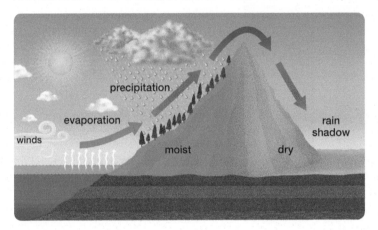

precipitation
evaporation
winds
moist
dry
rain shadow

Water Needed for Life

Students infer why light level determines what can live in an ocean zone.
Sample answer: Light affects how much food producers can make.

FORMATIVE ASSESSMENT

MAKING SENSE OF PHENOMENA

Students gain understanding that water supports and shapes the environment as they explore the **investigative phenomenon.** They should connect this to the **anchoring phenomenon** that the hydrosphere interacts with other Earth's systems and supports diverse ecosystems. Students should conclude that a rain shadow effect causes the plant growth color difference on the Hawaiian island as warm ocean currents and prevailing winds bring rain to only one side of a mountain.

REMEDIATION If students struggle to connect the **investigative phenomenon** back to the **anchoring phenomenon,** have them review the photo of the Hawaiian island mountain and note its location relative to the ocean and prevailing winds.

MAKING SENSE OF PHENOMENA IDEA ORGANIZER
After completing Exploration 4, students can fill in the **Idea Organizer** to summarize the connection between how water supports and shapes the environment and the anchoring phenomenon that the hydrosphere interacts with other Earth's systems and supports diverse ecosystems, including dense plant growth on a Hawaiian mountain side.

Engage • Explore/Explain • **Elaborate** • Evaluate

TIME ESTIMATE

45 min

These Take It Further paths may be completed to enrich and extend students' comprehension of content covered within this lesson.

ONLINE

People in Science & Engineering: Kang Hu

Students read about Kang Hu, an engineer from China who now lives and works in the United States. His career includes work in desalination.

Engineer It! Rainwater Harvest

Students engineer a model rain barrel for collecting and storing rainwater for practical uses at another time.

Gray Water

Students find out about how to reuse water that has been used for washing, which is clean enough to use for some things but not clean enough to drink or bathe in.

Lesson Check

Activity Guide, pages 205–207

Engage • Explore/Explain • Elaborate • **Evaluate**

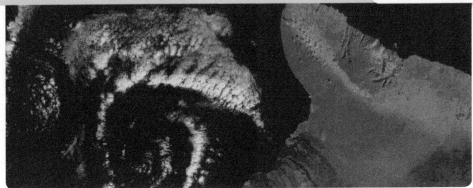

Can You Explain It?

Now I know or think that . . .

Sample answer: Water evaporates from the ocean, leaving salt behind; the moisture may fall as rain. Land and water temperature differences can cause winds and other weather. Warm, moist wind from the ocean interacts with a mountain range. It produces rain on the ocean-facing side and a rain shadow on the opposite side. More plants grow on the wetter side of the mountain.

After completing the lesson, use the **Making Sense Idea Organizer** to summarize the connections between the **investigative phenomena** and the **anchoring phenomenon.**

MAKING CONNECTIONS

After students complete the lesson, they should be able to answer a question about an alternative phenomenon to explain the interactions with water that might happen on the farm near a river.

Sample answer: River flooding could leave behind new soil and damage crops. Fertilizer, pesticide, and soil could be washed into the river.

Checkpoints

1. warm water; equator; poles; cold water; equator

2. **Sample answer:** Models should show the rain shadow effect with wind moving air in a path from the ocean to the land, interacting with a mountain to produce rain on the ocean-facing side and a rain shadow on the opposite side.

3. **Sample answer:** More rain would fall because more water would evaporate from the saltwater reservoir, then condensing to fall on the land.

4. b—land and sea breezes

5. a—90% salt water, 10% fresh water

6. **Sample answer:** The water is fresh because its source is rain that was soaked up by the ground.

7. **Sample answer:** Temperature; some organisms may not be suited to cold polar water currents or warm tropical water currents.

8. **Sample answer:** The desert does not get much rain, so it has few plants. The green forest receives enough rain for plants to grow.

 SOCIAL EMOTIONAL LEARNING

Have students reflect on the hands-on activities they explored throughout the lesson. As a class, discuss the need for responsible decision-making for the sake of safety and for other reasons. Have small groups or partners brainstorm a list of responsible actions students can take when doing hands-on activities. Then use the results to create a class list of ideas.

LESSON

03 Resource Use Affects the Environment

ANCHORING PHENOMENON

In order to meet people's need for water, an artificial river through the desert was designed and built.

ENGAGE Can You Explain It?

Students observe and ask questions about a desert aqueduct. They answer the Can You Explain It? question to identify what they will gather evidence about in the lesson.

EVALUATE Lesson Check

Students gauge their understanding of the anchoring phenomenon.

HANDS-ON ACTIVITY

EXPLORATION 1 Squeaky Clean Water (80 min)

Investigative Phenomenon People use technology to clean water before and after they use it.

Students connect back to the **anchoring phenomenon** that people often must transport or alter resources, such as water, before they can be used.

HANDS-ON ACTIVITY

EXPLORATION 2 Getting to a Resource (45 min)

Investigative Phenomenon Over time, extracting a resource requires more work for less return and causes more change.

Students connect back to the **anchoring phenomenon** that people can change the environment as they work to extract scarce resources.

EXPLORATION 3 Earth's Resources and Human Activities (30 min)

Investigative Phenomenon Earth's resources are things found in nature that people need.

Students connect back to the **anchoring phenomenon** that unwanted changes to the environment may occur in the pursuit of natural resources.

EXPLORATION 4 Getting and Using Resources (35 min)

Investigative Phenomenon Meeting human needs in housing, agriculture, and industry affects the environment.

Students connect back to the **anchoring phenomenon** that people change the environment as they use natural resources, but human impact can be minimized.

Making 3D Connections

The **anchoring phenomenon** in this lesson supports students' understanding of and application of these Next Generation Science Standards.

Building to the Performance Expectations

5-ESS3-1 Obtain and combine information about ways individual communities use science ideas to protect the Earth's resources and environment.

SEP	DCI	CCC

Obtaining, Evaluating, and Communicating Information
Obtain and combine information from books and/or other reliable media to explain phenomena or solutions to a design problem. *(Explorations 1, 3, 4)*

ETS1.C Optimizing the Design Solution Different solutions need to be tested in order to determine which of them best solves the problem, given the criteria and the constraints. *(Explorations 1, 2)*

ESS3.C Human Impacts on Earth Systems Human activities in agriculture, industry, and everyday life have had major effects on the land, vegetation, streams, ocean, air, and even outer space. But individuals and communities are doing things to help protect Earth's resources. *(Explorations 1, 2, 3, 4)*

Science Addresses Questions About the Natural and Material World Science findings are limited to questions that can be answered with empirical evidence. *(Explorations 1, 2, 3, 4)*

Systems and System Models
A system can be described in terms of its components and their interactions. *(Explorations 1, 2, 3, 4)*

Vocabulary

| Word Wall | A word wall, anchor chart, or Language Development chart can be used to support vocabulary.

You may want to include additional academic terms such as *contaminated* and any other terms students might struggle with.

Language Development Prompt students to complete the chart when they come to these highlighted terms within the lesson and to add their own terms as they come across unknown science terms.

Anchor Chart As you progress through the unit, you may want to make a vocabulary-based anchor chart using the Language Development chart as a guide that can be displayed and filled out as a whole group during each lesson.

03 Resource Use Affects the Environment

Activity Guide, pages 208–225

Students can engage in the Can You Explain It? content by observing the photograph or by exploring the corresponding video online.

ONLINE

View a video related to an aqueduct in a dry environment.

ANCHORING PHENOMENON

In order to meet people's need for water, an artificial river through the desert was designed and built.

PHENOMENON EXPLAINED

The aqueduct is a designed system. It was built, at great cost to people and the environment, to move water long distances to where it is needed.

Lesson Objective

Students obtain information to explain how human activities affect Earth's systems and its resources.

Support Discovery

The following prompts can be used to guide student-led discovery.

I notice . . .

After observing the photograph or watching the video, students should record what they noticed about the aqueduct. If students struggle to record observations, ask them to think about what is unusual about this large body of water in a dry environment.

Sample answers: The fields look very dry, the river's sides are unusually smooth, and it seems to start suddenly at a building.

I wonder . . .

After observing the photograph or watching the video, students should record what they want to find out more about aqueducts and resource use on islands.

Sample answer: How much effort is required to get fresh water and send it to where it's needed? Islands are surrounded by salt water, so getting fresh water might be hard.

Can You Explain It?

In the Can You Explain It?, students make an initial claim that explains the **Anchoring Phenomenon.**

Sample answer: People drill, mine, dig, and process geosphere materials to extract resources.

Students will gather evidence about getting and using resources. This will enable them to give a more complete explanation of the **Anchoring Phenomenon** at the end of the lesson.

Alternative Phenomenon

If students are unfamiliar with irrigation aqueducts (artificial rivers), guide them to think of other examples of things designed to transport resources over a distance, such as logging roads and high-voltage, cross-country electric wires. You may want to bring pictures of these examples to class so that students can observe how these resources function and interact with surrounding environments.

 SOCIAL EMOTIONAL LEARNING

Guide students to reflect on their goals from previous lessons and on any feedback they received from their teachers or peers. Then have each student set a personal goal for this lesson and make a plan for how to achieve the goal. Throughout the lesson, take daily breaks for students to track their progress in meeting their goals. As students move from lesson to lesson, they can continue to work towards their initial goals or set new ones. If students struggle setting goals for this lesson, share with them some of the following ideas: identifying how human activities and resource use affect the environment, communicating information, or persevering when a test or solution does not work as expected.

FUNomenal READER
X Is for Xeriscaping

WHEN TO USE

SCIENCE **30 min**

- Anchoring Phenomenon / Alternative Phenomenon
- Options for ELA Instruction
- Build on Prior Knowledge
- Preview the Phenomenon
- Read to Learn
- Support Sense Making
- Science Stretch
- Check for Comprehension

Option 1 Use before students begin the lesson in the Activity Guide to provide an engaging model to introduce the lesson's phenomenon.

Option 2 Use after students have completed the Activity Guide to reinforce students' understanding of the lesson phenomenon by exploring a related phenomenon.

ELA **20 min**

- Options for ELA Instruction
- Build on Prior Knowledge
- Read to Learn

Option 3 To use during designated ELA Reading time for independent reading, whole-class instruction, or small-group instruction, look for this icon: 🔖 **ELA**

Plan

ANCHORING PHENOMENON / ALTERNATIVE PHENOMENON

The anchoring phenomenon in the Activity Guide is *In order to meet people's need for water, an artificial river through the desert was designed and built.* The main example is an irrigation aqueduct, or artificial river, in the middle of a dry environment. The FUNomenal Reader presents a similar phenomenon (*To reduce water usage, one school limited its green space*), and the example is a story about a school that uses xeriscaping techniques to help reduce its water usage. Both present the same science concepts and cover the same standards but with different phenomena. Guide students to draw connections between the two situations and to understand the underlying principle: humans use Earth's resources and have an impact on Earth and its systems.

Options for ELA Instruction ELA

Choose one of the following anchor chart options and project it or print copies. Then display and introduce the chart before reading the text. Revisit the chart after reading the text and encourage students to discuss how the skill connects to the text.

Summarize After reading, have students use the *Summarize Anchor Chart* as a guide for summarizing the story. Help them notice the section headings throughout and summarize each section, removing unnecessary details. Remind them that a summary should be no more than about one-third as long as the original.

Make Connections Display the *Make Connections Anchor Chart* to help students relate what they read to their own experiences, to other stories they have read, and to the larger world. Give them these sentence starters: *This reminds me of when I..., This is like another story I read..., This is like something that happened in my community...*

Narrative Nonfiction Use the *Narrative Nonfiction Anchor Chart* to discuss the format of this story. Help students recognize that the story presents factual information and is written as a newspaper article, but it includes a fictional setting and characters.

Preview

ELA **Build on Prior Knowledge** Students already know that they use natural resources every day. Have them make a list of the ones they commonly use, such as air to breathe and water to drink, bathe in, and wash things. But they may not realize that natural resources are also being used up to make clothes for people to wear and technology for people to use.

Preview the Phenomenon Ask students to study the illustration on pages 2–3 of the story, which shows a boy and girl holding awards. Encourage students to record the first questions that come into their minds, focusing on how those awards might relate to the topic of resource use. Point out that their questions might change as they read through the story. Have them keep their questions handy and periodically check to see if any can be answered.

STANDARDS SUPPORTED

SEP
Obtaining, Evaluating, and Communicating Information

DCI
ESS3.C Human Impacts on Earth Systems

ETS1.C Optimizing the Design Solution

CCC
Science Addresses Questions About the Natural and Material World

Systems and System Models

X Is for Xeriscaping (continued)

Discover

Read to Learn ELA

The **Read to Learn** suggestions inside the book's front cover encourage students to interact with the book multiple times for different purposes.

> **Preview** Students look for unfamiliar words and share them with a partner. New terms may include *plaque, xeriscape,* and *drought.* Have students look up words they aren't sure about and notice how they are used in the context of the story.

> **Skim** Students skim the headings, illustrations, and captions. Have them turn to a partner and share what type of selection they think this is.

> **Read** As students read the story, ask them to look for connections to one of the following anchor chart skills. **Summarize, Make Connections, Narrative Nonfiction**

Support Sense Making

Choose one or more of the following:

▶ Be sure students can identify the phenomenon presented on the opening pages of the story: school leaders are worried about increasing water bills and want to solve the problem. The story follows the school's efforts, sparked by ideas from its fifth-grade science students, to investigate and implement water-saving methods.

▶ Have student pairs recall the ways they have used Earth's natural resources so far today. If students have trouble coming up with ideas, give a few examples; air to breathe, water to wash in or drink, and paper to write on. Challenge students to think about the lights they turn on and off, and where their books and chairs come from.

▶ Encourage a student-led discussion of what the fifth-graders in the story do to address the problem. Make a list on the board, which should include touring the building and making a map of water use, learning how to read the water meter and graphing usage, making a list of tips for saving water, listening to an expert, and making a proposal.

▶ Have interested students do research to learn more about xeriscaping and report their finding to the class. Discuss if such methods would be feasible in your area.

Extend

Science Stretch

The **Science Stretch** suggestions inside the book's back cover help students think about what they read. Students can complete one or more as time allows.

> Make a plan for starting a water-conservation program at your school. **Sample answer:** I would begin by doing a survey of water usage at my school.

> Do research about plants that are native to your area. Provide appropriate books or a set of links to approved webpages for students to use in their research.

> Find out what an environmental footprint is and what people can do to make theirs smaller. You might want to have students work in small groups and then report their findings to the class.

 SOCIAL EMOTIONAL LEARNING

How did the people in this story work together to solve a problem? **Sample answer:** The students worked together to come up with a plan, which the principal, superintendent, and school board reviewed and revised. The community held a fundraiser to help make it possible.

Check for Comprehension Have students write a paragraph that explains how the steps taken by East Millsburg Elementary School are designed to use less water and save money.

Engineer It • Squeaky Clean Water

Activity Guide, pages 210–213

TIME ESTIMATE

SHORT ON TIME?
Consider providing a filtration system for students to improve and test. Or you may wish to complete the activity as a whole class.

POSSIBLE MATERIALS

- ☐ 250 mL of dirty water
- ☐ graduated cylinder
- ☐ large jar
- ☐ rubber bands, stirring sticks, gauze squares, wire screen, coffee filters, cotton balls, paper towels, or gravel
- ☐ soil, grass, oil, pepper, orange rinds, etc., to make dirty water

Material Alert Remind students never to drink the water. Have students wash their hands afterward. Guide students to discard or recycle used materials.

PREPARATION
Prepare dirty water ahead of time. Prepare research materials for students.

INVESTIGATIVE PHENOMENON
People use technology to clean water before and after they use it.

Phenomenon Explained Students explore the **investigative phenomenon** by designing, building, and testing a water filtration system. They state a claim and use observations to support it.

Form a Question After they read about clean drinking water, students should form a question about cleaning water. If students struggle to form a question, ask them to consider what it takes to clean the water they drink. **Sample answer:** How many times does water need to be filtered to be clean enough to drink?

Explore

STEPS 1–3 Students research water filtration system define the problem, and brainstorm solutions. Review the meaning of "criteria" and "constraints." Make sure students understand that they'll be allowed to use only what they can afford. **Sample answer:** Criteria: Make a water filtration system to clean contaminated water; clarity 10 or less. Constraints: Must keep at least 200 mL of water; budget of $10.

Make and Test

STEP 4 Remind students to use the image to judge their water clarity after each step, and record their observations in the table. Students should use the photo of the five jars as a reference to determine the water clarity level.

Improve and Test

STEPS 5 and 6 Students analyze their results and recommend improvements. Have each group present their results to the class. Then, discuss which solutions worked best and why.

25   20   15   10   5

- **Make a Claim** Claims should reflect investigation results, such as that dirty water can be cleaned using a coffee filter and pebbles.

- **Evidence** Students should cite as evidence their observations from the activity, such as that each time they ran the water through the filter, it went down one level on the clarity scale.

- **Reasoning** Students should explain their reasoning, such as that the coffee filter and pebbles removed some dirt from the water each time it was filtered.

FORMATIVE ASSESSMENT ▪ ▫ ▫ ▫

MAKING SENSE OF PHENOMENA

Students gain understanding that people use technology to clean water before and after they use it as they explore the **investigative phenomenon.** They should connect this to the **anchoring phenomenon** that people change the environment as they use natural resources such as water to meet their needs and wants. Students should infer that people sometimes use systems to change or clean resources like water so they can be used safely.

REMEDIATION If students struggle to connect the **investigative phenomenon** back to the **anchoring phenomenon,** have a discussion about how students think their community provides clean water to its residents. They can think about how the water must be changed from its extracted form to be used safely.

Activity Outcome

Students should design, build, and test a water filtration system. They should also state a claim and use observations to support it.

Performance Indicators	
	design, build, and test a water filtration system
	make a claim based on investigation results
	support the claim using observations as evidence

MAKING SENSE OF PHENOMENA IDEA ORGANIZER

After completing Exploration 1, students can fill in the **Idea Organizer** to summarize the connection between how people use technology to clean water before and after they use it and the anchoring phenomenon that people change the environment as they use natural resources such as water to meet their needs and wants.

 SOCIAL EMOTIONAL LEARNING

After student partners discuss something that they learned from their design that didn't work, have them reflect quietly on the emotions they experienced during the process. Have students discuss with their partners how professional engineers might feel when designs don't work and what actions engineers might take.

Engineer It • Getting to a Resource

Activity Guide, pages 214–215

TIME ESTIMATE

45 min

....

SHORT ON TIME?

This activity can be done as a whole class activity or teacher demonstration to save time.

POSSIBLE MATERIALS

- ☐ sponge circle
- ☐ 2 clear plastic cups
- ☐ water
- ☐ paper towels
- ☐ graduated cylinder
- ☐ funnel
- ☐ pencil

PREPARATION

Cut sponges into circles to fit snuggly in the bottom of the cups.

INVESTIGATIVE PHENOMENON
Over time, extracting a resource requires more work for less return and causes more change.

Phenomenon Explained Students explore the **investigative phenomenon** by modeling the extraction of a resource.

Form a Question Students should form a question about getting a resource. If they struggle, have them consider how much effort it takes to get resources. Sample answer: How do the effort to get a resource and the amount of a resource harvested change over time?

STEPS 1 and 2 Students use a cup containing a sponge soaked with water to model a resource. They try three methods to remove the water, each time measuring the water removed. Allow students to interpret the method descriptions, or model the methods for students.

- **Make a Claim** Claims should indicate that the scarcer some resources become, the more effort and tools needed to get them.

- **Evidence** Students should cite their measurements as evidence that the amount of resource harvested decreases.

- **Reasoning** Students should relate the methods—pouring, pencil end, hand—and effort used in the model to real world drilling and mining methods. Students should also relate the amount of the resource harvested with each method.

FORMATIVE ASSESSMENT

MAKING SENSE OF PHENOMENA

Students gain understanding that, over time, extracting a resource requires more work for less return and causes more change as they explore the **investigative phenomenon.** They should connect this to the **anchoring phenomenon** that people use systems like the aqueduct to get and use resources. Students should understand that obtaining resources often gets more difficult over time and requires more complicated systems.

REMEDIATION If students struggle to connect the **investigative phenomenon** back to the **anchoring phenomenon,** have them review and discuss their results with a partner.

MAKING SENSE OF PHENOMENA
IDEA ORGANIZER

After completing Exploration 2, students can fill in the **Idea Organizer** to summarize the connection between how, over time, extracting a resource requires more work for less return and causes more change and the anchoring phenomenon that people change the environment as they use natural resources such as water to meet their needs and wants.

Activity Outcome

Students should model the extraction of a resource.

Performance Indicators
model the extraction of a resource
make a claim that effort increases and harvest decreases over time
support the claim using collected data as evidence

Earth's Resources and Human Activities

Activity Guide, pages 216–219

TIME ESTIMATE

Materials Alert Provide access to computers so students can use Internet resources to do research on how items are made.

INVESTIGATIVE PHENOMENON
Earth's resources are things found in nature that people need.

Phenomenon Explained Students explore the **investigative phenomenon** by exploring the types, characteristics, and uses of natural resources.

To compete a table, students identify human needs, items that meet the needs, and resources used to make the items.

Everyday Phenomenon **People use resources in many ways every day.**

Have students form pairs and recall the **everyday phenomena** of how they've used resources today. If students struggle, give examples: air to breathe, plants to eat, and paper to write on. Challenge students to think about resources used to get to school and to see at home after dark.

Lead them to connect the topic to the **anchoring phenomenon** that people change the environment as they get and use natural resources such as water to meet their needs and wants.

Results of Use

Have students compare and contrast renewable and nonrenewable resources. Have students list other uses for wood. **Sample answer:** Other uses of wood include paper, pencils, furniture, and fuel.

After students read about coal and water, they identify another resource delivered through a system and the need it meets. Sample answer: Natural gas is delivered through a system of pipes. People burn natural gas to heat homes and to cook food.

Complex Resource Situations

Ask students to write for themselves a personal or family value that affects resource use, for example, choosing whether to recycle.

Soil

After students read about negative effects of using resources, discuss agriculture's importance. **Ask:** Even though agriculture has negative impacts, do its benefits outweigh its negative effects? Why or why not? Sample answer: Yes, people need food. Bad effects can be minimized.

SOCIAL EMOTIONAL LEARNING

Model ways students can effectively communicate with a partner, such as taking turns to speak and repeating what was said back to the speaker. Then encourage students to apply what they learned when they talk with their partner and work together to add to their tables.

FORMATIVE ASSESSMENT

MAKING SENSE OF PHENOMENA

Students gain understanding that Earth's resources are things found in nature that people need as they explore the **investigative phenomenon.** They should connect this to the **anchoring phenomenon** that people build systems like the aqueduct to get and use natural resources such as water to meet their needs and wants. Students should understand that these systems can cause some unwanted changes to the environment.

REMEDIATION If students struggle to connect the **investigative phenomenon** back to the **anchoring phenomenon,** have them review the images and captions in this Exploration.

MAKING SENSE OF PHENOMENA IDEA ORGANIZER

After completing Exploration 3, students can fill in the **Idea Organizer** to summarize the connection between Earth's resources being things found in nature that people need and the anchoring phenomenon that people change the environment as they get and use natural resources such as water to meet their needs and wants.

Getting and Using Resources

Activity Guide, pages 220–222

TIME ESTIMATE

Misconception Alert Some students may think that space debris can be seen from Earth with a naked eye, since the space debris is closer to Earth than the stars. Scientists know space debris is out there not because of seeing it from Earth, but because of pictures taken of it from satellites orbiting Earth.

> **INVESTIGATIVE PHENOMENON**
> Meeting human needs in housing, agriculture, and industry affects the environment.

Phenomenon Explained Students explore the **investigative phenomenon** by exploring how people change the environment and space as they meet their needs and use natural resources.

Humans Cause Changes

Students work in a group to list at least two ways humans change the environment. **Sample answer:** Humans remove fish and other organisms from the oceans, lakes, and rivers for food. Humans burn fuels to travel and to manufacture things.

Space Junk

Remind students that the debris in space is an example of human impact on one of Earth's resources. Therefore, it is our responsibility as humans to remove the junk.

As a class, brainstorm a list of space elements any device for cleaning up space debris must withstand, such as radiation and internal pressure. Then, have students work in groups to design a device to clean up space debris. They should describe what the device will do and how the parts will work together as a system. Ask a volunteer from each group to show the design and explain how it would work. Encourage classmates to ask questions and offer constructive criticism. Designs should show the interactions among the parts that make up the whole.

Medium-Rare or None?

Students conduct research and provide an argument with evidence to support their ideas about whether or not Americans should eat less meat. **Sample answers: 1)** I think people should eat less meat. People can get the nutrition they need from plants. Oranges are a great source of calcium. Tofu and spinach contain iron. Eating less meat will help save our limited drinking water. Animal waste can seep into our water and pollute it. **2)** I think people should not eat less meat. It tastes great. It is also very nutritious. Protein helps build strong muscles and bones.

Materials Alert Provide access to computers or library resources so students can do research on the issue of eating less meat.

FORMATIVE ASSESSMENT

MAKING SENSE OF PHENOMENA

Students gain understanding that meeting human needs in housing, agriculture, and industry affects the environment as they explore the **investigative phenomenon.** They should connect this to the **anchoring phenomenon** that people change the environment as they use natural resources such as water to meet their needs and wants. Students should conclude that, because of how the resources are produced and transported, choices made about which resources to use can have both positive and negative effects. People can make choices to minimize harm based on their personal values.

REMEDIATION If students struggle to connect the **investigative phenomenon** back to the **anchoring phenomenon,** have them work with a partner to discuss and answer the Making Sense question.

MAKING SENSE OF PHENOMENA IDEA ORGANIZER

After completing Exploration 4, students can fill in the **Idea Organizer** to summarize the connection between how meeting human needs in housing, agriculture, and industry affects the environment and the anchoring phenomenon that people change the environment as they use natural resources such as water to meet their needs and wants.

Engage • Explore/Explain • **Elaborate** • Evaluate

TIME ESTIMATE

45 min

These Take It Further paths may be completed to enrich and extend students' comprehension of content covered within this lesson.

ONLINE

Careers in Science & Engineering: Marine Biologist & Ecologist

Students explore careers in the field of marine biology by researching and proposing responses to situations threatening a reef population. Then, students explore the field of ecology by researching and evaluating a wetland restoration program.

Sustainable Forests

Students explore the use of sustainable forests to supply wood for human use. Students use math to model the number of trees in a sustainable forest over time.

Overfishing

Students explore the issue of overfishing. Students make an infographic about overfishing based on research they conduct. Then, students debate the issue of overfishing in a small group.

Lesson Check

Activity Guide, pages 223–225

Engage • Explore/Explain • Elaborate • **Evaluate**

Can You Explain It?

Now I know or think that . . .

Sample answer: Water is obtained from natural sources. It needs to be filtered and treated to be safe for people to drink. Coal and natural gas are nonrenewable resources; wood and plants are renewable resources. Gathering or extracting resources can damage ecosystems. For example, building the aqueduct to transport water damaged and interrupted habitats. Using resources can add pollution to the environment.

After completing the lesson, use the **Making Sense Idea Organizer** to summarize the connections between the **investigative phenomena** and the **anchoring phenomenon.**

Checkpoints

1. b

2. b, d, e

3. c

4. **Sample answer:** To obtain a mineral resource, you need to build roads, transport equipment, store waste, and transport the mineral. These activities can interfere with an ecosystem.

5. **Sample answer:** Dams can generate electricity. Building a dam can destroy habitats and block fish movements up and down stream.

6. **Sample answer:** I ride the bus to school. The bus uses gasoline, a fossil fuel. Burning the fuel pollutes the air.

7. b, c

8. **Sample answer:** Wood is renewable because more can be grown relatively quickly, so there is not a limited supply.

MAKING CONNECTIONS

After students complete the lesson, they should be able to answer a question about an alternative phenomenon to explain what type of resource wood is and how it is used. **Sample answer:** Wood is a renewable resource. It can be used for buildings, furniture, pencils, or as raw material for making paper.

💬 SOCIAL EMOTIONAL LEARNING

Have students reflect on the goals they set at the beginning of the lesson. Ask them to think about whether the goals were accomplished or if there were challenges. Have students share the factors that contributed to their success. If the goals were not achieved, talk about what students can do to help them achieve the goals.

04 People Can Protect the Environment

ANCHORING PHENOMENON
People planted trees and other plants on these roofs.

ENGAGE Can You Explain It?
Students observe and ask questions about plants growing on rooftops. They answer the Can You Explain It? question to identify what they will gather evidence about in the lesson.

EVALUATE Lesson Check
Students gauge their understanding of the anchoring phenomenon.

HANDS-ON ACTIVITY

EXPLORATION 1 Pocket Park (75 min)
Investigative Phenomenon A park design that incorporates green features helps individuals and communities conserve resources and protect the environment.

Students connect back to the **anchoring phenomenon** that people design green spaces to conserve resources and protect the environment as do surface heating and cooling benefits from green roof systems.

HANDS-ON ACTIVITY

EXPLORATION 2 Reusing at Home (45 min)
Investigative Phenomenon Reusing materials at home is a conservation practice.

Students connect back to the **anchoring phenomenon** that designing a reuse of discarded materials such as jars and boxes reduces resource use like the green roof systems.

EXPLORATION 3 Conservation's Three R's (30 min)
Investigative Phenomenon The Three R's incorporate green practices and technologies that help people conserve resources and protect the environment.

Students connect back to the **anchoring phenomenon** that communities and individuals who practice reducing, reusing, and recycling also reduce resource use.

EXPLORATION 4 Conserve and Protect the Environment (30 min)
Investigative Phenomenon Green technology helps us minimize the impacts of human activity on the environment.

Students connect back to the **anchoring phenomenon** that green roof systems are a type of green technology that helps conserve resources and protect the environment.

Making 3D Connections

The **anchoring phenomenon** in this lesson supports students' understanding of an application of these Next Generation Science Standards.

Building to the Performance Expectations

5-ESS3-1 Obtain and combine information about ways individual communities use science ideas to protect the Earth's resources and environment.

SEP

Obtaining, Evaluating, and Communicating Information
Obtain and combine information from books and/or other reliable media to explain phenomena or solutions to a design problem. *(Explorations 1, 2, 3, 4)*

Engaging in Argument from Evidence Support an argument with evidence, data, or a model. *(Exploration 4)*

Using Mathematics and Computational Thinking
Describe and graph quantities such as area and volume to address scientific questions. *(Exploration 1)*

DCI

ESS3.C Human Impacts on Earth Systems Human activities have had major effects on the land, vegetation, streams, ocean, air, and even outer space. But individuals and communities are doing things to help protect Earth's resources and environments.
(Explorations 1, 2, 3, 4)

ETS1.B Developing Possible Solutions Research should be carried out before beginning to design a solution. Testing a solution involves investigating how well it performs. Communicating with peers is an important part of the design process. Tests are often designed to identify failure points.
(Explorations 1, 2, 3)

CCC

Science Addresses Questions About the Natural and Material World Science findings are limited to questions that can be answered with empirical evidence.
(Explorations 1, 2, 3, 4)

Systems and System Models
A system can be described in terms of its components and their interactions. *(Explorations 1, 2, 3, 4)*

Vocabulary

Word Wall   A word wall, anchor chart, or Language Development chart can be used to support vocabulary

green technology innovative ways of using resources that minimize human impact on the environment

recycle use materials in old things to make new things

You may want to include additional academic terms such as *conservation* and any other terms students might struggle with.

Language Development Prompt students to complete the chart when they come to these highlighted terms within the lesson and to add their own terms as they come across unknown science terms.

Anchor Chart As you progress through the unit, you may want to make a vocabulary-based anchor chart using the Language Development chart as a guide that can be displayed and filled out as a whole group during each lesson.

04 People Can Protect the Environment

Activity Guide, pages 226–243

Students can engage in the Can You Explain It? content by observing the photograph or by exploring the corresponding video online.

ONLINE ⊙ **Ed** View a video related to a rooftop garden.

ANCHORING PHENOMENON
People planted trees and other plants on these roofs.

PHENOMENON EXPLAINED
Green roofs are a conservation strategy to manage resources and protect the environment.

Lesson Objective

Students can obtain, evaluate, and communicate information about the importance of reducing, reusing, and recycling and other ways people protect the environment. They can also investigate technologies and ideas used to help protect Earth's resources and environments.

Support Discovery

The following prompts can be used to guide student-led discovery.

I notice . . .

After observing the photograph or watching the video, students should record what they noticed about the green roof. If students struggle to record observations, ask them to think about why plants might be grown on a roof, or focus on some of the other "green" things atop the buildings.

Sample answers: The rooftops are covered with grass, trees, and other plants.

I wonder . . .

After observing the photograph or watching the video, students should record what they want to find out more about.

Sample answer: I wonder what the costs and benefits are. Islands have limited resources so they need to use all available space.

Alternative Phenomenon

If students are unfamiliar with rooftop gardens or other green technologies and techniques, consider discussing small, hand-hold "green" technologies such as rechargeable batteries, solar-powered calculators, and self-powering watches. You may want to bring one or more of these examples to class so that students can make in-person observations of what these devices "save" or reduce in terms of resources.

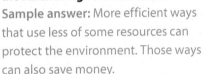

Can You Explain It?

In the Can You Explain It?, students make an initial claim that explains the **Anchoring Phenomenon**.

Sample answer: More efficient ways that use less of some resources can protect the environment. Those ways can also save money.

Students will gather evidence about ways that people can protect and maintain the environment. This will enable them to give a more complete explanation of the **Anchoring Phenomenon** at the end of the lesson.

SOCIAL EMOTIONAL LEARNING

Guide students to reflect on their goals from previous lessons and on any feedback they received from their teachers or peers. Then have each student set a personal goal for this lesson and make a plan for how to achieve the goal. Throughout the lesson, take daily breaks for students to track their progress in meeting their goals. As students move from lesson to lesson, they can continue to work towards their initial goals or set new ones. If students struggle setting goals for this lesson, share the following ideas: identifying ways people and communities are helping Earth's resources and environments; obtaining, evaluating, and communicating information; and working as a team to make decisions.

FUNomenal READER

Coastal Cleanup

WHEN TO USE

SCIENCE **30** min

- Anchoring Phenomenon / Alternative Phenomenon
- Options for ELA Instruction
- Build on Prior Knowledge
- Preview the Phenomenon
- Read to Learn
- Support Sense Making
- Science Stretch
- Check for Comprehension

Option 1 Use before students begin the lesson in the Activity Guide to provide an engaging model to introduce the lesson's phenomenon.

Option 2 Use after students have completed the Activity Guide to reinforce students' understanding of the lesson phenomenon by exploring a related phenomenon.

ELA **20** min

- Options for ELA Instruction
- Build on Prior Knowledge
- Read to Learn

Option 3 To use during designated ELA Reading time for independent reading, whole-class instruction, or small-group instruction, look for this icon: ELA

Plan

ANCHORING PHENOMENON / ALTERNATIVE PHENOMENON

The anchoring phenomenon in the Activity Guide is *People planted trees and other plants on these roofs,* and the main example is city rooftops covered with grass, trees, and other plants. The FUNomenal Reader presents a similar phenomenon *(The number of sea urchins on this beach has increased),* and the example is a beach with a newly-posted warning sign about sea urchins. Both present the same science concepts and cover the same standards but with different phenomena. Guide students to draw connections between the two situations and to understand the underlying principle: people use technologies and science ideas to help protect Earth's resources and environments from harm which may be caused by human activities.

Options for ELA Instruction

Choose one of the following anchor chart options and project it or print copies. Then display and introduce the chart before reading the text. Revisit the chart after reading the text and encourage students to discuss how the skill connects to the text.

Ask and Answer Questions Use the *Ask and Answer Questions Anchor Chart* when introducing, developing, or reviewing those skills. Have students consider how the story's main character starts his investigation with a question: "Why are there so many sea urchins on the beach?"

Present Information In the story, Tillman makes a multimedia report and presents it to his environmental club. Have students consult the *Tips on How to Present Anchor Chart* to see best practices for making an oral presentation.

Make Inferences Display the *Make Inferences Anchor Chart* to discuss how seeing trash at the beach and learning about sea otters helps Tillman make an inference about what might be causing the increase in sea urchins. He combines what he knows with what he learns to come up with a new understanding of the problem.

Preview

STANDARDS SUPPORTED

SEP
Obtaining, Evaluating, and Communicating Information

DCI
ESS3.C Human Impacts on Earth Systems

ETS1.B Developing Possible Solutions

CCC
Science Addresses Questions About the Natural and Material World

Systems and System Models

ELA **Build on Prior Knowledge** Students already know that people can do things to affect the world around them, including making choices that reduce their impact on the environment. Invite volunteers to name choices people can make to help their local environment. Students may suggest picking up trash, recycling paper, turning off lights when not in use, and carrying groceries in reusable bags.

Preview the Phenomenon Ask students to study the illustration on page 2 of the story, which shows a man and boy with surfboards at a beach. A sign says "Beware of Urchins." Encourage students to record the first questions that come into their minds, focusing on the sign and what it might mean to the surfers. Point out that their questions might change as they read through the story. Have them keep their questions nearby and periodically check to see if any can be answered.

Coastal Cleanup (continued)

Discover

Read to Learn

The **Read to Learn** suggestions inside the book's front cover encourage students to interact with the book multiple times for different purposes.

Preview Students look for unfamiliar words and share them with a partner. New terms may include *investigate, keystone species,* and *predator*. Have students look up words they aren't sure about and notice how they are used in the context of the story.

Skim Students skim the illustrations. Have them turn to a partner and share their predictions of what the story will be about.

Read As students read the story, ask them to look for connections to one of the following anchor chart skills. **Ask and Answer Questions, Present Information, Make Inferences**

Support Sense Making

Choose one or more of the following:

▶ Be sure students can identify the phenomenon presented on the opening pages of the story: Tillman and his father can't go surfing because they learn there has been an influx of sea urchins in the ocean and along the beach. The story follows Tillman's efforts to understand why sea urchins are increasing in this area. Have students name the steps he takes in his investigation.

▶ Have students analyze the claim-evidence-reasoning argument Tillman makes in the story. Is his claim (trash at the beach has led to fewer sea otters, which are predators of sea urchins) supported by the evidence he gathers? Is his

reasoning sound? Have them work in pairs to present their own claims, evidence, and reasoning related to the phenomenon.

▶ Encourage a student-led discussion of how Tillman's efforts lead to a change in the food web in his area. How do picking up trash, providing new trash containers, and setting up a fishing-line disposal station help restore balance to the food web?

▶ Tillman's assignment for the environmental club is to find an issue and take action. Have students brainstorm an issue your class could tackle together and then make a plan for taking action.

Extend

Science Stretch

The **Science Stretch** suggestions inside the book's back cover help students think about what they read. Students can complete one or more as time allows.

> Why are keystone species an important part of food webs? **Sample answer:** Other organisms depend on keystone species to keep the ecosystem in balance.

> Make a claim, supported by evidence, about how humans can harm the environment. Have students consult the online *Science and Engineering Practices Handbook* for more information on using claims, evidence, and reasoning.

> Make a model of a food web that includes sea otters. Students' models might take the form of drawings, photos connected by yarn, or a demonstration using small toys.

 SOCIAL EMOTIONAL LEARNING

How can you help your local environment? **Sample answer:** I can save water by turning off the faucet while I am brushing my teeth.

Check for Comprehension Have students write a short explanation of why protecting Earth's resources is important and how people can protect those resources.

Engineer It • Pocket Park

Activity Guide, pages 228–231

TIME ESTIMATE

75 min

POSSIBLE MATERIALS

☐ pencil, pen, or markers

☐ copy paper

☐ graph paper, 1/4" scale

☐ ruler

☐ sources of information about parks, community gardens, and accessible playgrounds, may be printed or through digital devices with Internet access

☐ large format paper and colored pencils (optional)

PREPARATION

Make arrangements for trips to the media center to allow students time for research, as well as gathering some books and magazines. Have group members decide on and divide up individual roles in the activity, such as budget controller and model presenter. All group members should take part in any decision making.

INVESTIGATIVE PHENOMENON
A park design that incorporates green features helps individuals and communities conserve resources and protect the environment.

Phenomenon Explained Students explore the **investigative phenomenon** by conducting research in order to design a pocket park to benefit the environment, and provide green space that is accessible to all students.

Form a Question After reading about pocket parks, students should form a question about how to design one. If students struggle to form a question, ask them to think of themselves as park designers in training. **Sample answer:** How can you plan the space inside a new park?

Explore

STEPS 1 and 2 Students conduct research about parks, accessible playgrounds, and community gardens. Student research will vary. Students use the scenario to find criteria and constraints. As needed, review the meaning of *criteria* and *constraints*. **Sample answer:** criteria: green features, dog park, rest areas, ground cover and lights, play area for children, accessible to all children; constraints: $10,000 budget, 8 x 8 m garden, 80-square-meter play area

STEP 3 Students discuss and decide how to make the park accessible. **Sample answer:** We'll plan an inclusive playground with paved walkways.

Make and Test

STEP 4 Students use graph paper to draw scale models of their park designs. Remind students to document park features and costs.

Improve and Test

STEPS 5 and 6 Have groups present their designs to community members who will use the park (the class) for feedback. After, students identify possible improvements to their models and describe tradeoffs.

- **Make a Claim** Claims should indicate how they balanced limited space and budget with environmental and community benefits.

- **Evidence** Students should cite evidence, such as having paved paths for accessibility and grassy areas for play and habitat.

- **Reasoning** Students should explain their reasoning, such as using recycled materials to reduce the need for new materials.

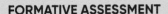

FORMATIVE ASSESSMENT

MAKING SENSE OF PHENOMENA

Students gain understanding that a park design with green features helps conserve resources and protect the environment as they explore the **investigative phenomenon.** They should connect this to the **anchoring phenomenon** that communities and individuals use science ideas and technology to conserve resources and protect the environment. Students should understand benefits of pocket parks, such as providing habitats and recreation areas.

REMEDIATION If students struggle to connect the **investigative phenomenon** back to the **anchoring phenomenon,** have them work with a partner to list three benefits of their park design.

Activity Outcome

Students should research to design an accessible pocket park to benefit the environment and increase green space.

Performance Indicators	
	conduct research and design a green, accessible pocket park
	make a claim about the benefits of their pocket park
	support the claim using evidence

MAKING SENSE OF PHENOMENA IDEA ORGANIZER

After completing Exploration 1, students can fill in the **Idea Organizer** to summarize the connection between how a park design that incorporates green features helps individuals and communities conserve resources and protect the environment and the anchoring phenomenon that communities and individuals use science ideas and technology such as the effect green spaces have on surface heating and cooling to conserve resources and protect the environment.

SOCIAL EMOTIONAL LEARNING

Students who fear being judged or teased may be reluctant to share the challenges they faced during the activity. Remind students that everyone struggles at times, and explain that sharing your struggles and coping strategies can help you as well as others. Consider sharing an example of a challenge you faced and how you coped with it.

Engineer It • Reusing at Home

Activity Guide, pages 232–233

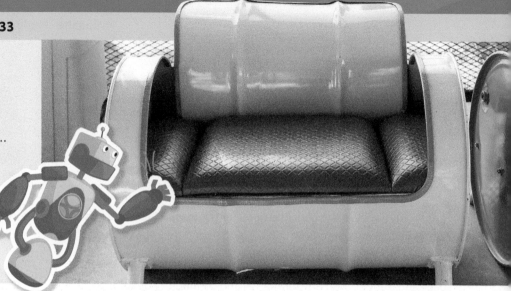

TIME ESTIMATE

45 min

SHORT ON TIME?

Steps 1 and 2 of this activity can be done by the class as a group. Then have pairs or small groups of students complete the activity.

POSSIBLE MATERIALS

☐ household items

☐ scissors

☐ masking tape

☐ glue

PREPARATION

In advance, gather a variety of household items likely to be discarded, such as cardboard boxes, plastic bottles, large salad boxes, and plastic jars. Or, ask students to bring some items from home. Screen for hazards such as sharp or fragile items.

INVESTIGATIVE PHENOMENON
Reusing materials at home is a conservation practice.

Phenomenon Explained Students explore the **investigative phenomenon** by designing, building, and testing ways to reuse materials at home or school.

Form a Question After they read about reusing items, students should form a question about ways items can be reused. If students struggle to form a question, ask them to consider how they reuse items. Sample answer: There are probably more options for durable materials such as wood, metal, and plastic.

STEP 1 Students look for items that are likely to be discarded and list them in a table. Sample answer: cardboard box, plastic bottle, large salad box, clothing

STEP 2 Students think of ways to reuse the items to solve a problem or to meet a need, then list their ideas in the table. Sample answers: storage (cardboard box), planter (plastic bottle), terrarium (large salad box), cleaning rag (clothing)

STEP 3 Review the engineering design steps with students. Then have them choose one of their reuse ideas and follow the steps to design a solution or meet a need. Review students' designs and, once they get your permission, have them build and test a prototype.

- **Make a Claim** Claims should indicate how items should be reused, such as that plastic bottles should be used as ice packs for coolers.

- **Evidence** Students should cite evidence from the activity, such as that testing of their prototype indicated that plastic bottle ice packs kept food cold.

- **Reasoning** Students should explain their reasoning, such as that plastic bottle ice packs are less messy than bagged ice and reusing them keeps plastic out of landfills.

FORMATIVE ASSESSMENT

MAKING SENSE OF PHENOMENA

Students gain understanding that reusing materials at home is a conservation practice as they explore the **investigative phenomenon.** They should connect this to the **anchoring phenomenon** that communities and individuals use science ideas and technology such as using materials such as plants and plant covering to reduce the use of energy to conserve resources and protect the environment. Students should understand that reuse can solve a problem for people, since fewer resources are needed to make new materials, which means less harm occurs to ecosystems from resource gathering.

REMEDIATION If students struggle to connect the **investigative phenomenon** back to the **anchoring phenomenon,** have the class discuss and guide students to understand the connection.

MAKING SENSE OF PHENOMENA IDEA ORGANIZER
After completing Exploration 2, students can fill in the **Idea Organizer** to summarize the connection between reusing materials at home being a conservation practice and the anchoring phenomenon that communities and individuals use science ideas and technology such as using materials such as plants and plant covering to reduce the use of energy to conserve resources and protect the environment.

Activity Outcome

Students should design, build, and test a solution to reuse materials at home. They state a claim about how items should be reused and use evidence to support it.

Performance Indicators
design, build, and test a solution to reuse materials
make a claim about how items should be reused
support the claim using collected data as evidence

Conservation's Three R's

Activity Guide, pages 234–236

TIME ESTIMATE

30 min

RECYCLE   RECYCLE

Misconception Alert Students may believe that because you are doing something good for the environment when you are recycling, then recycling should be free. But, collecting, processing, and transporting recyclables requires both expensive equipment and labor.

INVESTIGATIVE PHENOMENON
The Three R's incorporate green practices and technologies that help people conserve resources and protect the environment.

Phenomenon Explained Students explore the **investigative phenomenon** by exploring recycling, reducing, and reusing practices.

Back to Basics

Remind students that people can choose to change behaviors to lessen their impact. Ask students whether they think recycling is beneficial. Have them argue why or why not, and list any items they recycle. Ask whether it takes more energy to produce new things or to recycle old things. **Sample answer:** Making new things uses more resources and energy.

Students identify one reason people might choose to recycle and one they might choose not to. **Sample answer:** choose to recycle—to feel good about helping the environment; choose not to recycle—because there's no space to store messy waste

Students list recyclable items that they use every day and describe how recycling helps the environment. Before answering, ask them to start at the beginning of a typical day and think it through to the very end to consider objects that they might not normally think of as recyclable. **Sample answer:** I use plastic drinking bottles, glass containers, and magazines. Recycling helps conserve fossil fuels and trees, and helps save energy.

Using Less

Students identify the best items pictured for helping to reduce waste.

Bring to class a product that is overpackaged. Open it, discarding all unnecessary materials in a pile. Explain that products often include unnecessary, extra packaging that does not make the product better. Decreasing this wasteful packaging can decrease the total amount of generated waste. **Ask:** What happens to all the wasted packaging material? **Sample answer:** Some may be recycled, but much ends up as trash that is burned, buried, or litters the ground or water. What can you do to reduce the impact of wasteful packaging material? **Sample answer:** Choose products without extra packaging and repackage items in reusable containers

FORMATIVE ASSESSMENT

MAKING SENSE OF PHENOMENA

Students gain understanding that the Three R's incorporate green practices and technologies that help people conserve energy and resources and protect the environment as they explore the **investigative phenomenon.** They should connect this to the **anchoring phenomenon** that communities and individuals use science ideas and technology, such as using materials such as plants and plant covering to reduce the use of energy to conserve resources and protect the environment. Students should understand that reducing, reusing, and recycling saves resources, reduces pollution, and protects the environment.

REMEDIATION If students struggle to connect the **investigative phenomenon** back to the **anchoring phenomenon,** have a class discussion about the Three R's and their benefits to people and the environment.

MAKING SENSE OF PHENOMENA IDEA ORGANIZER

After completing Exploration 3, students can fill in the **Idea Organizer** to summarize the connection between how the Three R's incorporate green practices and technologies that help people conserve resources and protect the environment and the anchoring phenomenon that communities and individuals use science ideas and technology, such as using materials such as plants and plant covering to reduce the use of energy to conserve resources and protect the environment.

Conserve and Protect the Environment

Activity Guide, pages 237–240

TIME ESTIMATE

PREPARATION

Make arrangements for trips to the media center to allow students time to conduct research and have access to the internet.

INVESTIGATIVE PHENOMENON
Green technology helps us minimize the impacts of human activity on the environment.

Phenomenon Explained Students explore the **investigative phenomenon** by exploring examples of green technologies.

Green Technology

Everyday Phenomenon **Local communities are going green and using green technologies.**

Point out to students that there may be examples of the **everyday phenomenon** of going green in their neighborhoods such as parks, playgrounds, or waterways. Have them name examples found in homes or businesses. Help them connect examples of their community going green to the **anchoring phenomenon** that communities and individuals use science ideas and technology such as green roof systems to conserve resources and protect the environment.

Students do research on green technology used in their area, evaluate it, and report their findings. **Sample answer:** Our city has recycling bins. It would be helpful if the bins showed which products could go inside.

Paper or Plastic Bag Debate

Students research the pros and cons of plastic bags and paper bags. They state a claim about which least impacts the environment and support it with evidence. **Sample answer:** Claim: Paper bags are more environmentally friendly than plastic. Evidence: Paper bags are biodegradable and less likely end up in trees or oceans; they are not made from fossil fuels.

Students work in a group to develop and summarize an argument for or against a plastic bag ban. They tell how their group agreed on its position. **Sample answer:** Plastic bags are cheap and convenient. Don't ban them. They can be reused. Our group decided its position by voting.

SOCIAL EMOTIONAL LEARNING

Support students through the process of making decisions as a group. Have a class brainstorming session about appropriate ways to make group decisions. Encourage students to apply one of the strategies when their group works to agree on a position about using plastic bags.

Cities Conserving Resources

Tell students that while it is expensive initially to create a green roof, the investment pays off. **Ask:** What are some of the benefits of a green roof? **Sample answer:** Green roofs have a fairly stable surface temperature. They insulate and buffer temperature extremes.

Conserving at Home

Students study a room and apply what they know about conservation to describe changes they would make. **Sample answer:** Adjust the thermostat. Turn off the lights, fan, and computer. Fix the leaky faucet.

FORMATIVE ASSESSMENT

MAKING SENSE OF PHENOMENA

Students gain understanding that green technology helps us minimize the impacts of human activity on the environment as they explore the **investigative phenomenon.** They should connect this to the **anchoring phenomenon** that communities and individuals use science ideas and technology such as green roof systems to conserve resources and protect the environment. Students should understand the benefits of green technology, such as that green roofs lower energy use for heating and cooling. They are a new way to use a resource (rooftop space).

REMEDIATION If students struggle to connect the **investigative phenomenon** back to the **anchoring phenomenon,** have them work with a partner to write a paragraph summarizing the benefits of the green technologies described in this Exploration.

MAKING SENSE OF PHENOMENA IDEA ORGANIZER

After completing Exploration 4, students can fill in the **Idea Organizer** to summarize the connection between how green technology helps us minimize the impacts of human activity on the environment and the anchoring phenomenon that communities and individuals use science ideas and technology such as green roof systems to conserve resources and protect the environment.

Take It Further

Engage • **Explore/Explain** • **Elaborate** • Evaluate

TIME ESTIMATE

60 min

These Take It Further paths may be completed to enrich and extend students' comprehension of content covered within this lesson.

ONLINE

People in Science & Engineering: Dr. Mario Molina

Students learn about Dr. Mario Molina, a chemist who studied the effects of CFC's on the environment.

Landfills: How Long until It's Gone?

Students examine the purposes, pros, and cons of a landfill.

Can All Plastics Be Recycled?

Students examine many of the household products that come in plastic containers.

Careers in Science & Engineering: Sustainability Specialist

Students explore an environmental career that includes planning natural resource use.

Lesson Check

Activity Guide, pages 241–243

Can You Explain It?

Now I know or think that . . .

Sample answer: Green roofs protect the environment. The roofs help buildings use less energy to heat and cool. The roofs also improve air quality. The three R's—Reduce, Reuse, and Recycle—lower resource use. Less energy and fewer raw materials are needed compared to making totally new products.

After completing the lesson, use the **Making Sense Idea Organizer** to summarize the connections between the **investigative phenomena** and the **anchoring phenomenon.**

MAKING CONNECTIONS

After students complete the lesson, they should be able to answer a question about an alternative phenomenon to explain how composting is an example of green technology. **Sample answer:** Composting is a form of recycling where waste is turned into a new useful product instead of going to a landfill.

Checkpoints

1. c—a city with a large community garden and a recycling program

2. Possible answer: They lower the use of energy resources, so there's less pollution. Government websites are good resources.

3. c—Maria

4. a—by using more renewable energy sources; c—by establishing extensive recycling programs; d—by offering transit systems that run on clean energy

5. c— Use a filter to filter tap water.; d—Buy a smaller number of larger bottles of water.

6. nonrenewable; renewable; environment; energy efficiency

 SOCIAL EMOTIONAL LEARNING

Have students reflect on the concepts they have explored about protecting the environment. Have small groups make a list of additional questions they would like to investigate. Then have each group choose one question. Have students set short-term goals to help them go about finding answers to their question. Help students identify the number of goals and the amount of time needed to complete each.

The Unit review items enable you to assess student comprehension of core ideas, as well as cross cutting concepts and science and engineering practices.

1. **DOK 2** Hyd66rosphere interaction:
Sample answer: Lava boils ocean water.
Atmosphere interaction: Sample answer: Dust and gases are sent high into the air.
Biosphere interaction: Sample answer: Living things are killed or displaced by lava flows.
Review what a volcanic eruption does: releases gases and lava, can trigger earthquakes, bury organisms in ash, mud, lava. Have students identify what spheres are affected in each example.

2. **DOK 2** **a.** Most of it is salt water., **b.** Most of the fresh water is frozen., **c.** People are adding pollutants to the water.
Neither *d* nor *e* are true. Trees use water but water cycles through them. Even if there were more trees growing, which is untrue, this would not have a big impact on the amount of usable water. The amount of water on Earth is fixed.

3. **DOK 3** **Sample answer:** replace three-fourths of the paved areas with natural ground, leaving one-fourth of the city paved
Explain to students that water can seep down through grass, rocks, or dirt. Most water will not be absorbed by pavement, so it runs across the surface and can carry pollution it picks up, such as oil that has spilled on the road, and deposit it in a lake or stream.

4. **DOK 2** **Sample answer:** The hydrosphere and biosphere are most affected. Ecosystems are damaged by the blocked river flow. How did the dam change animal populations?
Remind students that dams redirect and reshape rivers, which are a part of the hydrosphere and a feature that shapes the geosphere.

5. **DOK 3** **b.** Draw a beach and waves crashing on it to show a way the hydrosphere and geosphere interact., **c.** Draw an erupting volcano to show how the geosphere and atmosphere interact., **d.** Add a river cutting through the land to show how the hydrosphere shapes the geosphere.
If students struggle to answer the question, step through each distractor and ask them to identify if the spheres identified are correct, based on the other details. For example, a river cutting through the land is indeed an example of the hydrosphere interacting with the geosphere.

6. **DOK 3** **Sample answer:** Surface mining of coal leaves scars in the landscape. Burning fossil fuels adds pollution to the atmosphere. But, coal is important for generating electricity. A cost and benefit comparison would support this answer. Student might conflate or confuse gathering with use. Remind them that mining and drilling are examples of resource extraction, while making and burning gasoline are examples of use.

7. **DOK 2** **d.** rewarding use of refillable water bottles
Students need to identify the "green" solution that would add to what the school is already doing, so not recycling, walking to school, or water conservation.

8. **DOK 2** **Sample answer:** Positive: farming, green roofs, dams, recycling bins; Negative: farming, dams; support for dams as negative—number of fish killed by dams
Clarify for students that they need to weigh positive or negative effects on the environment—not on humans or human activities. Support should be specific.

9. **DOK 3** Students' models should resemble the rain shadow illustration in Lesson 2. Models may include evaporation from the ocean, cloud formation, wind from the ocean to the mountain, rain from clouds on the ocean side, hot dry air flowing down into desert on the far side.

If students struggle, tell them to use the following labels: evaporation, condensation, rain.

10. **DOK 2** Engineers gather data by testing the prototypes. The city may have thousands of people, so the problem is too big for stream water. The ocean has much more water.

Students should connect the problem to knowledge about water resource distribution as well as understanding the importance of testing in engineering.

3D Item Analysis	1	2	3	4	5	6	7	8	9	10
SEP Developing and Using Models	•				•				•	
SEP Using Mathematics and Computational Thinking			•							
SEP Engaging in Argument from Evidence			•			•		•		
SEP Obtaining, Evaluating, and Communicating Information						•	•			
DCI Earth Materials and Systems	•	•		•	•				•	
DCI The Roles of Water in Earth's Surface Processes		•	•						•	•
DCI Human Impacts on Earth Systems		•	•	•		•	•	•		
DCI Optimizing the Design Solution										•
DCI Developing Possible Solutions			•							
CCC Systems and System Models	•	•	•	•	•				•	
CCC Scale, Proportion, and Quantity										•
CCC Science Addresses Questions About the Natural and Material World			•							

06 Patterns in the Sky

Activity Guide, page 247

Unit Storyline

In Unit 5, students explored Earth's systems and their interactions, including those that shape Earth's surface. They surveyed different components of Earth's systems, including rock, water, air, and organisms, and how they affect each other. In this unit, students will explore gravity and the sun, including their effects on Earth's systems and matter. They will also explore patterns in the night sky over time.

After completing Unit 6, you may want to administer the End-of-Year Test found online. A Modified End-of-Year Test is also available.

LESSON 1   PE 5-PS2-1

Gravity Affects Matter on Earth

Activity Guide. pp. 248–263

Students explore the **anchoring phenomenon** that there is no chance the skydivers will fall away from Earth's surface.

SEP Engaging in Argument from Evidence
DCI **PS2.B** Types of Interactions
CCC Cause and Effect

LESSON 2   PE 5-ESS1-2

Sky Patterns Over Time

Activity Guide, pp. 264–287

Students explore the **anchoring phenomenon** that from one day to the next, the time the sun sets at a location changes.

SEP Analyzing and Interpreting Data
DCI **ESS1.B** Earth and the Solar System
CCC Patterns

LESSON 3   PE 5-ESS1-1

The Sun

Activity Guide, pp. 288–307

Students explore the **anchoring phenomenon** that you can read by sunlight, but not by starlight at night.

SEP Engaging in Argument from Evidence
DCI **ESS1.A** The Universe and its Stars
CCC Scale, Proportion, and Quantity

Unit Review Activity Guide, pp. 308–310

Online-Only Resources

Supporting Unit Resources

You Solve It   SUPPORTS LESSON 2

Measuring Shadows is a virtual lab that offers practice in support of **Performance Expectation 5-ESS1-2.** Students will analyze data in a graph to reveal patterns in the length and direction of shadows over the course of one day.

- **SEP** Engaging in Argument from Evidence
- **DCI** **ESS1.B** Earth and the Solar System
- **CCC** Cause and Effect

Unit Project   SUPPORTS LESSONS 2 AND 3

90 min

Starry Sky provides students an opportunity to practice aspects of **Performance Expectation 5-ESS1-2.** Students will explore patterns caused by Earth's revolution around the sun, collect and analyze observational data, and analyze data to reveal monthly and seasonal patterns.

- **SEP** Analyzing and Interpreting Data; Engaging in Argument from Evidence
- **DCI** **ESS1.B** Earth and the Solar System
- **CCC** Patterns

Unit Performance Task   SUPPORTS LESSON 3

90 min

Solar Size provides an opportunity for students to practice or be assessed on aspects of **Performance Expectation 5-ESS1-1.** Students design scale 3D models of stars to convey distance, brightness, and size.

- **SEP** Developing and Using Models; Using Mathematics and Computational Thinking
- **DCI** **ESS1.A** The Universe and its Stars
- **CCC** Scale, Proportion, and Quantity

Language Development

This worksheet is used as students progress through the unit's lessons. As they come to a highlighted vocabulary term, they should come back to this chart and fill in the blanks with words or phrases.

Supporting Lesson Resources

Do the Math!

Lesson 1 Above and Beyond
Lesson 2 Daylight, Chart the Sun
Lesson 3 Determining Distance

Language SmArts

Lesson 1 Supporting Your Point of View, Supporting a Point of View
Lesson 2 Use Evidence from Text, Main Ideas and Details, Compare and Contrast, Summarize
Lesson 3 Understanding Logical Connections, Diving for Details, Providing Evidence

Take It Further

Lesson 1 Engineer a Parachute, Life in Space, Weighing In
Lesson 2 Careers in Science & Engineering: Astronomer, Foucault Pendulum, Seasonal Shadows, Ancient Calendars
Lesson 3 People in Science & Engineering: Dr. Beth Brown and Hibah Rahmani, Star Colors, People in Science & Engineering: William and Margaret Huggins, Careers in Science & Engineering: Aerospace Engineer

MAKING SENSE OF PHENOMENA

This idea organizer is used to make sense of the following **anchoring phenomena**:
Lesson 1—There is no chance the skydivers will fall away from Earth's surface.
Lesson 2—From one day to the next, the time the sun sets at a location changes.
Lesson 3—You can read by sunlight but not by starlight at night.

It also connects the investigative phenomena back to the anchoring phenomenon in each lesson.

Assessment

Unit Readiness Check: Are You Ready?
Lesson Quizzes: Can You Apply It?
Unit 6 Test
Performance-Based Assessment

Assessments are available in an editable, printable format or can be administered and auto-graded online.

01 Gravity Affects Matter on Earth

ANCHORING PHENOMENON

There is no chance the skydivers will fall away from Earth's surface.

ENGAGE **Can You Explain It?**

Students observe and ask questions about how skydivers fall to Earth rather than falling away from its surface. They answer the Can You Explain It? question to identify what they will gather evidence about in the lesson.

EVALUATE **Lesson Check**

Students gauge their understanding of the anchoring phenomenon.

HANDS-ON ACTIVITY

EXPLORATION 1
An Ant's View of the World

50 min

Investigative Phenomenon Earth's size makes it appear flat to people on its surface.

Students connect back to the **anchoring phenomenon** that Earth's surface may appear flat, but it is actually a sphere.

HANDS-ON ACTIVITY

EXPLORATION 2
A Trip around the World

45 min

Investigative Phenomenon Gravity affects objects on Earth's surface.

Students connect back to the **anchoring phenomenon** that gravity is a force that pulls objects anywhere on Earth's surface toward its center.

EXPLORATION 3
An Attractive Sphere

45 min

Investigative Phenomenon Everyday experiences on Earth's surface provide evidence for Earth's spherical shape and the pull of gravity.

Students connect back to the **anchoring phenomenon** that Earth is a sphere whose gravity pulls objects toward its center.

Making 3D Connections

The **anchoring phenomenon** in this lesson supports students' understanding of and application of these Next Generation Science Standards.

Building to the Performance Expectations

5-PS2-1 Support an argument that the gravitational force exerted by Earth on objects is directed down.

SEP	DCI	CCC
Engaging in Argument from Evidence Support an argument with evidence, data, or a model. *(Explorations 1, 2, 3)*	**PS2.B Types of Interactions** The gravitational force of Earth acting on an object near Earth's surface pulls that object toward the planet's center. *(Explorations 1, 2, 3)*	**Cause and Effect** Cause and effect relationships are routinely identified and used to explain change. *(Explorations 1, 2, 3)*

Vocabulary

Word Wall   A word wall, anchor chart, or Language Development chart can be used to support vocabulary.

gravity a force that pulls all objects in the universe toward one another.

You may want to include additional academic terms such as *sphere* and *hemisphere* and any other terms students might struggle with.

Language Development Prompt students to complete the chart when they come to these highlighted terms within the lesson and to add their own terms as they come across unknown science terms.

Anchor Chart As you progress through the unit, you may want to make a vocabulary-based anchor chart using the Language Development chart as a guide that can be displayed and filled out as a whole group during each lesson.

01 Gravity Affects Matter on Earth

Activity Guide, pages 248–249

Students can engage in the Can You Explain It? content by observing the photograph or by exploring the corresponding video online.

ONLINE  View a video related to skydiving.

ANCHORING PHENOMENON

There is no chance the skydivers will fall away from Earth's surface.

PHENOMENON EXPLAINED

Skydivers fall toward Earth. Earth's gravity pulls them toward Earth's center. Earth's gravity also keeps objects on its surface from flying off into space.

Lesson Objective

Students can gather evidence to explain that Earth's gravity pulls objects toward the planet's center. Through developing and using models, students use evidence to support an argument that Earth is a sphere and that gravity causes falling objects to move toward Earth's center.

Support Discovery

The following prompts can be used to guide student-led discovery.

I notice . . .

After observing the photograph or watching the video, students should record what they noticed about Earth's shape and the skydivers. If students struggle to record observations, ask them to compare the shape of Earth in the photograph or video with how Earth looks from the ground.

Sample answer: I notice that the edge of Earth looks curved. I notice that the skydivers are very high in the air.

I wonder . . .

After observing the photograph or watching the video, students should record what they want to find out more about regarding the cause of the skydivers' motion. If students struggle to record what they want to know more about, ask them to consider what might have happened five minutes before and five minutes after the images were taken to spark questions and curiosity.

Sample answer: I wonder what causes the skydivers to fall towards the ground.

Can You Explain It?

In the Can You Explain It?, students make an initial claim that explains the **Anchoring Phenomenon.**

Sample answer: Students may draw a model of the skydivers' path to the ground or write a sentence about what causes the skydivers to fall to the ground as opposed to falling away from Earth.

In the lesson, students gather evidence about Earth's shape and the effects of gravity. This will enable them to give a more complete explanation of the **Anchoring Phenomenon** at the end of the lesson.

Alternative Phenomenon

If students struggle to grasp the scale of motion involved in skydiving, guide them to think about another object moving toward Earth's surface, such as a ball they throw. You may want to bring in balls and provide an opportunity for students to throw them in an outdoor or gymnasium environment so that students can make in-person observations of objects pulled toward Earth's surface.

SOCIAL EMOTIONAL LEARNING

Guide students to reflect on their previous lesson goals and on any feedback. Then, have students set new personal lesson goals and make a plan to achieve the goals. Throughout the lesson, pause daily so students can track progress toward their goals. As students move through the unit, they can keep their initial goals or set new ones. If students struggle to set lesson goals, share these ideas: gather evidence for Earth's shape and the pull of gravity, identify cause-and-effect relationships, engage in argument from evidence, or ensure everyone in their group has a chance to share ideas during discussions.

Our Friends Are Falling

WHEN TO USE

SCIENCE **30 min**

- Anchoring Phenomenon / Alternative Phenomenon
- Options for ELA Instruction
- Build on Prior Knowledge
- Preview the Phenomenon
- Read to Learn
- Support Sense Making
- Science Stretch
- Check for Comprehension

Option 1 Use before students begin the lesson in the Activity Guide to provide an engaging model to introduce the lesson's phenomenon.

Option 2 Use after students have completed the Activity Guide to reinforce students' understanding of the lesson phenomenon by exploring a related phenomenon.

ELA **20 min**

- Options for ELA Instruction
- Build on Prior Knowledge
- Read to Learn

Option 3 To use during designated ELA Reading time for independent reading, whole-class instruction, or small-group instruction, look for this icon: **ELA**

Plan

ANCHORING PHENOMENON / ALTERNATIVE PHENOMENON

The anchoring phenomenon in the Activity Guide is *There is no chance the skydivers will fall away from Earth's surface.* The main example is a group of four skydivers who are holding onto one another as they fall toward the ground. The FUNomenal Reader presents a similar phenomenon *(People who live in the Southern Hemisphere don't fall off Earth),* and the example is a group of students who explore why people in Australia don't fall off Earth. Both present the same science concepts and cover the same standards but with different phenomena. Guide students to draw connections between the two situations and to understand the underlying principle: Earth is a sphere, and gravity pulls objects toward Earth's center.

Options for ELA Instruction

Choose one of the following anchor chart options and project it or print copies. Then display and introduce the chart before reading the text. Revisit the chart after reading the text and encourage students to discuss how the skill connects to the text.

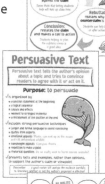

Argument Have students consult the online *Science and Engineering Practices Handbook* for more information on the claim-evidence-reasoning format the characters use in the story. They can also use the *Parts of an Argument Anchor Chart* as a reference.

Persuasive Text Maddie makes an argument about how gravity affects objects. Display the *Persuasive Text Anchor Chart* to provide tips for analyzing evidence to determine whether an argument is effective.

Discussion Use the *How to Have a Discussion Anchor Chart* to talk about how the two fifth-grade classes in the story communicate via technology. Which speaking and listening skills do students think are the most important when two groups aren't in the same room?

Preview

Build on Prior Knowledge Affix a small plastic figure to a ball and then have students rotate the ball to show how the figure changes position. Ask how a person standing on the round Earth can always be standing upright. Ask why it's difficult to know that you are living on a sphere when you are standing on Earth.

Preview the Phenomenon Ask students to study the illustration on pages 2–3 of the story, which shows a teacher holding a globe as his students look on. Remind students that they are studying the effects of gravity on Earth. Encourage them to record the first questions that come into their minds about gravity and Earth, as represented by the globe. Point out that their questions might change as they read through the selection. Have them keep their questions nearby and periodically check to see if any can be answered.

Our Friends Are Falling (continued)

Discover

Read to Learn

The **Read to Learn** suggestions inside the book's front cover encourage students to interact with the book multiple times for different purposes.

> **Preview** Students look for unfamiliar words and share them with a partner. New terms may include *gravity* and *hemisphere*. Have students look up words they aren't sure about and notice how they are used in the context of the story.

> **Skim** Students skim the illustrations. Have them turn to a partner and share their predictions of what the story will be about.

> **Read** As students read the story, ask them to look for connections to one of the following anchor chart skills. **Argument, Persuasive Text, Discussion**

Support Sense Making

Choose one or more of the following:

▶ Be sure students can identify the phenomenon presented on the opening pages of the reader: Zack's little brother wants to know how people in Australia stay put if gravity is always pulling things down. The story follows students' efforts to understand that Earth is spherical and gravity pulls things toward the center of Earth.

▶ Have students analyze the claim-evidence-reasoning argument the characters make at the end of the story. Does their evidence support the claim that gravity is a force that pulls objects toward the center of Earth? Is their reasoning sound? Have students work in pairs to present their own claim, evidence, and reasoning related to the phenomenon.

▶ If the diagrams on pages 8 and 9 are confusing to students, have them model the phenomena with a small toy car and a beach ball—or other objects that students choose for modeling. Discuss how a 3D model can help you understand something in a way that a flat image may not.

▶ Encourage a student-led discussion of the pull of gravity on growing plants. Have students draw a model of a plant, using labels to describe its different parts. Ask them to develop an argument that uses gravity and sunlight as evidence to support these growth patterns: plants' roots grow down toward the ground while stems and leaves grow upward toward the sky.

Extend

Science Stretch

The **Science Stretch** suggestions inside the book's back cover help students think about what they read. Students can complete one or more as time allows.

> Make an organizer to compare and contrast magnetism and gravity. Students can use a T-chart, a Venn diagram, or another format.

> Support an argument that you should not use the word down when describing gravity. **Sample answer:** The word down is a matter of perspective and can lead people to think Australians are upside down. It is better to say gravity pulls things toward the center of Earth.

> Which evidence that Earth is not flat was most convincing? **Sample answer:** The pictures of a car driving toward a mountain convinced me because I have experienced seeing only the tops of mountains until getting closer to them.

 SOCIAL EMOTIONAL LEARNING

How could you help someone who was upset about making the wrong claim? **Sample answer:** I would tell them that scientists and engineers often make initial claims that aren't supported by facts. This can lead them to make a better claim or even a new discovery.

Check for Comprehension Have students pause to think about gravity on Earth and then respond to the following prompts: *I became more aware of . . ., I didn't realize that . . ., I still don't understand . . .* Ask volunteers to share their responses with the class.

An Ant's View of the World

Activity Guide, pages 250–251

TIME ESTIMATE

50 min

POSSIBLE MATERIALS

☐ small ball, such as a golf ball

☐ medium ball, such as a basketball

☐ large ball, such as a large beach ball

☐ ruler (optional)

PREPARATION

Make sure you have three spheres of different sizes. Remind students that the spheres are models of Earth and they shouldn't be bounced. Model for the students how to look at each ball from various angles. You may choose to provide rulers so students can consistently hold the balls the same distance from their faces.

INVESTIGATIVE PHENOMENON
Earth's size makes it appear flat to people on its surface.

Phenomenon Explained Students explore the **investigative phenomenon** by using models to make and record observations to explain how Earth's size affects our perception of its shape.

Form a Question After they study a photograph of Earth's surface, students should form a question about the fact that the surface appears flat to people standing on the ground. If students struggle to form a question, ask them to consider how the ground appears in the photo and how it might appear in a different location. **Sample answers:** Why does Earth's surface appear flat? Does Earth's surface look mostly flat everywhere, or is it different in different places? How can something round look flat?

STEPS 1 and 2 Students observe three balls of different sizes from the same distance and draw what they see. **Sample answer:** Students' drawings of the small and medium ball should show spheres. Their drawings of the large ball should show a portion of the ball. They will not be able to see the entire shape of the ball.

Students infer what an ant on a large ball would see and experience of the ball. **Sample answer:** The ball would look flat to the ant because it only sees a small part of the ball. It likely would not know it was on a ball.

Students complete a table summarizing the effect of the size of the ball on whether it appears round or flat. Help students understand that their perception of the ball's shape depends on its size.

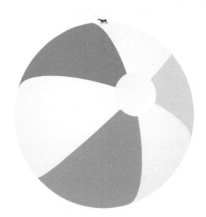

- **Make a Claim** Claims should indicate that Earth's surface appears flat to people standing on the ground because of Earth's large size.

- **Evidence** Students should cite as evidence their observations of the surfaces of balls of different sizes.

- **Reasoning** Students should explain their reasoning that Earth's surface appears flat from the ground because it is large, just like the surface of the balls appeared flatter the larger the ball.

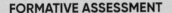

FORMATIVE ASSESSMENT

MAKING SENSE OF PHENOMENA

Students gain understanding that Earth's size makes it appear flat to people on its surface as they explore the **investigative phenomenon.** They should connect this to the **anchoring phenomenon** that Earth's surface may appear flat, but the world is actually a sphere. Students should understand that, just as a larger beach ball appears flat to a tiny ant, Earth's large size makes it appear flat to the much smaller people on its surface. From greater distances or heights, such as at the height of skydivers high in the sky, Earth's round or spherical shape is easier to see.

REMEDIATION If students struggle to connect the **investigative phenomenon** back to the **anchoring phenomenon,** have them discuss which one the balls they observed appeared flat and why.

MAKING SENSE OF PHENOMENA IDEA ORGANIZER

After completing Exploration 1, students can fill in the **Idea Organizer** to summarize the connection between Earth's size making it appear flat to people on its surface and the anchoring phenomenon that Earth's surface, on which the skydivers will land, is actually a sphere.

Activity Outcome

Students should use models to make and record observations to explain that Earth appears flat to people on its surface because Earth is very large.

Performance Indicators	
	use models to make observations
	record observations of the models
	explain how Earth's size affects our perception of Earth's shape

A Trip around the World

Activity Guide, pages 252–255

TIME ESTIMATE

45 min

SHORT ON TIME?
You may opt to inflate the globes prior to class and tape on the figures. Then, have students skip Steps 1 and 2.

POSSIBLE MATERIALS

☐ clear, inflatable globe with labeled continents and compass rose

☐ small plastic figures

☐ transparent tape

PREPARATION
Before the activity, you may want to review the seven continents and how to use a compass rose on a globe to determine direction. Set up the investigation space in a well-lit section of the classroom to make observations easier. Clear, inflatable globes can be found at toy stores and convenience stores. Tell students you intend to reuse these globes, so they should not bounce or throw them. Ask them to use care when removing tape so they don't rip the globes.

INVESTIGATIVE PHENOMENON
Gravity affects objects on Earth's surface.

Phenomenon Explained Students explore the **investigative phenomenon** by using a model to observe how gravity affects objects on Earth's surface. They state a claim and support it with evidence.

Form a Question After learning about antipodes, students should form a question about how people on different parts of Earth's surface experience the ground and sky. If students struggle to form a question, ask them to identify anything they find surprising or unexpected from the pictures of the cities and their locations on Earth's surface. **Sample answer:** How do people on opposite sides of Earth experience the direction of the ground and sky in the same way?

STEPS 1 and 2 Students inflate the globes and tape a plastic figure to each continent. If the adhesive tape does not affix the figures to the globe, try using small pieces of duct tape or shorter objects with flatter bases, such as golf tees.

STEP 3 Students look through the globe to observe the figure in Africa and describe the figure's position. **Sample answer:** The figure appeared to be standing almost sideways.

STEP 4 Students describe what they can see of the other figures when they observe from near the feet of one of the figures. Remind students to look across the globe's surface to mimic the perspective of the figure. **Sample answer:** I can see the heads of some of the figures.

STEPS 5, 6, and 7 Students describe the figures in the Southern Hemisphere with the North Pole facing up. Then, students describe the figure in North America with Australia facing up. Many people think of the Southern Hemisphere as the bottom of Earth, but that is arbitrary. Some images of Earth taken from space show Africa pointing in the opposite direction from most world maps. In space, planets do not have a top or bottom.

- **Make a Claim** Claims should indicate that because gravity pulls us toward the center of Earth, we feel upright anywhere on Earth's surface.

- **Evidence** Students should cite as evidence their observations from the activity about the orientations of the figures in their model.

- **Reasoning** Students should explain their reasoning that, as in their model, at every location on Earth the surface is "down" and the sky is "up" from the point of view of a person standing at that location.

FORMATIVE ASSESSMENT

MAKING SENSE OF PHENOMENA

Students gain understanding that gravity affects objects on Earth's surface as they explore the **investigative phenomenon.** They should connect this to the **anchoring phenomenon** that gravity is a force that pulls objects on Earth's surface toward its center. They should understand gravity pulls the skydivers toward the ground and will keep pulling them toward the ground when they land.

REMEDIATION If students struggle to connect the **investigative phenomenon** back to the **anchoring phenomenon,** have student pairs discuss how the gravity that affects people all over the world would affect the skydivers.

Activity Outcome

Students should use a model of Earth to support a claim that gravity affects objects on different parts of Earth's surface in the same way.

Performance Indicators	
	use a model of Earth to make observations
	make a claim that gravity affects objects on Earth's surface in the same way
	support the claim using observations as evidence

MAKING SENSE OF PHENOMENA IDEA ORGANIZER

After completing Exploration 2, students can fill in the **Idea Organizer** to summarize the connection between gravity affecting objects on Earth's surface and the anchoring phenomenon that gravity is a force that pulls objects and people anywhere on Earth's surface, like the landing skydivers, toward its center.

SOCIAL EMOTIONAL LEARNING

As students consider people living in other parts of the world, help them connect with others near and far by reminding them that the world is their community. Encourage them to periodically ask themselves questions such as: How can I help my community? What problem can our school help solve in the community?

An Attractive Sphere

Activity Guide, pages 256–260

Preconception Alert While students may state that Earth is a sphere, many do not perceive it that way themselves. It is difficult to comprehend that people can live on the bottom of a ball. The pull of gravity, interpreted by our senses, is what makes us feel upright and determines what we call "up" and "down."

Materials Alert Gather small toy boats and a large ball for students to use to model the boat going over the horizon. Gather balls or marbles for students to use when exploring the **everyday phenomenon.**

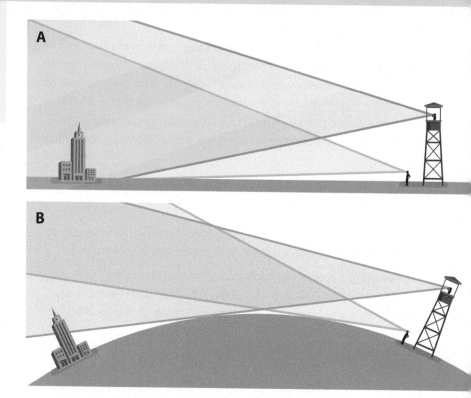

INVESTIGATIVE PHENOMENON
Everyday experiences on Earth's surface provide evidence for Earth's spherical shape and the pull of gravity.

Phenomenon Explained Students explore the **investigative phenomenon** by analyzing models to explain how observations of distant objects can provide evidence of Earth's shape. They also use models to predict how gravity affects objects on Earth.

The View from Above

You may wish to have students discuss the diagrams in this Exploration in pairs. First, have students write their responses to the questions. Then, pair students to share their answers. In this way, students can explain their thinking to a partner. When they are done sharing, discuss as a class.

If the images of the ships in this Exploration are confusing to students, have them model the phenomena with small toy boats and a ball in the classroom. Have the students move the toy boat different distances to represent the boat sailing over the horizon.

Earth's Shape and Gravity

Everyday Phenomenon Objects on Earth fall to the ground because of gravity.

Ask students to list some everyday objects they observed falling (such as raindrops, balls, and leaves) and identify the direction in which they fell. To reinforce this everyday experience, provide small balls or marbles, and have students drop the balls from desk height to observe how gravity affects the objects.

Playing Ball

Students predict how a ball will move and explain how location affects their prediction. **Sample answer:** The soccer ball will move toward the boy, dropping towards the ground as it moves through the air. This is true anywhere on Earth, and it does not depend on where the boy is playing.

SOCIAL EMOTIONAL LEARNING

Encourage students to think of you, their teacher, as part of their team in learning reflection and self-assessment. Students can engage in this reflective activity by writing out their ideas. Other students may find it helpful to assess their understanding by making a graphic organizer or drawing. As a group, brainstorm ways for students to organize their thoughts during self-assessment.

FORMATIVE ASSESSMENT

MAKING SENSE OF PHENOMENA

Students gain understanding that everyday experiences on Earth's surface provide evidence for Earth's spherical shape and the pull of gravity as they explore the **investigative phenomenon.** They should connect this to the **anchoring phenomenon** that Earth is a sphere whose gravity pulls objects and people like the falling skydivers toward its center. Students should understand that observations of what can be seen from different heights and of ships moving over the horizon provide evidence of Earth's spherical shape. The information that people all over the world experience the ground as "down" is evidence that gravity pulls objects towards the center of Earth.

REMEDIATION If students struggle to connect the **investigative phenomenon** back to the **anchoring phenomenon,** have them make a two-column chart for Earth's spherical shape. In one column, students should list their evidence for the Earth's shape, and in the second column, students should describe how Earth's shape affects the skydivers. They can then make a second chart focusing on their evidence for the pull of gravity and how that affects the skydivers.

MAKING SENSE OF PHENOMENA IDEA ORGANIZER

After completing Exploration 3, students can fill in **the Idea Organizer** to summarize the connection between everyday experiences on Earth's surface providing evidence for its shape and the pull of gravity and the anchoring phenomenon that Earth is a sphere whose gravity pulls objects and people like the skydivers toward its center.

01

Take It Further

Engage • Explore/Explain • **Elaborate** • Evaluate

TIME ESTIMATE

45 min

These Take It Further paths may be completed to enrich and extend students' comprehension of content covered within this lesson.

ONLINE

Engineer a Parachute

Students use an engineering design process to build and test a parachute. In the process, they gather evidence to explain forces that can oppose Earth's gravity.

Life in Space

Students learn about and research how astronauts deal with everyday activities in space.

Weighing In

Students calculate weights on other planets based on a weight on Earth.

Lesson Check

Can You Explain It?

Now I know or think that . . .

Sample answer: The skydivers will not fall away from Earth's curved surface because gravity pulls everything towards Earth's center. People describe this as "down," so an object that falls and is pulled towards Earth's center by gravity is said to "fall down." People all over the world experience the ground as down because of gravity, so no matter where the skydivers are falling towards, they will fall towards the ground.

After completing the lesson, use the **Making Sense Idea Organizer** to summarize the connections between the **investigative phenomena** and **anchoring phenomenon.**

MAKING CONNECTIONS

After students complete the lesson, they should be able to answer a question about an alternative phenomenon to explain why satellites don't fly away from Earth. **Sample answer:** Gravity pulls objects near Earth's surface toward Earth's center. If the satellites are relatively close to Earth, gravity will pull them towards Earth's center as they go around the planet, keeping them in orbit.

Checkpoints

1. a—Higher elevations allow you to see around the curve of Earth's horizon.; b—You see only the top part of a ship as it sails over the horizon.

2. b—gravity

3. toward Earth's center; away from Earth's center

4. **Sample answer:** Both of us will observe that the balls fall toward the ground, toward Earth's center. All over the world, people experience the ground as down because gravity pulls objects towards Earth's center.

5. **Sample answer:** Earth appears flat to people on its surface because Earth is very big compared to people and what we can perceive.

6. image 2

7. **Sample answer:** Gravity pulls everything toward the center of Earth. This is why people all over the world always feel like Earth is beneath them.

8. a—Gravity is a force.; b—Gravity affects all matter on Earth.

 SOCIAL EMOTIONAL LEARNING

Have students reflect on the goals they set at the beginning of the lesson. Ask them to think about whether the goals were accomplished or if there were challenges. Have students share the factors that contributed to their success. If the goals were not achieved, talk about what students can do to help them achieve the goals.

02 Sky Patterns Over Time

ANCHORING PHENOMENON
From one day to the next, the time the sun sets at a location changes.

ENGAGE Can You Explain It?
Students observe and ask questions about sunsets and their timing. They answer the Can You Explain It? question to identify what they will gather evidence about in the lesson.

EVALUATE Lesson Check
Students gauge their understanding of the anchoring phenomenon.

HANDS-ON ACTIVITY

EXPLORATION 1 Shadows `50 min`
Investigative Phenomenon The length and direction of a shadow changes throughout the day.

Students connect back to the **anchoring phenomenon** that the apparent motion of the sun across the sky due to Earth's motion in space causes patterns that can be observed.

HANDS-ON ACTIVITY

EXPLORATION 2 The Night Moves `40 min`
Investigative Phenomenon Earth's revolution around the sun can explain patterns in the sky.

Students connect back to the **anchoring phenomenon** that Earth has regular patterns of motion, which can explain how and when objects become visible and appear to move in the sky.

EXPLORATION 3 Objects in the Sky `40 min`
Investigative Phenomenon Patterns can be observed in the position, apparent motion, and time of day the sun, moon, and stars appear in the sky.

Students connect back to the **anchoring phenomenon** that Earth has regular patterns of motion, which can explain how and when objects become visible and appear to move in the sky.

EXPLORATION 4 What Patterns Do the Sun and Moon Cause During the Year? `40 min`
Investigative Phenomenon Monthly and yearly patterns in the sky are caused by Earth's and the moon's motions in space.

Students connect back to the **anchoring phenomenon** that the apparent motion of the sun across the sky due to Earth's rotation and revolution causes patterns that can be observed, such as changes in the time the sun appears to set at a location.

Making 3D Connections

The anchoring phenomenon in this lesson supports students' understanding of and application of these Next Generation Science Standards.

Building to the Performance Expectations

5-ESS1-2 Represent data in graphical displays to reveal patterns of daily changes in length and direction of shadows, day and night, and the seasonal appearance of some stars in the night sky.

SEP	DCI	CCC
Analyzing and Interpreting Data Represent data in graphical displays (bar graphs, pictographs and/or pie charts) to reveal patterns that indicate relationships. *(Explorations 1, 2, 3, 4)*	**ESS1.B Earth and the Solar System** The orbits of Earth around the sun and of the moon around Earth, together with the rotation of Earth about an axis between its North and South poles, cause observable patterns. These include day and night; daily changes in the length and direction of shadows; and different positions of the sun, moon, and stars at different times of the day, month, and year. *(Explorations 1, 2, 3, 4)*	**Patterns** Similarities and differences in patterns can be used to sort, classify, communicate and analyze simple rates of change for natural phenomena. *(Explorations 1, 2, 3, 4)*

Vocabulary

Word Wall   A word wall, anchor chart, or Language Development chart can be used to support vocabulary.

constellation group of stars that appears to make a pattern in the night sky

orbit path of one object in space around another

revolution a full movement of an object in space around another

You may want to include additional academic terms such as *altitude* and *rotation* and any other terms students might struggle with.

Language Development Prompt students to complete the chart when they come to these highlighted terms within the lesson and to add their own terms as they come across unknown science terms.

Anchor Chart As you progress through the unit, you may want to make a vocabulary-based Anchor Chart using the Language Development chart as a guide that can be displayed and filled out as a whole group during each lesson.

02 Sky Patterns Over Time

Activity Guide, pages 264–265

Students can engage in the Can You Explain It? content by observing the photograph or by exploring the corresponding video online.

ONLINE  View a video related to sunsets.

ANCHORING PHENOMENON
From one day to the next, the time the sun sets at a location changes.

PHENOMENON EXPLAINED
Sunsets at the same location on consecutive days may look exactly the same, but because of Earth's motion in space the sunsets' times are different.

Lesson Objective

Students can explore patterns observed over different time scales and caused by Earth's motion and its interactions with the sun and moon. They collect and analyze data to detect patterns, including the path of the sun across the day sky, the movements of constellations in the night sky, and hours of sunlight.

Support Discovery

The following prompts can be used to guide student-led discovery.

I notice . . .

After observing the photograph or watching the video, students should record what they noticed about the sunset. If students struggle to record observations, ask them to focus on changes in the amount and color of light in the sky as the sun's position changes in the video, or ask them to focus on how the sky in the photograph looks different than the daytime sky.

Sample answer: I notice that the sky is multiple colors. I notice that the landscape is darker than it would be during the day.

I wonder . . .

After observing the photograph or watching the video, students should record what they want to find out more about regarding the time the sun appears to set. If students struggle to record what they want to know more about, ask them to work with a partner to brainstorm as many questions as they can.

Sample answer: I wonder if the sun sets at the same time every day. I wonder what determines when the sun sets. The sun looks like it disappears because Earth is round and spinning.

Can You Explain It?

In the Can You Explain It?, students make an initial claim that explains the **Anchoring Phenomenon.**
Sample answer: Students may draw a model of a sunset with Earth and the sun, or they may write a sentence proposing a cause for the variation in the time of sunset.

In the lesson, students gather evidence about the motion of Earth in space. This will enable them to give a more complete explanation of the **Anchoring Phenomenon** at the end of the lesson.

Alternative Phenomenon

If students are unfamiliar with observing the position or timing of the setting sun, discuss other observations they might have made of the sun, such as how high it gets in the sky in summer versus winter or how the path it takes across the sky varies with the seasons.

SOCIAL EMOTIONAL LEARNING

Guide students to reflect on their goals from previous lessons and on any feedback they received from their teachers or peers. Then, have each student set a personal goal for this lesson and make a plan for how to achieve the goal. Throughout the lesson, take daily breaks for students to track their progress in meeting their goals. As students move from lesson to lesson, they can continue to work towards their initial goals or set new ones. If students struggle setting goals for this lesson, share with them some of the following ideas: connecting Earth's motion in space to observable patterns in the sky, interpreting data, identifying patterns in natural phenomena, or participating more during activity/group work.

Searching for Sunrise

WHEN TO USE

SCIENCE (30 min)

- Anchoring Phenomenon / Alternative Phenomenon
- Options for ELA Instruction
- Build on Prior Knowledge
- Preview the Phenomenon
- Read to Learn
- Support Sense Making
- Science Stretch
- Check for Comprehension

Option 1 Use before students begin the lesson in the Activity Guide to provide an engaging model to introduce the lesson's phenomenon.

Option 2 Use after students have completed the Activity Guide to reinforce students' understanding of the lesson phenomenon by exploring a related phenomenon.

ELA (20 min)

- Options for ELA Instruction
- Build on Prior Knowledge
- Read to Learn

Option 3 To use during designated ELA Reading time for independent reading, whole-class instruction, or small-group instruction, look for this icon: ELA

Plan

> ### ANCHORING PHENOMENON / ALTERNATIVE PHENOMENON
>
> The anchoring phenomenon in the Activity Guide is *From one day to the next, the time the sun sets at a location changes.* The main example is a photo of the sun appearing to set over mountains. The FUNomenal Reader presents a similar phenomenon *(From one day to the next, the time the sun rises at a location changes)*, and the example is a girl who wonders why the sun appears in a different place in the sky each day at 7 a.m. Both present the same science concepts and cover the same standards but with different phenomena. Guide students to draw connections between the two situations and to understand the underlying principle: daily patterns in the sky are caused by interactions and relative positions of bodies in the solar system.

Options for ELA Instruction

Choose one of the following anchor chart options and project it or print copies. Then display and introduce the chart before reading the text.

Retell Use the *Retell Anchor Chart* to help gauge students' understanding of the concepts in the story. Pair students and have them take turns retelling the story, focusing on the problem the main character addresses (why it gets light later each morning) and the resolution of that problem (learning about the effects on Earth of bodies in the solar system).

Synthesize Have students take what they already know about patterns in the sky and add it to what they learn in the story. After reading, they can synthesize their new understanding by applying it to their own daily schedule and future plans. They can use the *Synthesize Anchor Chart* as a guide.

Research In the story, Rylie does online research to learn more about sunrise times throughout the year. Have students refer to the *Research Anchor Chart* as a reminder of good sources to use when doing their own research.

Preview

© Houghton Mifflin Harcourt Publishing Company • Image Credits: ©HMH

ELA **Build on Prior Knowledge** Have students discuss the kinds of patterns they see in relation to day and night. For example, they know that the sun "comes up" every morning and "goes back down" at night. They know that on most nights the moon can be seen, although it may appear to vary in size and shape.

Preview the Phenomenon Ask students to study the photos and illustrations on pages 2–3 of the story, which show a girl getting ready to ride her bike to school at 7 a.m. The two scenes are alike except for the clothes she is wearing, the color of the sky behind her, the sun's position, and that her bike light is on. Encourage students to record the first questions that come into their minds about why the scenes might be slightly different. Point out that their questions might change as they read through the selection. Have them keep their questions nearby and periodically check to see if any can be answered.

STANDARDS SUPPORTED

SEP
Analyzing and Interpreting Data

DCI
ESS1.B Earth and the Solar System

CCC
Patterns

Searching for Sunrise (continued)

Discover

Read to Learn

The **Read to Learn** suggestions inside the book's front cover encourage students to interact with the book multiple times for different purposes.

> **Preview** Students look for unfamiliar words and share them with a partner. New terms may include *axis, revolve,* and *hemisphere.* Have students look up words they aren't sure about and notice how they are used in the context of the story.

> **Skim** Students skim the photos and illustrations. Have them turn to a partner and share their predictions of what the story will be about.

> **Read** As students read the story, ask them to look for connections to one of the following anchor chart skills. **Retell, Synthesize, Research**

Support Sense Making

Choose one or more of the following:

▶ Be sure students can identify the phenomenon presented on the opening pages of the reader: Rylie wonders why the sun's position changes over several weeks when she leaves home for school at 7 a.m. The story follows her efforts to understand how Earth's rotation, revolution around the sun, and tilt cause the time of sunrise to change.

▶ In the story, Rylie keeps track of sunrise and sunset times in a chart. Have students work in small groups to discuss the benefits of using charts and graphs to analyze data. Elicit that this is one way scientists organize information to help themselves and others understand concepts.

▶ Discuss the steps Rylie takes to answer her question about why the sun rises later and later each day. Write the steps on the board as students

call them out. The list should include that Rylie first asks questions. Then she does research on the computer to find answers. She adds the data she finds to a chart and makes observations of the daytime and nighttime sky. At the science center, she watches a planetarium show, looks at models, and uses an interactive program.

▶ Challenge students to chart their own observations of sunrise or sunset times over several weeks and share their findings with the class. Discuss the role the sun plays in sustaining life on Earth. Help students understand that Earth's rotation and revolution around the sun affects the number of hours of daylight each day, which, in turn, has an impact on temperature, climate, and food chains.

Extend

Science Stretch

The **Science Stretch** suggestions inside the book's back cover help students think about what they read. Students can complete one or more as time allows.

> Have students research how moons move around a planet such as Saturn. Provide books and links to approved websites for students to use as they do their research.

> Students may discover how Earth's tilt affects climate. Students can work in pairs or small groups to make a model for demonstrating their findings.

> Make a claim about the position of a constellation in the evening. Collect data to support your claim. Refer students to the online *Science and Engineering Handbook* for more information on using claims, evidence, and reasoning.

 SOCIAL EMOTIONAL LEARNING

Make a plan to find out more about a topic that interests you. As needed, guide students in setting short-term goals on how they will go about finding answers to their questions.

Check for Comprehension Have students write three things they found out in this story, two things they found particularly interesting, and one question they still have about sunrise, sunset, and the seasons.

Shadows

Activity Guide, pages 266–269

TIME ESTIMATE

50 min

POSSIBLE MATERIALS

- ☐ new pencil or dowel
- ☐ modeling clay
- ☐ posterboard
- ☐ metric ruler
- ☐ marker
- ☐ other objects students may need to complete their plans

PREPARATION

Plan the activity for a sunny day. Set aside time for students to participate in this activity by scheduling it out in advance. Keep in mind that this activity will require data collection over the course of a full day. The materials listed are a starting point. You can replace the pencil or dowel with different cylindrical objects, such as a cardboard paper towel tube.

> ## INVESTIGATIVE PHENOMENON
> The length and direction of a shadow changes throughout the day.

Phenomenon Explained Students explore the **investigative phenomenon** by planning and conducting an investigation to gather evidence and explain how the sun's apparent motion across the sky causes shadows to change.

Form a Question After viewing the photograph of the shadows, students should form a question about how shadows change throughout the day. If students struggle to form a question, ask them to remember a time when they saw objects casting very long shadows and think of a question about those shadows. Sample answer: When are shadows shortest or longest? Why do shadows change throughout the day?

STEP 1 As a class, students choose and record the most important questions about shadows. Sample answer: How does a change in the position of a light cause a shadow to change?

STEP 2 Students list needed materials and develop a plan. Make sure their plans carefully show each step in their process.

Everyday Phenomenon **Shadows happen when objects block light.**

Students should be familiar with shadows. As students plan their investigations, encourage them to consider gathering data about the objects blocking light and the light source.

STEP 3 Students carry out their plan and record data in the format of their choice.

- **Make a Claim** Claims should indicate that as the light source (sun) appears to move across the sky, the shadow changes size and position.

- **Evidence** Students should cite as evidence the data from the activity that an object's shadow points in a different direction in the afternoon than in the evening, and the shadow also likely changes length.

- **Reasoning** Students should explain their reasoning, such as because the shadow changed size and position from morning to afternoon, the changes are related to the apparent motion of the sun across the sky.

FORMATIVE ASSESSMENT

MAKING SENSE OF PHENOMENA

Students gain understanding that the length and direction of a shadow changes throughout the day as they explore the **investigative phenomenon.** They should connect this to the **anchoring phenomenon** that the apparent motion of the sun across the sky causes patterns that can be observed, including patterns in the time the sun appears to set.

REMEDIATION If students struggle to connect the **investigative phenomenon** back to the **anchoring phenomenon,** have them review their data on the apparent motion of the light source (sun) in the sky and reflect on how the sun appears to move as it sets.

Activity Outcome

Students should plan and conduct an investigation to record data on how shadows change throughout the day in order to infer that the changes are caused by the apparent motion of the sun across the sky.

Performance Indicators	
	plan and conduct an investigation
	record data on how shadows change throughout the day
	make and support a claim that the sun's apparent motion across the sky causes changes in shadows during the day

MAKING SENSE OF PHENOMENA IDEA ORGANIZER

After completing Exploration 1, students can fill in the **Idea Organizer** to summarize the connection between the changing length and direction of a shadow throughout the day and the anchoring phenomenon that the apparent motion of the sun across the sky due to Earth's motion in space causes patterns that can be observed, such as the changing time of sunset.

SOCIAL EMOTIONAL LEARNING

Students should identify at least one positive contribution from every member of the group. Encourage them to reflect on the full activity, from forming questions through planning and carrying out their investigation and ending in analyzing their data. Invite students to share this positive feedback with the members of their group while emphasizing the importance of recognizing each person's value on the team.

The Night Moves

Activity Guide, pages 270–271

TIME ESTIMATE

40 min

POSSIBLE MATERIALS

☐ butcher paper

☐ string

☐ star maps for each season, labeled with the season

PREPARATION

Make a large sun out of butcher paper by cutting a circle. Ideally this should be very large, about 6 feet in diameter. Hang the model sun in the center of the room. Tell students it is the sun and they must look in the opposite direction from the sun throughout the activity. Make large copies of star maps of constellations for each season—one for each station students will stop at as they revolve around the sun. See page 282 for examples of seasonal constellations. Hang or tape the star maps on each wall of the room; label the maps with the appropriate season. Have students begin with summer.

INVESTIGATIVE PHENOMENON
Earth's revolution around the sun can explain patterns in the sky.

Phenomenon Explained Students explore the **investigative phenomenon** by using a model to gather evidence and explain how Earth's motion around the sun causes the apparent position of stars in the sky to change over the course of a year.

Form a Question After reading about constellations and observing the photograph, students should form a question about how Earth's motion relates to which constellations are visible. If students struggle to form a question, have them brainstorm ideas with a partner. Sample answer: What causes different constellations to be visible at different times?

Everyday Phenomenon   **Objects blocking our view affect what we can see.**

Students should understand that we cannot see through objects such as desks or books. Ask students to identify objects in the classroom that block their view of another object in the classroom. As students work through this modeling activity, encourage them to think about which objects in space affect the view of the constellations from Earth.

STEP 1   Students position themselves with their backs to the sun and record the constellations they observe in front of them.

STEP 2   Students model one-quarter revolution of Earth and record their observations, then repeat the same step twice.

STEP 3 Students model one rotation of Earth and record their observations. **Sample answer:** It was daytime when I faced the sun.

- **Make a Claim** Claims should indicate that the constellations appear to move as Earth revolves around the sun.

- **Evidence** Students should cite as evidence the data from the activity that they observed different constellations with each partial revolution.

- **Reasoning** Students should explain their reasoning that relates Earth revolving around the sun as the cause of the changes in which constellations are observable from Earth.

FORMATIVE ASSESSMENT

MAKING SENSE OF PHENOMENA

Students gain understanding that Earth's revolution around the sun can explain patterns in the sky as they explore the **investigative phenomenon.** They should connect this to the **anchoring phenomenon** that Earth has regular patterns of motion which can explain how and when objects become visible and appear to move in the sky. Students should understand that patterns in the constellations visible at different times of the year and in the time of sunset can be explained by Earth's revolution around the sun.

REMEDIATION If students struggle to connect the **investigative phenomenon** back to the **anchoring phenomenon,** have a class discussion of what students modeled in the activity and how they could make a model to investigate patterns in the time of sunset.

MAKING SENSE OF PHENOMENA IDEA ORGANIZER

After completing Exploration 2, students can fill in the **Idea Organizer** to summarize the connection between Earth's revolution around the sun explaining patterns in the sky and the anchoring phenomenon that Earth has regular patterns of motion, which can explain patterns in the sky, such as the time the sun appears to set.

Activity Outcome

Students should use a model to observe changes in the apparent position of the stars in the sky in order to make and support a claim connecting those changes to Earth's revolution around the sun.

Performance Indicators	
	use a model to observe changes in the apparent position of the stars in the sky
	make a claim that Earth's revolution around the sun causes different stars to be visible during different times of the year
	support the claim using observations as evidence

Objects in the Sky

Activity Guide, pages 272–278

TIME ESTIMATE

40 min

Materials Alert A time zone map and globe may be helpful in this Exploration in clarifying concepts of Earth's rotation and changing time zones.

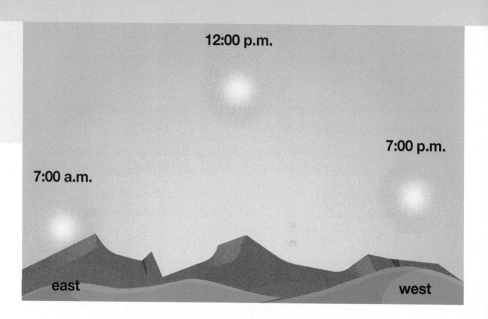

12:00 p.m.

7:00 p.m.

7:00 a.m.

east   west

> ## INVESTIGATIVE PHENOMENON
> Patterns can be observed in the position, apparent motion, and time of day that the sun, moon, and stars appear in the sky.

Phenomenon Explained Students explore the **investigative phenomenon** by interpreting data and making a model to identify daily patterns and explain how objects appear to move in the sky.

The Moving Sun

After students study the image at the top of the page, emphasize the concept of patterns. Point out that because this is the sun's cycle every day, it is considered a pattern.

Students interpret a graph to describe daily patterns in the sun's altitude. **Sample answer:** The sun is low in the sky in the mornings and late afternoons; its angle is about 25°. The sun is highest in the sky around noon; its angle is about 70°.

The Night Sky

Students analyze a model of changes in the night sky overnight to describe patterns. **Sample answer:** a. The stars are in a specific place in the sky.; b. The stars all shifted to the right. I see a new constellation, Hercules, on the left.; c. The stars appear to move across the night sky to the right.; d. Orion moved so far to the right that it can't be seen anymore.

Your Turn

Students draw a diagram to model the cause of the apparent motion of the sun and stars across the sky. **Sample answer:** Student diagrams should show Earth rotating from left to right, giving the sun and stars their apparent movement across the sky.

Have students compare their models in small groups and look for common patterns and themes about how Earth moves in space. Encourage groups to also discuss differences in their models. As students work through the rest of this Exploration and the lesson, encourage them to revisit these models, using all of the evidence they gather to resolve differences in their understanding.

As the World Turns

Some students may be thrown off by the time difference between the United States (Gabriella) and New Zealand (Sophie). They might wonder how Sophie could be eating breakfast if the people to her west are in bed or eating dinner. Explain that it is Monday afternoon for Gabriella and Tuesday morning for Sophie. Use a time zone map for clarity and help students relate the different time zones to Earth's one rotation on its axis every 24 hours.

Students infer why different places have different times. **Sample answer:** Patterns of night and day are related to Earth's rotation. As Earth rotates, different parts of it experience day, and others experience night.

SOCIAL EMOTIONAL LEARNING

Students may consider cultural factors, methods of communication, shared interests, and other aspects of building and maintaining friendships. As students discuss their friendships, use the opportunity to reinforce the importance of building and maintaining relationships. Encourage students to share ways they build and keep local and long-distance friendships and why they do so.

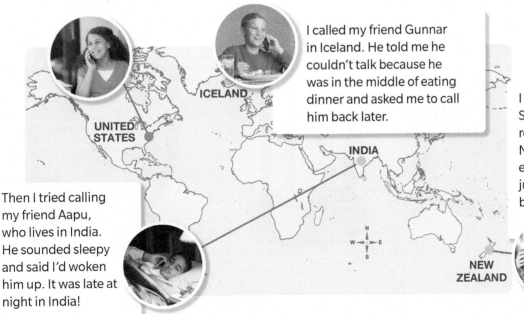

I called my friend Gunnar in Iceland. He told me he couldn't talk because he was in the middle of eating dinner and asked me to call him back later.

I called my friend Sophie, who'd recently moved to New Zealand. It was early, and she had just started eating breakfast.

Then I tried calling my friend Aapu, who lives in India. He sounded sleepy and said I'd woken him up. It was late at night in India!

ICELAND

UNITED STATES

INDIA

NEW ZEALAND

Objects in the Sky (continued)

Daylight

Students use sunrise and sunset data to calculate the number of daylight hours for several days. Then, they use the data to make a bar graph and identify and use a pattern to predict the number of upcoming nighttime hours.

Review the table with students, pointing out that the first row has been completed for them. Model how to continue filling out the rest of the table using data they calculate, based on patterns. Ask students what kind of pattern they see in the chart. They should identify the number of daylight hours as increasing as the time of sunrise gets earlier and the time of sunset gets later.

History of Telling Time

Students learn about time-keeping devices throughout history. Invite volunteers to read aloud the description of each device. Have students discuss which devices on the page are reliant on the interactions of the sun and Earth. **Sample answer:** Sundials rely on sun–Earth interactions.

Then discuss with students the advantages and disadvantages of the device being reliant on the sun and Earth interacting. Have students identify an example of each. **Sample Answer:** An advantage is that a sundial needs only sunlight to work. A disadvantage is that a sundial doesn't work indoors, in the shade, or on a cloudy day.

Around We Go

Students complete a paragraph to summarize what they have learned about the effects of Earth's rotation. Before they begin, review in a class discussion the patterns that students have learned about so far. For example, the sun appears to rise in the east, cross the sky, and set in the west; constellations appear to move across the sky at night; and the time of sunrise and sunset and duration of daylight shifts a little from day to day.

6:45 p.m.

3:00 a.m.

FORMATIVE ASSESSMENT

MAKING SENSE OF PHENOMENA

Students gain understanding that patterns can be observed in the position, apparent motion, and time of day that the sun, moon, and stars appear in the sky as they explore the **investigative phenomenon.** They should connect this to the **anchoring phenomenon** that Earth has regular patterns of motion, which can explain how and when objects become visible and appear to move in the sky, including when the sun sets.

REMEDIATION If students struggle to connect the **investigative phenomenon** back to the **anchoring phenomenon,** have them work with a partner and make a model to explain how Earth's motion in space causes sunset.

MAKING SENSE OF PHENOMENA
IDEA ORGANIZER
After completing Exploration 3, students can fill in the **Idea Organizer** to summarize the connection between how patterns can be observed in the position, apparent motion, and time of day objects appear in the sky and the anchoring phenomenon that Earth has regular patterns of motion, which can explain how and when objects are visible and appear to move in the sky, as the sun appears to move at sunset.

What Patterns Do the Sun and Moon Cause During the Year?

Activity Guide, pages 279–284

TIME ESTIMATE

Materials Alert You may wish to provide students with colored pencils and poster paper for drawing their models.

> **INVESTIGATIVE PHENOMENON**
> Monthly and yearly patterns in the sky are caused by Earth's and the moon's motion in space.

Phenomenon Explained Students explore the **investigative phenomenon** by interpreting data and making a model to explore and explain how Earth's revolution around the sun and the moon's revolution around Earth cause observable monthly and yearly patterns in the sky.

Round and Round

Use the illustrations to contrast *orbit* and *revolution*. Explain that *orbit* can be a noun or a verb. For example, in "Earth *orbits* the sun," it's a verb. *Revolution,* on the other hand, is always a noun. Its verb form is *revolve*.

Students infer patterns caused by the revolutions of Earth and the moon. **Sample answer:** the apparent shape of the moon and the seasons; Accept all preliminary ideas based on what students have learned so far.

Moon Shapes

Students interpret a lunar calendar, determine the time from one full moon to the next, and describe patterns. **Sample answer:** In about a month's time, the moon changes from partial moons on the right side to full moon. Then, it goes from full to partial moons on the left side and ends as a dark moon. Finally, it repeats the pattern on the right side.

Revolution and Patterns

Students interpret data and graph seasonal patterns in the sun's position in the sky. Discuss how the illustrations and the graph suggest that seasonal changes repeat yearly due to Earth's motion in space.

Shifting Stars and Changing Constellations

Students analyze images and answer questions in order to explore a pattern in the positions of stars as Earth revolves around the sun.

Students explain why you can't see Pegasus in the spring.
Sample answer: Pegasus is located on the opposite side of the sun from where Earth is located during springtime.

Students record observations of constellations and complete a data chart. They use the data to identify constellations visible in winter.

Campus Constellations

Students choose a daily, monthly, or yearly pattern to model. They make a model showing how objects in space, including Earth and the sun, moon, and stars, interact to cause a pattern people observe from Earth's surface.

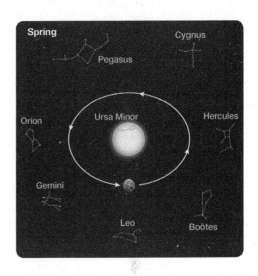

FORMATIVE ASSESSMENT

MAKING SENSE OF PHENOMENA

Students gain understanding that monthly and yearly patterns in the sky are caused by Earth's and the moon's motion in space as they explore the **investigative phenomenon.** They should connect this to the **anchoring phenomenon** that the apparent motion of the sun across the sky due to Earth's rotation and revolution causes patterns that can be observed, such as changes in the time the sun sets at a location. Students should understand that the observed yearly patterns in the position of the sun in the sky support an explanation of Earth's revolution around the sun, and that Earth's revolution around the sun causes Earth to be in a different position with respect to the sun each day at sunset, causing the time of sunset to change.

REMEDIATION If students struggle to connect the **investigative phenomenon** back to the **anchoring phenomenon,** have small groups of students explain in words or drawings how Earth's revolution around the sun causes the time of sunset to change.

MAKING SENSE OF PHENOMENA IDEA ORGANIZER

After completing Exploration 4, students can fill in the **Idea Organizer** to summarize the connection between Earth's and the moon's motion in space causing monthly and yearly patterns in the sky and the anchoring phenomenon that the apparent motion of the sun across the sky due to Earth's rotation and revolution causes patterns that can be observed, including changes in the time the sun sets at a location.

02 Take It Further

Engage • Explore/Explain • **Elaborate** • Evaluate

TIME ESTIMATE

60 min

These Take It Further paths may be completed to enrich and extend students' comprehension of content covered within this lesson.

ONLINE

Careers in Science & Engineering: Astronomer

Students explore careers in science, focusing on astronomy and the study of space.

Foucault Pendulum

Students explore the invention and use of the Foucault pendulum and what it demonstrates.

Seasonal Shadows

Students explore how the lengths of shadows change through the seasons and how the shadow lengths and seasons are related.

Ancient Calendars

Students learn that Stonehenge may have been an ancient calendar. They then research other ancient calendars.

Lesson Check

Can You Explain It?

Now I know or think that. . .

Sample answer: The sun appears to move across the sky because Earth rotates on its axis. This causes the angle of the sun to change throughout the day. Low angles in the morning and evening cause long shadows, and the high angle in the middle of the day causes short shadows. As Earth revolves around the sun, it is in a slightly different position with respect to the sun each day, so the timing of the sunset changes slightly.

After completing the lesson, use the **Making Sense Idea Organizer** to summarize the connections between the **investigative phenomena** and **anchoring phenomenon.**

MAKING CONNECTIONS

After students complete the lesson, they should be able to answer a question about an alternative phenomenon to explain why the time that the sun rises changes from one day to the next. **Sample answer:** Earth's revolution around the sun and rotation on its axis also explain why the sun rises at a slightly different time from one day to the next.

Checkpoints

1. 1:00 p.m.; 6:00 a.m.; 7:00 p.m.

2. Student graphs should show a repeating pattern with the sun low in the morning of each day, high in the middle of the day, and low in the evening.

3. b—It will rotate and face the sun.

4. a—Because Earth revolves around the sun, Earth is in different positions each season. In summer, Earth is on one side of the sun, and in then in winter, it is on the opposite side. This changes what can be seen.

5. sun; 365; moon; month

6. 4.0 meters at 8:00 a.m.; 2.1 meters at 10:00 a.m.; 0.2 meters at 12:00 p.m.

SOCIAL EMOTIONAL LEARNING

Have students reflect on the goals they set at the beginning of the lesson. Ask them to think about whether the goals were accomplished or if there were challenges. Have students share the factors that contributed to their success. If the goals were not achieved, talk about what students can do to help them achieve the goals.

03 The Sun

ANCHORING PHENOMENON
You can read by sunlight, but not by starlight at night.

ENGAGE **Can You Explain It?**
Students observe and ask questions about light availability from stars at night and a student using a head lamp to read a book under a dark night sky. They answer the Can You Explain It? question to identify what they will gather evidence about in the lesson.

EVALUATE **Lesson Check**
Students gauge their understanding of the anchoring phenomenon.

HANDS-ON ACTIVITY

EXPLORATION 1 **Glowing Light**    50 min
Investigative Phenomenon Distance from Earth affects the apparent brightness of stars.

Students connect back to the **anchoring phenomenon** that we receive more sunlight than starlight.

HANDS-ON ACTIVITY

EXPLORATION 2 **Color Provides the Final Clue**   60 min
Investigative Phenomenon Stars are bodies that emit light.

Students connect back to the **anchoring phenomenon** that the sun and other stars are similar sources of light.

EXPLORATION 3 **How Does Distance Affect the Apparent Size of Objects?**   30 min
Investigative Phenomenon Distances in space are very large.

Students connect back to the **anchoring phenomenon** that distance from Earth affects the amount (intensity) of sunlight and starlight that we receive.

EXPLORATION 4 **What Are the Sun's Characteristics?**   30 min
Investigative Phenomenon Proximity to Earth makes the sun appear larger and brighter than all other stars in the sky.

Students connect back to the **anchoring phenomenon** that the sun is Earth's nearest star and we experience it differently from other stars.

Making 3D Connections

The **anchoring phenomenon** in this lesson supports students' understanding of and application of these Next Generation Science Standards.

Building to the Performance Expectations

5-ESS1-1 Support an argument that differences in the apparent brightness of the sun compared to other stars is due to their relative distances from Earth.

SEP	DCI	CCC
Engaging in Argument from Evidence Support an argument with evidence, data, or a model. *(Explorations 1, 2, 3, 4)*	**ESS1.A The Universe and its Stars** The sun is a star that appears larger and brighter than other stars because it is closer. Stars range greatly in their distance from Earth. *(Explorations 1, 2, 3, 4)*	**Scale, Proportion, and Quantity** Natural objects exist from the very small to the immensely large. *(Explorations 1, 2, 3, 4)*

Vocabulary

Word Wall A word wall, anchor chart, or Language Development chart can be used to support vocabulary.

You may want to include additional academic terms such as *spectrum* and *characteristics* and any other terms students might struggle with.

Language Development Prompt students to add their own terms as they come across unfamiliar science terms.

Anchor Chart As you progress through the unit, you may want to make a vocabulary-based anchor chart using the Language Development chart as a guide that can be displayed and filled out as a whole group during each lesson.

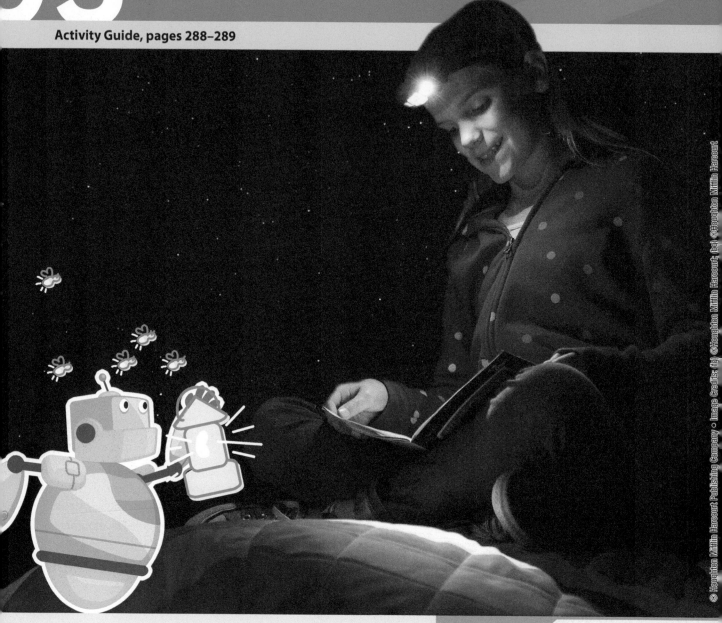

Students can engage in the Can You Explain It? content by observing the photograph or by exploring the corresponding video online.

ONLINE  View a video related to reading at night.

ANCHORING PHENOMENON
You can read by sunlight but not by starlight at night.

PHENOMENON EXPLAINED
The sun is a star. All other stars are so far away from Earth that they appear as tiny points of light. Distance from Earth makes it possible to read by sunlight but not by the light reaching Earth from other stars.

Lesson Objective

Students use models and gather evidence to support arguments that the sun is a star and appears larger and brighter than other stars due to its distance from Earth.

Support Discovery

The following prompts can be used to guide student-led discovery.

I notice . . .

After observing the photograph or watching the video, students should record what they noticed about the levels of light available at night as the student attempts to read. If students struggle to record observations, ask them to think about how easy it is for them to do things outside at nighttime when there are few sources of light available.

Sample answers: I notice that it is dark outside. I notice that the student is using a lamp to see her book.

I wonder . . .

After observing the photograph or watching the video, students should record what they want to find out more about regarding why the student is using a lamp to read. If students struggle to record what they want to know more about, ask them to think about natural and human-made objects that help them see outside at night and during the day, focusing on how much light each provides.

Sample answer: I wonder why this student needs a lamp to see her book. I wonder why the stars do not provide as much light to Earth as the sun. The sun is always giving light but Earth is a spinning ball and we can't always see it.

Can You Explain It?

In the Can You Explain It?, students make an initial claim that explains the **Anchoring Phenomenon.**
Sample answer: Students may draw a model of the sun, Earth, and stars, or they may write a sentence proposing a reason the sun looks larger and brighter. Students may propose that the difference is due to size, distance, or some other factor.

In the lesson, students gather evidence about the sun and relative distances in space. This will enable them to give a more complete explanation of the **Anchoring Phenomenon** at the end of the lesson.

Alternative Phenomenon

If students are unfamiliar with outside environments that get dark enough at night to prevent reading, guide them to think of other ways the amount of light coming from the sun differs from the amount of light coming from the stars. People can safely look at the stars at night, but we cannot safely look at the sun. In fact, the sun is so bright that people use sunglasses to protect their eyes during the day, even though they are not looking directly at the sun.

SOCIAL EMOTIONAL LEARNING

Guide students to reflect on their goals from previous lessons and on any feedback they received. Then, have each student set a personal goal for this lesson and make a plan for how to achieve the goal. Throughout the lesson, take daily breaks for students to track their progress in meeting their goals. If students struggle setting goals, share with them some ideas: explaining why the sun appears different from other stars, engaging in argument from evidence, or persevering when a topic is difficult.

Our Star, the Sun

WHEN TO USE

SCIENCE **30 min**

- Anchoring Phenomenon / Alternative Phenomenon
- Options for ELA Instruction
- Build on Prior Knowledge
- Preview the Phenomenon
- Read to Learn
- Support Sense Making
- Science Stretch
- Check for Comprehension

Option 1 Use before students begin the lesson in the Activity Guide to provide an engaging model to introduce the lesson's phenomenon.

Option 2 Use after students have completed the Activity Guide to reinforce students' understanding of the lesson phenomenon by exploring a related phenomenon.

ELA **20 min**

- Options for ELA Instruction
- Build on Prior Knowledge
- Read to Learn

Option 3 To use during designated ELA Reading time for independent reading, whole-class instruction, or small-group instruction, look for this icon: ELA

Plan

ANCHORING PHENOMENON / ALTERNATIVE PHENOMENON

The anchoring phenomenon in the Activity Guide is *You can read by sunlight, but not by starlight at night*. The main example is a student reading by lamplight at night. The FUNomenal Reader presents a similar phenomenon (*You can safely look at stars that are far away, but you can't safely look directly at the sun*), and the example is a story about a girl who looks at stars through a telescope at night but wonders how scientists can safely study the sun. Both present the same science concepts and cover the same standards but with different phenomena. Guide students to draw connections between the two situations and to understand the underlying principle: the sun appears larger and brighter than other stars due to its distance from Earth.

Options for ELA Instruction

Choose one of the following anchor chart options and project it or print copies. Then display and introduce the chart before reading the text.

Ask and Answer Questions Use the *Ask and Answer Questions Anchor Chart* when introducing, developing, or reviewing those skills. Have students consider how questioning helps Asha find out more information about how scientists are able to study the sun.

Following and Giving Instructions Have students refer to the *Following and Giving Instructions Anchor Chart* to discuss how Asha and her mother built a pinhole projector. Student pairs can take turns giving and following instructions on how to do something.

Respond to Text Display the *Respond to Text Anchor Chart* before reading and tell students they will use one of these methods to respond to the story after they have finished reading: think, connect, remember, create. After reading, have individuals choose the method they prefer and take 5–10 minutes to craft a response.

Preview

ELA **Build on Prior Knowledge** Ask students to describe to a partner a time when they saw a sunset or sunrise. Ask them to discuss the scale and proportion of objects in the day and night sky. Invite pairs to discuss their answers with the rest of the class.

Preview the Phenomenon Ask students to study the illustration on pages 2–3 of the story, which shows a girl and her father using a telescope to look at a starry night sky. Encourage students to record the first questions that come into their minds about what the characters are doing and why. Point out that their questions might change as they read through the selection. Have them keep their questions nearby and periodically check to see if any can be answered.

STANDARDS SUPPORTED

SEP

Engaging in Argument from Evidence

DCI

ESS1.A The Universe and Its Stars

CCC

Scale, Proportion, and Quantity

Our Star, the Sun (continued)

Discover

Read to Learn

The **Read to Learn** suggestions inside the book's front cover encourage students to interact with the book multiple times for different purposes.

> **Preview** Students look for unfamiliar words and share them with a partner. New terms may include *observatory* and *pinhole projector*. Have students look up words they aren't sure about and notice how they are used in the context of the story.

> **Skim** Students skim the illustrations and photos. Have them turn to a partner and share their predictions of what the story will be about.

> **Read** As students read the story, ask them to look for connections to one of the following anchor chart skills. **Ask and Answer Questions, Following and Giving Instructions, Respond to Text**

Support Sense Making

Choose one or more of the following:

▶ Make sure students can identify the phenomenon presented on the opening pages of the story: Asha can look at stars at night safely through a telescope, but she knows that the sun is dangerous to look at directly. The story is about her efforts to find out how scientists are able to study the sun without harming their eyesight. Steps she takes include visiting an observatory, asking an astronomer questions, doing online research, and making a pinhole projector for viewing the sun.

▶ Ask students if they have seen a solar eclipse—when the sun is partially or completely obscured by the moon for several minutes or hours. This occurs when the sun, moon, and Earth are aligned. Discuss how the solar projector Asha and her mother build can help protect the eyes of someone looking through it as an eclipse takes place.

▶ In the story, Asha spots Betelgeuse through her telescope. Tell students that this star's name is pronounced BEET-l-jooz. Betelgeuse is a bright-red star, approximately 500 light years away from Earth, in the constellation Orion (oh-RY-uhn). Have interested students do research to learn more about this or another star and report their findings to the class.

Extend

Science Stretch

The **Science Stretch** suggestions inside the book's back cover help students think about what they read. Students can complete one or more as time allows.

> How could you use two flashlights to model the brightness of the sun? Make a plan. **Sample answer:** A friend and I can shine two identical flashlights on the wall from different distances to show that the closer a star is to Earth, the brighter it seems.

> Build a pinhole projector and use it to view an image of the sun. Draw what you see. Provide materials for students that are similar to the ones Asha and her mother use in the story. Have students work in pairs or small groups to complete the activity.

> Write a blog post that identifies three reasons that the sun is important. **Sample answer:** The sun provides us with heat, light, and it allows plants to make their own food.

SOCIAL EMOTIONAL LEARNING

Why is it important to follow directions, such as not looking directly at the sun? **Sample answer:** If you ignore directions about looking at the sun, you could harm your eyes.

Check for Comprehension Ask students: *What evidence from the story could be used in an argument to support the claim that scientists are able to study the sun safely?* **Sample answer:** Scientists use solar observatories in space as well as telescopes with special filters on Earth to study the sun. Have students turn to a partner and compare their answers.

Glowing Light

Activity Guide, pages 290–291

TIME ESTIMATE

50 min

....

SHORT ON TIME?

Conduct the tests as a class to reduce the time needed for setup and clean up.

POSSIBLE MATERIALS

☐ 4 glow sticks (one large and three small)

☐ water

☐ cups

☐ thermometers

PREPARATION

You rather than students should activate the glow sticks. Two small glow sticks tied together can take the place of one large one in this investigation. Either conduct Step 3 as a class or prepare in advance three containers of water at different temperatures to provide to students in Step 3. Make sure the warm water is at a safe temperature that will not cause burns. Remind students never to put anything in their mouths during a lab activity and to wash their hands after the activity. The materials inside a glow stick may be harmful if swallowed.

INVESTIGATIVE PHENOMENON
Distance from Earth affects the apparent brightness of stars.

Phenomenon Explained Students explore the **investigative phenomenon** by conducting an investigation to explain why the sun looks brighter than other stars.

Form a Question After observing the photograph and reading the text, students should form a question about why the sun appears brighter than other stars in the sky. If students struggle to form a question, have them compare the two images and ask them to think about how the sun and stars differ. **Sample answer:** What causes the sun to look brighter than other stars?

STEP 1 Students compare a large and a small glow stick to observe how size affects the amount of light that's given off. To enhance the glow effect, have students place the two sticks a few inches apart on a desk or table so that the light reflects off the surface.

STEP 2 Divide students into two groups at least 10 feet apart, such as at each end of the room. Have them place one glow stick somewhere that will be visible from across the room, such as on a shelf or desk. Then, have them switch places to compare their remaining glow stick with the one farther away.

STEP 3 You may want to have students complete the previous two steps in groups and then come together for this last step. That way, you can set up the cups one time in order to control and maintain the different temperatures. Label the temperature for each cup. Have students gather in a circle or line up in rows to take turns observing the three cups.

- **Make a Claim** Claims should indicate that size, distance, and temperature affect how bright a star appears.

- **Evidence** Students should cite as evidence their recorded observations from the data table.

- **Reasoning** Students should explain their reasoning that the glow sticks represent glowing stars and that their brightness varies depending on size, distance, and temperature.

FORMATIVE ASSESSMENT

MAKING SENSE OF PHENOMENA

As they explore the **investigative phenomenon**, students gain understanding that distance from Earth affects the apparent brightness of stars. They should connect this to the **anchoring phenomenon** that we can read by light from the sun because it is brighter than other stars. At this stage, students identify that the sun is brighter because it is bigger, closer, or hotter than other stars. They may not have evidence yet to select distance as the key factor.

REMEDIATION If students struggle to connect the **investigative phenomenon** back to the **anchoring phenomenon,** have them discuss with a partner what data they collected could help them explain why we need extra light to read outside at night.

MAKING SENSE OF PHENOMENA IDEA ORGANIZER

After completing Exploration 1, students can fill in the **Idea Organizer** to summarize the connection between distance affecting the apparent brightness of light-emitting objects and the anchoring phenomenon that we receive more light from the sun than from other stars.

Activity Outcome

Students should carry out an investigation in order to observe that size, distance, and temperature affect our perception of light brightness.

Performance Indicators	
	complete the steps of the activity and record observations
	make a claim that size, distance, and temperature affect brightness
	support the claim using recorded observations as evidence

Color Provides the Final Clue

Activity Guide, pages 292–295

TIME ESTIMATE

SHORT ON TIME?
Skip Step 5 where students try to improve the spectroscope.

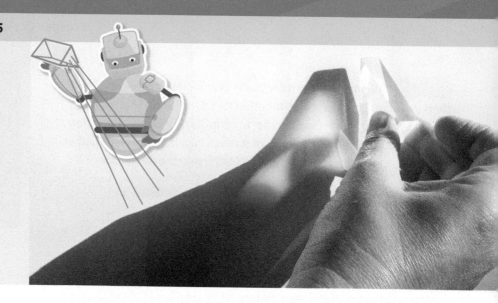

POSSIBLE MATERIALS
- ☐ cardboard tube
- ☐ diffraction grating slide, linear
- ☐ electrical tape, black
- ☐ masking tape
- ☐ various lights, including fluorescent and incandescent

PREPARATION
Preassemble the materials so that each student or team has the same materials available to them. Label the light bulbs. Linear diffraction gratings are preferred because they will show clearer, simpler spectra than double-axis gratings will. While students are handling the grating or the spectroscope, remind them to avoid looking directly or even indirectly at the sun and any very bright lights.

INVESTIGATIVE PHENOMENON
Stars are bodies that emit light.

Phenomenon Explained Students explore the **investigative phenomenon** by using tools to explain that the sun and stars emit light that can be studied.

Form a Question After observing the photograph and reading the text, students should form a question about how scientists have learned that the sun is a star. If students struggle to form a question, have them think about how scientists gather information to study things, such as by observation or measurement. Sample answer: How can scientists study the sun when it is so far away?

STEP 1 Before you begin, remind students not to look directly at the sun or any other very bright lights during the activity. Make sure that students are holding the diffraction grating slide properly by the edges.

STEPS 2 and 3 Students use the slide to look at different kinds of lights. They should look below the bulb to avoid hurting their eyes. If you have enough lights, hand them out and have students share. Otherwise, set up stations for each light and have students take turns examining each one. Remind students to record their observations. Depending on the type of light they are observing, students will likely see red, green, and blue as the brightest and clearest colors. Differences may include seeing different colors or seeing the same colors with a greater separation. Students should understand that the colors come from the light, and the diffraction grating makes it possible to see them.

STEP 4 Students work in groups to build spectroscopes. Support students as they interpret the instructions in the text. The spectroscope blocks out light from the room, so colors appear brighter and clearer.

STEP 5 Groups brainstorm improvements for their spectroscopes. Students implement their plans and continue observations.

- **Make a Claim** Claims should indicate that scientists can study the sun and stars by studying the light they emit that reaches Earth.

- **Evidence** Students should cite as evidence their data that with a spectroscope they could see differences in light from different sources.

- **Reasoning** Students should reason that scientists could use tools like spectroscopes to study similarities and differences in light coming from objects in space such as stars and the sun.

FORMATIVE ASSESSMENT

MAKING SENSE OF PHENOMENA

Students gain understanding that stars emit light as they explore the **investigative phenomenon.** They should connect this to the **anchoring phenomenon** that the sun and stars are similar sources of light. They should understand that because the light is similar, the brightness difference is from a factor in the last activity.

REMEDIATION If students struggle to connect the **investigative phenomenon** back to the **anchoring phenomenon,** remind them that the sun is also a star, but we can read by sunlight because the sun appears brighter from Earth.

MAKING SENSE OF PHENOMENA IDEA ORGANIZER

After completing Exploration 2, students can fill in the **Idea Organizer** to summarize the connection between stars emitting light that can be studied with spectroscopes and the anchoring phenomenon that the sun and stars are similar sources of light that appear to have different brightnesses.

Activity Outcome

Students should build and use a spectroscope in order to observe and compare different light spectra.

Performance Indicators	
	record observations of light spectra
	make a claim that scientists used light spectra to determine that the sun is a star
	support the claim with evidence from their observations

SOCIAL EMOTIONAL LEARNING

Remind students that people communicate in different ways, and not everyone is the same. Encourage them to find multiple ways for team members to express their ideas, including speaking, writing, and drawing.

How Does Distance Affect the Apparent Size of Objects?

Activity Guide, pages 296–299

TIME ESTIMATE

30 min

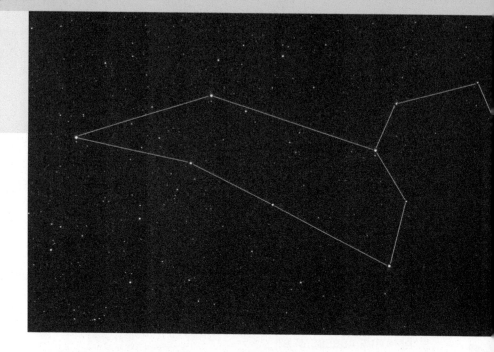

INVESTIGATIVE PHENOMENON
Distances in space are very large.

Phenomenon Explained Students explore the **investigative phenomenon** by analyzing data to explain how distances between objects are measured in the vastness of space.

Light-Years

Explain to students that light-years measure extremely large distances. For comparison, remind them that sunlight travels about 150 million kilometers from the sun to Earth in just a little more than eight minutes. Light-years allow scientists to describe more easily the vast distances between stars and other far away objects in space.

Students may have a difficult time interpreting the data presented in the graphic. Make sure they understand that the higher the number of light-years, the farther the star is from Earth. You might want to have students number the stars on page 296 from the closest to the farthest from Earth before placing them on the diagram. The correct order from closest to farthest is Denebola, Zosma, Regulus, Algieba, Rasalas, Algenubi, and Adhafera.

It's a Matter of Perspective

Everyday Phenomenon **Objects that are farther away appear smaller.**

Have students illustrate a scene that is familiar in their own lives that includes objects of the same size appearing different sizes based on distance. Familiar objects may include vehicles, fence posts, animals, or trees. Encourage students to share their illustrations with peers.

Observed Sizes

Students compare chairs of the same size, seen from different distances. The observed size of a more distant chair is smaller, even though the chair's actual size is the same. Observing from a distance makes an object appear smaller than it is, and the farther away it is, the smaller it appears.

FORMATIVE ASSESSMENT

MAKING SENSE OF PHENOMENA

Students gain understanding of that distances in space are very large as they explore the **investigative phenomenon**. They should connect this to the **anchoring phenomenon** that distance from Earth affects the intensity of light we receive from the sun and stars.

REMEDIATION If students struggle to connect the **investigative phenomenon** back to the **anchoring phenomenon**, have them compare the street lights in the image with the sun and stars to identify which lights best represent the sun and stars.

SOCIAL EMOTIONAL LEARNING

Encourage students to reflect on the importance of both speaking and listening as part of good communication. As students listen to each other's ideas, ask them to listen for any new ideas or new ways of thinking about how distance affects our perception of size. Remind students that they can learn from each other through exploring different ways of thinking.

MAKING SENSE OF PHENOMENA IDEA ORGANIZER

After completing Exploration 3, students can fill in the **Idea Organizer** to summarize the connection between the large distances in space and the intensity of light Earth receives from the sun and the stars, which can explain why people cannot read by starlight.

What Are the Sun's Characteristics?

Activity Guide, pages 300–304

TIME ESTIMATE

30 min

Materials Alert Consider printing out additional images of the sun or any of the celestial objects in the photos to show different perspectives. You might also refer to a scale model of solar system objects or a scale model of solar system distances if either is available.

> **INVESTIGATIVE PHENOMENON**
> Proximity to Earth makes the sun appear larger and brighter than all other stars in the sky.

Phenomenon Explained Students explore the **investigative phenomenon** by gathering evidence about the characteristics of the sun to support a claim for how its proximity relates to its apparent brightness.

A Close-Up View

We see the sunset all the time, but this view of the sun is only from our limited perspective far away on Earth. As students analyze and compare the two images, have them make a list of words to describe each image. They can use these words to fill out the chart.

Stellar Details, Solar System Giant, and Traveling by Light Speed

As you review the text with students, emphasize the concept of scale or relative size. Point out that when students compare the relative rather than the full, actual sizes of objects, such as planets and stars, they're using a scale model.

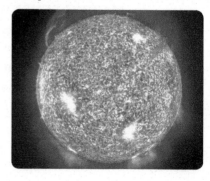

Objects in the Night Sky

Remind students that only stars give off their own light. Other objects in the night sky such as the moon and planets appear to glow, but they are only reflecting light from the sun. Halley's Comet and Mars are not stars.

Let It Shine!

Remind students that the sun is a star like other stars, but it appears bigger and brighter because it is closer to Earth. The other stars in the night sky are much farther away, too far to provide much light.

The Modest Sun

Comparison is needed in order to understand the scale of objects relative to each other, and that can be difficult when they are spread out. This image helps students compare the relative size of these four stars as if they were next to each other. Students should understand that even a very large star may not look bright because of its distance from Earth.

FORMATIVE ASSESSMENT

MAKING SENSE OF PHENOMENA

Students gain understanding of the sun's characteristics and its proximity to Earth as they explore the **investigative phenomenon**. They should connect this to the **anchoring phenomenon** that the sun is Earth's nearest star and we perceive it differently than other stars, which includes being able to read by light from the sun.

REMEDIATION If students struggle to connect the **investigative phenomenon** back to the **anchoring phenomenon,** have students revisit and discuss the image of the brightness of the sun and three stars and the table of their distances from Earth on page 303 to make a case for why the sun is the only star that provides enough light to read by on Earth's surface.

MAKING SENSE OF PHENOMENA
IDEA ORGANIZER

After completing Exploration 4, students can fill in the **Idea Organizer** to summarize the connection between the sun appearing larger and brighter than other stars because of its proximity to Earth and the anchoring phenomenon that we cannot read by starlight because stars other than the sun are too far away to appear as bright.

03

Take It Further

Engage • Explore/Explain • **Elaborate** • Evaluate

TIME ESTIMATE

60 min

These Take It Further paths may be completed to enrich and extend students' comprehension of content covered within this lesson.

ONLINE

People in Science & Engineering: Dr. Beth Brown and Hibah Rahmani

Students learn about Dr. Beth Brown, an African-American astronomer, and Hibah Rahmani, a Pakistani-American engineer, who have had an impact on the study of space.

Star Colors

Students explore the different colors produced by starlight. They can use this information to figure out the temperature of stars.

People in Science & Engineering: William and Margaret Huggins

Students meet scientists who made discoveries using a spectroscope.

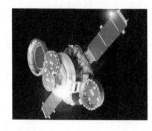

Careers in Science & Engineering: Aerospace Engineer

Students find out what it takes to be an aerospace engineer.

Lesson Check

Can You Explain It?

Sample answer: Objects that are closer appear larger, and closer objects that emit light appear brighter. The sun looks much brighter and larger than other stars because it is much closer to Earth than other stars. This explains why the student does not have enough light from just the stars to read.

After completing the lesson, use the **Making Sense Idea Organizer** to summarize the connections between the **investigative phenomena** and **anchoring phenomenon.**

MAKING CONNECTIONS

After students complete the lesson, they should be able to cite what they have learned about the amount of light we see from distant stars and the much closer sun. They should apply this understanding to the alternative phenomenon that people need to protect themselves from the light energy from the sun.

Sample answer: The sun is much closer to Earth than other stars. So much energy from the sun reaches Earth that people need to protect their skin and eyes from it. Because other stars are so far away, people do not need to protect themselves from the relatively small amount of energy from other stars that reaches Earth.

Checkpoints

1. a—The sun only appears brighter than other stars because it is closer to us.; b—The sun only appears larger than other stars because it is closer to us.

2. b—Neptune

3. Student models should show that the sun is much closer to Earth than other stars.

4. **Sample answer:** The left and right pictures are stars. The middle picture is not a star. Possible evidence: The outside objects are stars because they emit light and are made of gases. The object in the middle is made of rock and has shadows on it, so it appears to be reflecting rather than emitting light.

5. b—Temperatures on its surface are very high.; c—It makes its own light.; d—It is made of gases.

6. light-year; light; the sun

SOCIAL EMOTIONAL LEARNING

Have students reflect on the goals they set at the beginning of the lesson. Ask them to think about whether the goals were accomplished or if there were challenges. Have students share the factors that contributed to their success. If the goals were not achieved, talk about what students can do to help them achieve the goals.

The Unit Review items enable you to assess student comprehension of core ideas as well as crosscutting concepts and science and engineering practices.

1. **DOK 2** **b.** climbing to the top of a mountain to see more of Earth's surface, **c.** standing on a beach and watching a ship disappear over the horizon

   Climbing down into a valley would not provide a good vantage point for seeing more of Earth's surface. Choices b and c both describe valid ways of observing the non-flat shape of Earth, as described in Lesson 1.

2. **DOK 1** Students should circle the person in mid-air.

   No other objects in the image appear to be falling relative to Earth or in position that would cause them to fall. Students unfamiliar with the inflatable beach ball might not realize that it would float on the pool's surface.

3. **DOK 1** **a.** pulls everything to the center of Earth.

   If students choose b, c, or d, remind students that objects near Earth are not drawn to any particular side or pole; they are drawn toward the center. Refer back to Lesson 1 as needed.

4. **DOK 3** **Sample answer:** The moon's lit face appears to grow until it becomes a full circle, and then it shrinks until you can't see it at all. This pattern repeats about once a month. The moon's revolution around Earth causes this pattern.

   Remind students that the visible amount of the moon's surface that is lit by the sun is a function of Earth's relative position to the sun and moon. These relative positions change over the course of a month, causing the cycle of the moon's appearance. Refer back to Lesson 2 as needed.

5. **DOK 3** **b.** It is 7:00 a.m. in Seattle. The time difference is caused by Earth's daily rotation.

   Students should discount choice *a* because according to the map, Seattle and Miami are not in the same time zones. Choice *c* is incorrect because it cites Earth's revolution around the sun as a cause, rather than Earth's rotation. Choice *d* is incorrect because it is not 4:00 a.m. in Seattle, and the moon has no relevance.

6. **DOK 2** **b.** around noon

   Remind students that sunrise and sunset refer to times when the sun is very low in the sky. The sun is highest in the middle of the day, though the precise time of this varies within time zones. Review the patterns in Lesson 2.

7. **DOK 3** **Sample answer:** The sun appears larger and brighter because it is the closest star to Earth. If you see an airplane in the sky, it appears small because it is far away. Some other stars are brighter than our sun, but they look dimmer to us because of how far away they are.

   Students can refer to explorations in Lesson 3 as evidence or examples.

8. **DOK 1** difficult, great, the sun

   If students struggle, talk through each sentence, or rephrase them as questions. For example, ask if it's easy to judge the sizes of stars with the naked eye. Revisit Lesson 3 as needed.

9. **DOK 2** c. season 3

Help students interpret the data in the graph by asking them what the bars mean. Ask which season in the graph has the most hours of daylight, and then ask which season in their experience has the longest days. Review the patterns in Lesson 2.

10. **DOK 2** b. *image showing Orion in the same orientation but to the right*

If students struggle to answer the question, have them review how views of constellations shift over the course of weeks or months. Orion's orientation does not flip (choice *a*), nor would it be higher in the sky (choice *c*). It shifts and rotates slightly counterclockwise, as in choice *b*. Review Lesson 2 for more practice.

3D Item Analysis	1	2	3	4	5	6	7	8	9	10
SEP Analyzing and Interpreting Data		•		•	•				•	•
SEP Engaging in Argument from Evidence	•			•	•		•			
DCI Types of Interactions	•	•	•							
DCI The Universe and its Stars							•	•		
DCI Earth and the Solar System				•	•	•			•	•
CCC Cause and Effect		•	•	•	•					
CCC Patterns				•	•	•	•	•	•	•
CCC Scale, Proportion, Quantity	•						•	•		

Notes:

Index

Index

Index

Index

Index

Index

Index

Index